L. T. Kick

$206 E. 12th.

ΣΠ   427

CK
8⁵⁰

HYDROMETALLURGY
OF BASE METALS

Hydrometallurgy of Base Metals

George D. Van Arsdale, *Editor-in-Chief*

Prepared with the assistance of the Dorr Company Staff

1953 | FIRST EDITION

McGRAW-HILL BOOK COMPANY, INC.

NEW YORK   TORONTO   LONDON

THE MAPLE PRESS COMPANY, INC., YORK, PA.

Garrie L. Tufford
MNO 620900 8199

This book is dedicated to the memory of
DR. JAMES DOUGLAS
Pioneer U.S. Hydrometallurgist
and to
DR. J. V. N. DORR
without whose inventions modern
leaching would not be possible

FOREWORD

Forty years of ripe experience in hydrometallurgy, particularly with copper, emphasizes Mr. Van Arsdale's authority and competence to act as editor-in-chief of this volume. His familiarity with the subject was contemporaneous with the early research, development, and practical application of hydrometallurgy to the copper ores of Southwestern United States. Working there under the stimulating direction of the late Dr. James Douglas, he played an important part in the evolution of the industry. Working more recently in close collaboration with his professional colleagues in the Dorr Company, both here and abroad, he ably headed the "task force" of experts who pooled their knowledge and experience.

Skilled in chemistry, the editor early investigated a number of promising leaching processes. He elucidated the basic principles of the Rio Tinto process, which were obscure at that time and which were subsequently applied by Dr. Douglas in the pioneer commercial treatment of waste ore from Sacramento Hill at Bisbee, Arizona. The editor's research also banished those twin bugbears of electrolytic deposition—disintegrating anodes and foul solutions—by demonstrating the durability of either lead or graphite anodes if depolarized by ferrous sulfate, and the control of ferric iron in solution by reduction with sulfur dioxide. These procedures were subsequently adopted, practically without change, by the New Cornelia Copper Company at Ajo, Arizona. Later, Mr. Van Arsdale became consulting engineer for Inspiration Consolidated Copper Company in the development of a leaching process, similar to that at Ajo, but in which soluble copper sulfide in the ore took the place of sulfur dioxide as a reducing agent for ferric iron. Such, briefly, was the broad background of the editor's intimate familiarity with his subject.

As with other methods of ore treatment, early attempts to recover base metals by leaching were marked by indifferent success or failure. Excluding those abortive processes which have been aptly described as "over-invented and underengineered," others were soundly conceived but practically inoperative at the time for lack of mechanical equipment suitable for the unit operations of classifying, settling, agitating, and filtering.

In the intervening years this deficiency was remedied by the development of auxiliary devices, primarily for cyanidation, which were readily adapted to the operations of base-metal hydrometallurgy. Conspicuous among these were Dorr's inventions for classifying sand and slime and continuously thickening the latter, and the development by Oliver, Moore, and others of vacuum filtration and washing. It would be difficult to exaggerate the value of this equipment in implementing wet metallurgical processes, the chemical principles of which were well known.

The evolution of base-metal hydrometallurgy from the empirical to the scientific stage has followed a familiar pattern—scientific research to establish fundamental principles, and engineering ingenuity in their application. But successful research is compounded of at least two ingredients that are not always in happy conjunction. It calls for knowledge and imagination on the part of the scientist and patient dollars on the part of someone who is willing to assume a risk in hope of future reward. Faithfully followed, this formula offers the best insurance of eliminating the element of surprise that has so often proved costly and disastrous.

With the chemistry and mechanics of hydrometallurgy fairly well established, the outlook seems favorable for a wider application of the process, either as a primary or auxiliary method for increased recovery of base metals. Not all problems have been solved nor has full advantage been taken of promising new developments, but rather the obstacles do not seem insurmountable in the face of further research. Greater efficiency is still in prospect in the technique of flash roasting and in methods of chemical precipitation of copper to replace the conventional iron-cementation process.

It is from this point of vantage that the professional staff of the Dorr Company, working under the editorship of the late Mr. Van Arsdale, offers both student and operator a complete survey of the field—past, present, and future—in a timely volume that fills a void in the literature on hydrometallurgy of the base metals.

H. C. Parmelee

Bradenton, Fla.
September, 1952

ACKNOWLEDGMENTS

Preparation of this volume would have been a practical impossibility had it not been for the encouragement and co-operation of many professional associates of the editor, the officers and operating officials of the metallurgical plants described in it and, finally, the aid and assistance of a technical editor, skilled in the art, who stepped into the void created by the untimely death of the editor-in-chief, and added the finishing touches to the then almost-completed manuscript.

In August, 1950, Mr. Van Arsdale died. The first draft of the volume was then practically completed, lacking only a general editing and rearrangement to make it ready for the publishers. None of his associates in the Dorr Company felt qualified to perform this final and most important task. Fortunately for all concerned with the project, Robert Ramsey, Editor of *Engineering and Mining Journal*, proferred his services, and it was under the skillful hand of this experienced writer on mining and metallurgical subjects that the manuscript emerged in a final and acceptable form.

Sincere expressions of appreciation are due certain of Mr. Van Arsdale's colleagues in the Dorr Company, especially Dr. John V. N. Dorr, for the conception of the idea of this book; Anthony Anable, for the planning and executive direction of its preparation; and Messrs. Georgini of Italy, Alex D. Marriott of South Africa, J. Mikolajczak of Belgium, A. W. Beauger of the Netherlands, the late R. C. Gibbs of England, and S. V. Anspach of Sweden, for collecting up-to-date information on current leaching practices in their respective areas. The contributions of these men have given this project the international perspective that is today a prerequisite of any treatise that aims to depict the status of a branch of engineering.

Thanks are also due to many friends of the Dorr Company, versed in the art of leaching, who have either directly assisted the editor's co-workers in various parts of the mining world mentioned above, or have provided new data on operations for which they are responsible, or have graciously given permission to republish here material that previously appeared in the engineering press on their operations. Among these are Professor Caron of the University of Delft, the Netherlands, on his ammonia-nickel leaching process; Professor L. Cambi of the University of Milan, Italy, for notes on Italian zinc-leaching practice; P. J. Gleason of Rhodesia-Broken Hill Development Corporation, on zinc and vanadium leaching in South Africa; H. L. Talbot, consultant to Anglo-American Corporation, and his assistant H. N. Hepker, and officials of that company; and the officials of the Rhokana Corporation and of N'Changa Copper Mines, Ltd., for data on copper and cobalt leaching in South Africa.

Many engineers, associated with representative leaching operations here and abroad, have given generously of their time in checking published material for accuracy under present-day conditions, notably: A. C. Jephson of the American Smelting & Refining Company, Wallace Woolf of Bunker Hill & Sullivan Mining & Concentrating Company, L. P. Davidson of the American Zinc Company of Illinois, and W. C. Snow of the Electrolytic Zinc Company of Australasia, Ltd. In many cases entirely new data, not available elsewhere, have been furnished, for example, by D. N. Vedensky of the M. A. Hanna Company and James L. Bruce of Cyprus Mines Corporation.

Acknowledgment has been made throughout this volume of the source of a considerable number of references from published works, including special papers of the Institution of Mining and Metallurgy, London; *Mine and Quarry Engineering*, London; *Industrial Chemist*, London; and *Chemical Industries* (now *Chemical Week*), New York. Blanket permission to republish any of their material pertinent to this subject was given by the American Institute of Mining and Metallurgical Engineers, *Mining Engineering*, and *Engineering and Mining Journal*.

Especially appreciated are the interest and co-operation of F. C. Laist of Anaconda Copper Company, who arranged for a final review of the manuscript by experts on his staff after the manuscript had been reviewed and rechecked by the editor's associates, F. L. Bosqui, Westport, Connecticut, and J. D. Grothe, Stamford, Connecticut. Through the good offices of Mr. Laist, an authoritative review was made by P. D. I. Honeyman and Charles B. Kettering of Inspiration, Arizona; Russell Caples of Great Falls, Montana; and Burr Wheeler of New York.

If this volume fills, as expected, a need for an up-to-date treatise on hydrometallurgy as applied to the treatment of nonprecious metal ores, this will be due in no small part to efforts so unselfishly furnished by these associates and friends of the company whose contributions it is a very great pleasure to acknowledge.

The Dorr Company

CONTENTS

CHAPTER 1

CHEMISTRY OF ROASTING AND LEACHING

To state its purpose in simple terms, this book deals with the theory and practice of recovering metals other than gold and silver from their ores or concentrates by dissolving them with some solvent and then precipitating them in a pure state. To do that, certain basic processes have to be carried out. They are generally performed, and will be discussed, in the following order.

Crushing, grinding, and *classification* are required to break the ore down to a particle size (1) that can easily be handled in bulk and (2) that will give the solvent access to the desired mineral. In general, the aim of this step is to break the ore no finer than is absolutely necessary and, if needed, to separate coarse and fine fractions so that they can be treated in the way best suited to each one.

Roasting, by one of several techniques, is required for certain ores or concentrates to set the stage properly for subsequent leaching. Roasting may be varied to produce a sulfate, an oxide, a reduction in oxide content, a chloride, or combination of these. Equipment has been devised so that the sometimes complex reactions of roasting can be precisely controlled.

Leaching is the process of dissolving the desired mineral by the chosen solvent. The problem in leaching is to set up the mechanical, chemical, and economic conditions that will permit a maximum dissolution of the desired metal, at a profit.

Solution separation involves getting rid of the now-barren gangue from which the valuable mineral has been leached. This may vary from simple draining and washing to more elaborate techniques of countercurrent decantation or filtration.

Precipitation is the final step, in which metal is produced as such, and lacks only refining to be ready for use. Electrolytic methods of precipitation recover by far the greater part of the metal produced by techniques involving leaching. There are, however, chemical methods, such as precipitation of copper by iron, that account for substantial tonnages of metal.

The chemical reactions involved in these processes are not complex, but a clear understanding of them is essential to a detailed discussion of

1

techniques. Omitting crushing and classification, the discussion of chemistry will follow the foregoing outline.

CHEMISTRY OF ROASTING

Roasting base-metal ores or concentrates, as a preliminary to the leaching process, takes one of the following forms: oxidizing, reducing, sulfatizing, or chloridizing. Each has a special purpose, the attainment of which is a matter of operating measurement and control.

Oxidizing roast for copper ores is not used in any modern copper-leaching plant. This arises from no deficiency of the roasting process, but from the fact that it has usually been cheaper to build and operate a flotation mill and smelter for copper sulfide ores than to roast, leach, and refine them.

Roasting and leaching might, however, be considered for handling a copper sulfide concentrate that is low in precious-metal content or has to be shipped a long distance to a smelter.

Sulfides of iron and other metals, as well as various gangue minerals, complicate the reactions involved in roasting copper sulfides. The literature has many references to these reactions, and it would be impossible here to reproduce all variations of them. Only simplified basic reactions can be given for the behavior of copper sulfide in oxidizing roasting. These are as follows:

$$Cu_2S + 3O = Cu_2O + SO_2 \tag{1}$$
$$Cu_2S + 4O = 2CuO + SO_2 \tag{2}$$
$$CuS + 3O = CuO + SO_2 \tag{3}$$

These indicate that a restricted air supply helps form Cu_2O, which is soluble only in acid ferric sulfate leach solutions. With ample air, fairly high temperature, and enough time, all the copper will convert to CuO, which is soluble in a weak sulfuric acid leach solution.

Copper sulfate can be produced directly from the sulfide, according to the equation:

$$Cu_2S + 5O = CuO + CuSO_4 \tag{4}$$

This indicates that a considerable excess of air is required to produce a high concentration of sulfate in the calcine. Copper sulfate can also come from a reaction between CuO and SO_3.

$$Cu_2S + 2O_2 = 2CuO + SO_2 \tag{5}$$
$$SO_2 + O_2 = 2SO_3 \tag{6}$$
$$CuO + SO_3 = CuSO_4 \tag{7}$$

The trioxide is formed by catalysis from SO_2, either from the copper sulfide or from iron sulfide. In the latter case the catalytic agent is probably the iron oxide left from the oxidation of pyrite. This is indicated by the fact that in a sulfatizing roast, the presence of iron sulfide helps produce more sulfate. Iron sulfate may be, and usually is, produced by similar reaction.

Both iron and copper sulfates decompose at high temperatures (see Table 1 for decomposition temperatures), and differential decomposition is also possible. For example, iron sulfate may be converted to the oxide and to SO_2 below the decomposition temperature of $CuSO_4$.

It is therefore possible, by using the foregoing methods, to roast copper sulfides completely to the oxides or to the oxide plus varying percentages of the sulfate with resulting low iron solubility. The insoluble copper ferrite may form if the temperature is carried too high.

The quantity of water-soluble copper to be left in the calcine depends on the subsequent treatment. For example, if the calcine is to go eventually to electrolysis, theoretically there need be no sulfate left in the calcine at all. Electrolysis regenerates sulfuric acid in proportion to the copper precipitated. Therefore, to maintain an acid balance, if the acid consumption in leaching is 1 mol acid to 1 mol copper, the calcine should contain 100 per cent of its soluble copper as oxide. However, acid-consuming elements other than copper are usually present.

If electrolysis is used, some copper sulfate does have to be left in the calcine to provide the extra acid needed in leaching. This requirement can easily be met, as in zinc-leaching practice, by raising the final temperature of the roast and allowing enough time to decompose the excess copper sulfate that will be present down to the desired percentage.

Oxidizing roast for zinc ores can bring about a number of reactions. These may be expressed as follows:

$$2ZnS + 3O_2 = 2ZnO + 2SO_2$$
$$2ZnO + 2SO_2 + O_2 = 2ZnSO_4$$

A catalyst is required for the second reaction.

As is true of copper roasting, zinc sulfide roasting must be done with an eye to the final treatment, which in present practice means electrolysis. Because sulfuric acid is produced in the electrolytic cells in proportion to the zinc plated out, any extra acid produced by zinc sulfate coming in with the calcine builds up in repeated passes through the leaching cycle unless it is in some manner used up, neutralized, or discarded.

It is possible to control formation of zinc sulfate in roasting, and the aim is to produce only enough to make up for any excess acid required in leaching. From 2 to 3 per cent of sulfate sulfur in the calcine is usually enough. Control of the quantity of sulfate in the calcine is obtained by regulating the temperature in the lower hearths of the roaster.

It is usually necessary to raise the temperature of the lower hearths to complete the oxidation of zinc sulfide and to hold down the formation of zinc sulfate. Any sulfur left in the calcine as sulfide is insoluble in the leach solution and therefore causes the loss of about twice its own weight of zinc.

Maximum roasting temperatures for zinc sulfides are about 650°C for complex zinc concentrates, and about 750°C for concentrates very high in zinc. Complex concentrates are harder to handle if, for example, lead and iron sulfides are present. Initial roasting temperatures must be held well below 600°C to prevent fusion of the lead sulfides and excessive formation of insoluble ferrites.

Under certain conditions of roasting, zinc and iron oxides combine to form zinc ferrite ($ZnO\cdot Fe_2O_3$) which is insoluble in warm dilute sulfuric acid. This reaction is the greatest source of loss of zinc in the whole. electrolytic zinc process. Much time has therefore been spent on devising means to recover zinc from ferrites, although only a few such processes have proved to be of commercial value.[1]

For example, zinc lost as ferrite in leaching-plant residue can be converted to sulfate by roasting in an atmosphere of sulfur dioxide at a temperature between 500 and 550°C. Some iron sulfate is formed, but this can be controlled by careful regulation of temperature. The reaction is probably due to the catalytic action of iron oxide in converting a mixture of SO_2 and O_2 to SO_3.

At Trail, British Columbia, such a residue was treated in a multiple-hearth furnace, pyrite being added to the lower hearths to furnish the needed SO_2.

Another method is the so-called residue fuming, which depends on decomposition of zinc ferrite and formation of zinc sulfate by roasting at high temperatures with sulfuric acid. The reaction is probably represented by this equation:

$$ZnO\cdot Fe_2O_3 + 4H_2SO_4 = ZnSO_4 + Fe_2(SO_4)_3 + 4H_2O$$

The amount of ferric sulfate in the finished product can be controlled by regulating the temperature of the roast. If the temperature is held above 600 but below 650°C, ferric sulfate rapidly decomposes into insoluble ferric oxide. Zinc sulfate, on the other hand, remains practically untouched (see Table 1 for decomposition temperatures of anhydrous sulfates).

[1] F. Laist, R. B. Caples, and G. T. Wever, "The Electrolytic Zinc Process," in D. M. Liddell's *Handbook of Nonferrous Metallurgy*, McGraw-Hill Book Company, Inc., New York, 1945.

Sulfatization of copper ores can occur by direct air oxidation, as follows:

$$Cu_2S + 5O = CuO + CuSO_4$$

This is in addition to any amounts of copper sulfate that may be formed by various reactions of sulfur dioxide and sulfur trioxide.

It seems evident that several of the reactions that produce copper sulfate from copper sulfide ores have appreciable velocities at ordinary temperatures. Thus, the ore of Cyprus Mines Corp., which consists largely of pyrite carrying about 4 per cent copper as chalcocite and no copper sulfate, produces in the mining, crushing, and grinding steps, at ordinary temperatures, enough copper sulfate to interfere seriously with recovery of the copper by flotation. Sulfatization at ordinary temperatures is also indicated in the heap leaching of heavy pyrite ore, containing copper sulfides, at Rio Tinto in Spain.

In practice, it is most important in sulfatization to establish precise control of temperature as well as of other conditions of the roast. Wedge describes[1] roasting a pyrite ore containing 1.07 per cent copper. He was able to render only 27.8 per cent of the copper water-soluble because of the excessive temperature reached during the roast, owing to the large excess of sulfur present. With an ore containing less pyrite, where the temperature could be more closely controlled, 60 to 80 per cent of the copper was rendered water-soluble.

Large-scale tests run by the Phelps Dodge Corp. at Douglas, Ariz., have shown that it is impossible in an ordinary unmuffled multiple-hearth furnace to convert more than about 50 per cent of the copper in a sulfide ore to the water-soluble form, because of the lack of precise control of roasting conditions. The same tests showed, on the other hand, that the better control possible in a muffled furnace of the Wedge type brought about a yield under favorable conditions of as much as 60 to 80 per cent water-soluble copper.

To produce bluestone (copper sulfate) directly from copper concentrates, or for processes involving chemical precipitation (*e.g.*, hydrogen sulfide) or reaction with iron, it is important to produce a calcine in which the copper sulfate content is as high as possible. The goal, of course, would be 100 per cent copper sulfate. Owing to the aforesaid, lack of precise control of roasting, even in the muffled furnace, it has heretofore been impossible to get more than 60 to 80 per cent copper sulfate.

Introduction of the Dorrco FluoSolids process for roasting, however,

[1] Utley Wedge, Sulphating Roasting of Copper Ores and Concentrates, *Trans. AIME*, Vol. 44, p. 818.

made it easily possible to get a practically complete sulfatization of copper sulfide concentrates or similar material (see page 58).

In roasting for copper leaching, it should be noted that iron and copper oxides may combine at sufficiently high temperatures to form acid-insoluble compounds. These are probably ferrites, similar to the zinc ferrites formed in zinc roasting.

TABLE 1. DISSOCIATION OF ANHYDROUS SULFATES

Sulfate	Temperature of beginning of decomposition, °C	Temperature of energetic decomposition, °C	Products of decomposition
$FeSO_4$	167	480	$Fe_2O_3 \cdot 2SO_3$
$Fe_2O_3 \cdot 2SO_3$	492	560	Fe_2O_3
$Bi_2(SO_4)_3$	570	639	$5Bi_2O_3 \cdot 4(SO_3)_4$
$Al_2(SO_4)_3$	590	639	Al_2O_3
$PbSO_4$	637	705	$6PbO \cdot 5SO_3$
$CuSO_4$	653	670	$2CuO \cdot SO_3$
$MnSO_4$	699	790	Mn_3O_4
$ZnSO_4$	702	720	$3ZnO \cdot 2SO_3$
Cu_2SO_3	702	736	CuO
$NiSO_4$	702	764	NiO
$CoSO_4$	720	770	CoO
$3ZnO \cdot 2SO_3$	755	767	ZnO
$CdSO_4$	827	846	$5CdO \cdot SO_3$
$5Bi_2O_3 \cdot 4(SO_3)_3$	870	890	$Bi_2O_3(?)$
$5CdO \cdot SO_3$	878	890	CdO
$MgSO_4$	890	972	MgO
Ag_2SO_4	917	925	Ag
$6PbO \cdot 5SO_3$	952	962	$2Pb \cdot SO_3(?)$
$CaSO_4$	1200	...	CaO
$BaSO_4$	1510	...	BaO

The decomposition temperatures of various sulfates are important in roasting for leaching. Note Tables 1 and 2, showing these temperatures, given by Hofman and Wanjukov.[1] These tables indicate that some sulfates are converted directly into oxides; others change first to a basic salt at the temperature at which the first sulfur trioxide is driven off. Copper, with the highest atomic weight of group VIII of Mendelyeev's table, forms a basic salt. Iron, with a lower atomic weight, does not form a ferrous basic salt. In groups IV and V, the metals with higher atomic weights (bismuth and lead) form basic salts.

[1] Hofman and Wanjukov, The Decomposition of Metallic Sulphides, *Trans. AIME.* Vol. 43, p. 523.

Normal sulfates that do not form basic salts on dissociation show both sulfur dioxide and trioxide in the gaseous product. Normal sulfates that do form basic salts on dissociation evolve only SO_2 when they pass from the normal basic state. Basic sulfates, on dissociation into the

TABLE 2. DECOMPOSITION OF HYDRATED SULFATES

Salt	Temperature of beginning of dehydration, °C	Product formed
$FeSO_4 \cdot 7H_2O$	21	$FeSO_4 \cdot 4H_2O$
$FeSO_4 \cdot 4H_2O$	80	$FeSO_4 \cdot H_2O$
$FeSO_4 \cdot H_2O$	406	$Fe_2O_3, 2SO_3$
$Al_2(SO_4)_3 \cdot 16H_2O$	51	$Al_2(SO_4)_3 \cdot 13H_2O$
$Al_2(SO_4)_3 \cdot 13H_2O$	82	$Al_2(SO_4)_3 \cdot 10H_2O$
$Al_2(SO_4)_3 \cdot 10H_2O$	94	$Al_2(SO_4)_3 \cdot 7H_2O$
$Al_2(SO_4)_3 \cdot 7H_2O$	109	$Al_2(SO_4)_3 \cdot 4H_2O$
$Al_2(SO_4)_3 \cdot 4H_2O$	180	$Al_2(SO_4)_3 \cdot H_2O$
$Al_2(SO_4)_3 \cdot H_2O$	316	$Al_2(SO_4)_3$
$CuSO_4 \cdot 5H_2O$	27	$CuSO_4 \cdot 3H_2O$
$CuSO_4 \cdot 3H_2O$	93	$CuSO_4 \cdot H_2O$
$CuSO_4 \cdot H_2O$	155	$CuSO_4$
$MnSO_4 \cdot 5H_2O$	25	$MnSO_4 \cdot 2H_2O$
$MnSO_4 \cdot 2H_2O$	60	$MnSO_4 \cdot H_2O$
$MnSO_4 \cdot H_2O$	152	$MnSO_4$
$ZnSO_4 \cdot 7H_2O$	25	$ZnSO_4 \cdot 6H_2O$
$ZnSO_4 \cdot 6H_2O$	28	$ZnSO_4 \cdot 2H_2O$
$ZnSO_4 \cdot 2H_2O$	115	$ZnSO_4 \cdot H_2O$
$ZnSO_4 \cdot H_2O$	225	$ZnSO_4$
$NiSO_4 \cdot 7H_2O$	40	$NiSO_4 \cdot 4H_2O$
$NiSO_4 \cdot 4H_2O$	106	$NiSO_4 \cdot H_2O$
$NiSO_4 \cdot H_2O$	279	$NiSO_4$
$CoSO_4 \cdot 7H_2O$	19	$CoSO_4 \cdot 4H_2O$
$CoSO_4 \cdot 4H_2O$	58	$CoSO_4 \cdot H_2O$
$CoSO_4 \cdot H_2O$	276	$CoSO_4$
$CdSO_4 \cdot \frac{8}{3}H_2O$	30	$CdSO_4 \cdot 2H_2O$
$CdSO_4 \cdot 2H_2O$	41	$CdSO_4 \cdot H_2O$
$CdSO_4 \cdot H_2O$	170	$CdSO_4$

oxides, release only SO_3. Metallic sulfates of the type formed by trivalent and monovalent manganese do not form basic sulfates on dissociation. The former releases SO_3 on dissociation; the latter, SO_2.

According to Table 1, it is theoretically possible to roast a mixture of iron and copper sulfides to produce cupric sulfate with only small amounts of ferrous sulfate, since the latter dissociates energetically at 480°C, and the former requires 670°C.

Sulfatization of zinc ores is required only to produce the small amount of zinc sulfate needed for make-up acid in leaching and electrolysis of zinc concentrates. Although several early processes required high percentages of zinc sulfate in the calcine, none of these methods is used today. The usual multiple-hearth roasting furnace would probably be no more capable of producing a calcine in which the zinc is completely water-soluble than it was for copper.

Actually, a high water-soluble content of zinc would be most desirable in a calcine used to produce lithopone, made for example from Tri-State zinc concentrates. In producing lithopone, there is no regeneration of acid as there is in electrolysis. The acid required for leaching is a charge against the product. This charge for acid would be reduced in proportion to the amount of water-soluble zinc produced in roasting.

Here again, the Dorrco FluoSolids reactor, with its precise control, gives promise of being able to produce a calcine with a high water-soluble metal content, in roasting of zinc as well as copper. When roasting zinc, iron sulfide must be added to furnish the necessary excess of sulfur dioxide and the required ferric oxide catalyst, unless enough iron sulfide is already present in the raw material.

Reduction roasting of copper ores is not practiced at present on a large scale. It is interesting to note, however, that copper silicate, like nickel silicate, may be partly or completely converted to metal by reduction roasting.

Years ago Hample described the complete reduction of copper sulfide to metal in a reaction that is, however, no longer used commercially:

$$Cu_2S + 2H = 2Cu + H_2S$$

Similarly copper sulfide may be reduced to metal by methane:

$$2Cu_2S + CH_4 = 4Cu + 2H_2S + C$$

Nickel that occurs as the silicate (garnierite) can be recovered by a reduction roast followed by ammonia leaching. This is known as the Caron process, after Prof. Caron of Delft University, Holland. It was used on a large scale by the Nicaro Nickel Co. in Cuba during the Second World war. For a full description of the process, see Chap. 8.

Roasting in the Caron process involves reduction of the nickel silicate $[H_2(NiMg)SiO_4 \cdot H_2O)]$ to metallic nickel, which can be dissolved by the ammonia.

Reduction roasting is also used in treating manganese ores as a preliminary to electrolysis, either for the metal or manganese oxides. The latter may be reduced by heating with coal to form manganous oxide, (MnO), which is soluble in sulfuric acid:

$$2MnO_2 + C = 2MnO + CO_2$$
$$2Mn_3O_4 + C = 6MnO + CO_2$$

Because the principal source of tin is the oxide, cassiterite (SnO_2), which is insoluble in any commercial solvent, no direct leaching method for recovery of tin is feasible. Tin ores are treated by leaching, as at the Longhorn tin smelter in Texas, but this is for the removal of impurities rather than for the dissolution of the tin mineral. This process is described in Chap. 8, page 290.

Nevertheless, tin metallurgy leaves much to be desired, considering the losses in slags and the difficult processes required. It seems probable that some day improved methods will be devised that will be both cheaper and more efficient than the smelting techniques now used.

For example, tin oxide is readily reduced to metal by reduction roasting, and a method for tin production by this route has been tested by Mantell and Fink. Hydrogen was used as the reducing agent, and the roasted ore was leached with strong acids or bases.

More recently Fink and Strauss[1] have proposed a method of reduction roasting of cassiterite, to be followed by leaching, that makes use of a controlled mixture of carbon monoxide and carbon dioxide as the reducing medium. They state that the reduction of tin oxide could be made to proceed in two distinct steps:

$$SnO_2 + CO = SnO + CO_2$$
$$SnO + CO = Sn + CO_2$$

This is accomplished by using varying ratios of CO and CO_2 in the furnace atmosphere. The SnO could then be dissolved by either acid or base, and the tin recovered electrolytically, if desired. Experimental evidence was presented to indicate the commercial feasibility of the method.

Chloridizing roasting by modification of the original Longmaid-Henderson process is used for extracting copper from pyrite cinders. These may carry 1 to 3 per cent of copper, and may also hold appreciable quantities of zinc, lead, cobalt, gold, and silver. In roasting the cinder, sulfur must be present in sufficient amounts to satisfy the ratio of 3.5S to 2Cu. Pyritic ore must be added to make up for any lack of sulfur.

Salt, amounting to 8 to 10 per cent of the charge, is added to the

[1] Fink and Strauss, *Engineering and Mining Journal*, December, 1950.

cinders, and the whole mixed and crushed to pass a 3-mm screen. The reaction is exothermic, addition of producer gas being necessary only to start the chloridizing reaction.

Roasting reactions[1] cited are

$$2Cu_2S + 8NaCl + 4FeSO_4 + 5O_2 = 4CuCl_2 + 4Na_2SO_4 + 2Fe_2O_3$$
$$+ 2SO_2 \quad (1)$$
$$4NaCl + 2CuO + 2S + 3O_2 = 2Na_2SO_4 + 2CuCl_2 \quad (2)$$
$$2NaCl + CuS + 2O_2 = Na_2SO_4 + CuCl_2 \quad (3)$$

Cinders containing more than 3 per cent of zinc are difficult to treat by this method, owing to the formation of ferrites. This reaction renders the zinc insoluble and also locks other metals up with the ferrites.

In the past, chloridizing roasting was often suggested for various recovery problems but was seldom actually used. For example, roasting with salt was thought to be a good means of getting rid of copper as a cyanicide in treating copper-silver ores, but the method was abandoned. Later work showed that the chlorides of copper and some other metals were quite volatile, and this circumstance resulted in attempts to develop a means of recovering copper based on this volatility.

Chloridizing roasting is used in a number of cyanide plants treating arsenical or telluride gold ores. A description of this technique does not fall within the purview of this book, but it is mentioned because of its similarity to the roasting practice used for the secondary uranium ores, especially of the Colorado plateau. As described by F. W. McQuiston, Jr.,[2] the uranium-vanadium ores are crushed to minus 14 mesh, then roasted with 6 to 10 per cent of salt in multiple-hearth furnaces. Sodium vanadate is formed and hydrochloric acid released, the acid later serving to leach out the uranium minerals.

Temperature is the most important single factor in the salt roasting, according to McQuiston. Optimum temperature is 850°C, from the standpoint of both uranium and vanadium recovery. Water scrubbing of the roaster gases also provides a cheap source of leach solution. Lime content has to be below 2.5 per cent, so that too much hydrochloric acid is not lost in roasting and leaching. Under best conditions, 1 ton of ore when roasted yields 50 lb of hydrochloric acid. An increase of 1 per cent of lime cuts down the hydrochloric acid yield by 10 lb per ton of ore. With lime content greater than 5 per cent, almost no water-soluble

---

[1] W. H. Dennis, Recovery of Non-ferrous Metals from Pyrite, *Mine and Quarry Engineering*, December, 1947.

[2] F. W. McQuiston, Jr., "Processing Uranium Ores," American Mining Congress, Salt Lake City, Utah, August, 1950.

vanadium is formed in the roast, thus inhibiting the subsequent leaching cycle.

A salt roast is also used prior to carbonate leaching of certain uranium ores (Chap. 8).

CHEMISTRY OF LEACHING

Aside from the solvent used, the raw material of leaching is the ore, concentrate, or calcine to be leached. Generally speaking, an ore that is considered suitable for leaching is one that does not respond well to gravity concentration, flotation, or other simple process. The desired metal may occur free, or as the sulfide, the carbonate, the silicate, the oxide, or the sulfate. In any case, it is almost certain to present some difficulty. Likewise, the concentrate to be leached usually presents a problem, for there would be no need to leach it directly unless it were necessary to dispose of or to circumvent some troublesome impurity that could not be handled otherwise.

Calcines fall into a different category, inasmuch as the roasting process, when properly carried out, establishes a condition that facilitates leaching. The metal, as indicated in the foregoing pages, may be rendered soluble, and the impurities made insoluble. Make-up acid may be produced without cost. Indeed, modern roasting techniques have gone far to simplify and to widen the scope of leaching practice.

Solvents for leaching include both acids and bases, as well as some salts, but sulfuric acid is by far the most widely used. This is due partly to its effectiveness as a solvent, and partly to its wide availability and low cost. It is easy to handle and losses in process are low.

Hydrochloric acid, though used in several plants, is harder to handle than sulfuric, and losses are likely to be higher. Sulfur dioxide and ammonia, being very volatile, are also hard to handle and are not widely used. However, leaching processes using ammonia are under development for copper sulfide ores. Sodium carbonate is used for leaching secondary uranium ores. Sodium hydroxide is used in some pilot plants for leaching tin ores, and the U.S. Bureau of Mines has proposed using nitrates for several leaching jobs.

Accessory reagents in leaching are those which, like ferrous and ferric sulfate, assist in the dissolution reactions without acting as the principal solvent. Ferric sulfate helps dissolve a number of copper sulfides, and ferrous sulfate acts as a depolarizing agent in copper electrolysis. Iron oxide acts as a catalyst to produce sulfur trioxide in sulfating roasting. Sodium chloride is an accessory reagent in some roasting processes and in the subsequent leaching.

Leaching of Copper. The various commercially important minerals of copper are given in Table 3, together with their theoretical composi-

TABLE 3. COMMERCIALLY IMPORTANT MINERALS OF COPPER AND THEIR
SOLUBILITIES*

Mineral	Composition	% Cu	Solubility (Cu)
Azurite............	$2CuCO_3 \cdot Cu(OH)_2$	55.3	Readily acid-soluble
Malachite..........	$CuSO_3 \cdot Cu(OH)_2$	57.6	Readily acid-soluble
Chrysocolla........	$CuSiO_3 \cdot 2H_2O$	36.1	Acid-soluble
Tenorite...........	CuO	79.7	Acid-soluble
Cuprite............	Cu_2O	88.8	Acid- and ferric iron-soluble
Dioptase...........	$CuSiO_3 \cdot H_2O$	57.9	Acid-soluble (HCl)
Brochantite........	$CuSO_4 \cdot 3Cu(OH)_2$	56.2	Acid-soluble
Metallic copper.....	Cu	....	Acid-, ammonia-, and ferric iron-soluble
Chalcocite.........	Cu_2S	79.8	Acid- and ferric iron-soluble
Covellite..........	CuS	66.4	Acid- and ferric iron-soluble
Bornite............	Cu_5FeS_4	63.3	Partly soluble, acid and ferric iron
Chalcopyrite.......	$CuFeS_2$	34.6	Partly soluble, acid and ferric iron

* These solubilities are general statements only and solubilities depend on a number
of factors, including size of particle, strength of acid or ferric iron, time of contact,
temperature, etc.

tions and solubilities.   The reactions by which these minerals are dissolved in leaching, either with sulfuric acid or sulfuric plus ferric iron, are
as follows:

Azurite

$$Cu_3(OH)_2 \cdot (CO_3)_2 + 3H_2SO_4 = 3CuSO_4 + 2CO_2 + 4H_2O \tag{1}$$

Malachite

$$Cu_2(OH)_2 \cdot CO_3 + 2H_2SO_4 = 2CuSO_4 + CO_2 + 3H_2O \tag{2}$$

Chrysocolla

$$CuSiO_3 \cdot 2H_2O + H_2SO_4 = CuSO_4 + SiO_2 + 3H_2O \tag{3}$$

Cuprite

$$Cu_2O + H_2SO_4 = CuSO_4 + Cu + H_2O \tag{4}$$
$$Cu + Fe_2(SO_4)_3 = CuSO_4 + 2FeSO_4 \tag{5}$$
$$Cu_2O + H_2SO_4 + Fe_2(SO_4)_3 = 2CuSO_4 + H_2O + 2FeSO_4 \tag{6}$$

Chalcocite

$$Cu_2S + Fe_2(SO_4)_3 = CuS + CuSO_4 + 2FeSO_4 \tag{7}$$
$$CuS + Fe_2(SO_4)_3 = CuSO_4 + 2FeSO_4 + S \tag{8}$$
$$Cu_2S + 2Fe_2(SO_4)_3 = 2CuSO_4 + 4FeSO_4 + S \tag{9}$$

Covellite

$$CuS + Fe_2(SO_4)_3 = CuSO_4 + 2FeSO_4 + S \qquad (10)$$

Bornite. Bornite has the formula Cu_5FeS_4, which may be written $FeS \cdot 2Cu_2S \cdot CuS$. Practically all the copper can be dissolved from bornite by leaching with hot acid plus ferric sulfate. The reactions are probably similar to (7), (8), and (9) in the foregoing text. However, with bornite the iron is also attacked. This is probably due to the iron sulfide which is present in bornite in a different and more soluble form than in pyrite or chalcopyrite. The iron sulfide in these two minerals is not attacked by acid, or acid plus ferric iron, under leaching conditions.

Chalcopyrite. Only part of the copper in chalcopyrite is soluble in acid plus ferric iron, and to get even this solubility, fine grinding, heating of solutions, and a long period of contact are required. It seems probable that the iron sulfide in chalcopyrite is in a form similar to that in pyrite, which is not acted on by the usual leaching solvents. The solvent is thus permitted only partial action by the presence of this insoluble constituent.

Pyrite. Pyrite is not acted on appreciably by either sulfuric acid alone or with ferric iron under leaching conditions.

Pyrrhotite is readily acted on by sulfuric acid, and by acid plus ferric iron.

Among others, John D. Sullivan[1] has investigated the solubility of various pure copper minerals. A partial summary of results of his research is given in Table 4.

Conclusions from Sullivan's work may be drawn as follows:

Azurite, malachite, tenorite, and *chrysocolla* are completely soluble at room temperature in the usual strength of acid used in leaching, and in less time than the usual percolation-leaching cycle.

Cuprite requires acid ferric sulfate and is completely dissolved by it in less time than the usual percolation-leaching cycle.

Chalcocite, bornite, and *covellite* require acid ferric sulfate and elevated temperature. At 35 to 50°C, nearly complete extractions are possible in the usual percolation-leaching time.

Chalcopyrite does not give practical extraction percentages under the usual percolation-cycle conditions. Treatment at room temperature gives little or no extraction with acid ferric sulfate and only 40 to 50 per cent at higher temperature.

It should be understood that copper minerals in ores, especially sulfides,

[1] John D. Sullivan, Chemical and Physical Features of Copper Leaching, *Trans. AIME*, Vol. 106, p. 515, 1933.

are not always of theoretical composition and their solubilities and behavior on leaching may vary considerably.

TABLE 4. SOLUBILITIES OF VARIOUS PURE COPPER MINERALS

Mineral	Mesh	Solvent	Extraction and time	Temperature
Azurite........	$-100 +200$	1–5% H_2SO_4	100%, 1 hr	Room
Malachite.....	$-100 +200$	1–5% H_2SO_4	100%, 1 hr	Room
Tenorite......	$-100 +200$	1% H_2SO_4	98%, 1 hr	Room
Chrysocolla...	-0.525 in. $+3$ mesh	5% H_2SO_4	100%, 30 hr	Room
	$-10 +28$	5% H_2SO_4	97%, 6 hr	Room
Dioptase......	$-10 +28$	1% H_2SO_4	79%, 60 days	Room
	$-10 +28$	2% H_2SO_4	98%, 60 days	Room
	$-10 +28$	5% H_2SO_4	100%, 37 days	Room
Cuprite.......	$-10 +28$	Acid $Fe_2(SO_4)_3$	99%, 3 days	Room
	$-100 +200$	Acid $Fe_2(SO_4)_3$	100%, 1 hr	Room
Chalcocite.....	$-100 +200$	Acid $Fe_2(SO_4)_3$	50%, 24 hr	$35°C$
	$-100 +200$	Acid $Fe_2(SO_4)_3$	100%, 21 days	$35°C$
	$-100 +200$	Acid $Fe_2(SO_4)_3$	50%, 8 days	$23°C$
	$-100 +200$	Acid $Fe_2(SO_4)_3$	95%, 8 days	$50°C$
Bornite.......	$-100 +200$	Acid $Fe_2(SO_4)_3$	95%, 14 days	Room
	$-100 +200$	Acid $Fe_2(SO_4)_3$	45%, 5 days	$23°C$
	$-100 +200$	Acid $Fe_2(SO_4)_3$	85%, 3 days	$50°C$
Covellite......	$-100 +200$	Acid $Fe_2(SO_4)_3$	35%, 11 days	$35°C$
	$-100 +200$	Acid $Fe_2(SO_4)_3$	70%, 13 days	$50°C$
Chalcopyrite..	$-100 +200$	Acid $Fe_2(SO_4)_3$	2%, 43 days	Room
	-350	Acid $Fe_2(SO_4)_3$	38–39%, 57 days	Room
	-350	Acid $Fe_2(SO_4)_3$	44%, 14 days	$50°C$

Leaching of copper is conditioned by a number of factors, all of them common to the leaching of other metals as well:

1. Mesh to which the ore is ground.
2. Composition and strength of solvent.
3. Time of contact.
4. Temperature of solvent.

In addition to these more or less obvious factors, the physical character of the ore and its method of formation are of importance.

1. The object of crushing and grinding for leaching is obviously to permit contact of solvent and mineral, and subsequent removal of solution in a reasonable time. Run-of-mine material, *e.g.*, low-grade ore from stripping operations, may be leached without crushing, and a fairly high copper recovery made by heap leaching.

This method, which usually takes years, may be greatly accelerated to days, or even hours, by sufficient reduction in particle size. The usual procedure in percolation leaching is to crush and grind the ore to a degree sufficient to permit free percolation.

At the usual size to which ore is crushed and ground for percolation leaching (*e.g.*, ¼ to ⅜ in.), leach solution and wash waters are able to penetrate the particles and take effect in the usual cycle time.

Obviously, fines or slimes when leached separately permit penetration in much shorter time. Also sands ground to agitation size and treated by agitation, as at Katanga, probably leach faster than by percolation.

2. Choice of strength of solution and solvent is a question of balancing several factors. Practically, the acidity of liquors used for copper leaching is less than 10 per cent, the average figures for Inspiration, Chile, and Andes being 4.1, 6, and 7.6 per cent, respectively. In copper leaching, this acid cannot be neutralized completely because compounds of iron and aluminum precipitate from solutions that are too nearly neutral. These precipitates, if allowed to form on the ore in percolation leaching, not only carry down copper but also interfere with percolation. Another reason for not neutralizing all the acid is that a certain minimum of free acid, usually about 16 gpl, is necessary for good copper tank-house operation.

Ferric iron is used at Inspiration as a solvent for sulfides. It is regenerated during electrolysis by anodic oxidation and is reduced by contact with the sulfides in the ore. The solution to leaching usually carries about 1 per cent ferric iron, and the solution after leaching, about 0.5 per cent.

The solvent may contain several other acid-soluble elements, in addition to copper. These may be iron (both ferrous and ferric), alumina, potassium, sodium and magnesium sulfates, arsenic, chlorine, nitric acid, molybdenum, etc. These may cause harm by building up to an extent requiring their removal by solution discard or otherwise. Other elements, such as arsenic, chlorine, and nitric acid, may be directly injurious. Sulfates of sodium, potassium, magnesium, and aluminum are not harmful, and aluminum sulfate in sufficient concentration may even be beneficial, if ferric sulfate is present, in that it results in an appreciably higher deposition efficiency in electrolysis.

Solutions are purified at Katanga, Andes, and Chuquicamata. Purification by solution discard was carried out at Ajo. Neither purification nor discard is necessary at Inspiration, where there may be a deficiency of iron dissolved from the ore, which deficiency is made up by iron used for cementation of wash liquors.

It has been said that iron is harmful in electrolytic solutions because of its conversion to the ferric form, which reduces cathodic deposition efficiency. It should not be overlooked that aside from use of ferric iron for leaching sulfides, ferrous iron is useful for two reasons: (1) because its depolarizing action appreciably reduces deposition voltage; (2) this same depolarization acts to prevent lead anodes from peroxidation and disintegration. The possible voltage reduction by anodic depolarization is considerable, when sufficient ferrous iron is present.

3. Time of contact is a very important factor, especially when leaching slowly soluble sulfides. Usually "time of contact" includes only that time during which fresh leach liquor is brought into contact with the ore. In agitation leaching as at Katanga, constant relative movement of ore and solution is brought about. At Chuquicamata, however, the practice is different, in that "soaking" periods are used, during which there is no relative movement of ore and solution (see Chap. 6, page 151).

At Inspiration acid-solution contact time is about 8 days, the total cycle being 13 days. At Andes, the total cycle is 9 days, divided as follows: charging 1 day, leaching (acid contact) 6 days, washing 1 day, excavating 1 day.

At the Union Miniere plant at Katanga[1] leaching is entirely by agitation and the estimated leaching time (time of contact) from pilot-plant data was 48 hr for 3-mesh material and 9 hr for 10-mesh material.

4. Temperature is important inasmuch as solubility of copper sulfides is raised appreciably by increasing the temperature of the solvent carrying ferric iron. Inspiration finds it necessary to heat the solution from the tank house on its way to the leaching system. This heating is done by steam at 5 lb pressure flowing through 1-in. chemical lead pipes having a $\frac{3}{16}$-in. wall, the pipes being immersed in lead-lined tanks through which the solution flows. By heating the solvent from about 20°C to an average temperature of about 35°C, sulfide copper extraction was increased from between 40 and 50 per cent to about 75 per cent.

Leaching of Zinc. As far as is known, no ores of zinc are leached directly to recover the metal. Zinc occurs in commercial quantities as the sulfide (sphalerite), the carbonate (smithsonite), the silicate (calamine), or oxide (franklinite, zincite). The sulfide is most important as a source of zinc, and it is easily treated by roasting, followed by leaching

[1] A. H. Wheeler and H. Y. Eagle, Leaching Operations of Union Miniere du Haut Katanga, *Trans. AIME,* Vol. 106, p. 609, 1933.

and electrolysis, or by one of the pyrometallurgical processes. The zinc oxides are mined at only one location in the world, the New Jersey Zinc Co's. operations in the Eastern United States, and have their own special treatment. Carbonate and silicate ores have yet to be handled with complete success and perhaps a leaching method will some day prove suitable for treating them.

Roasting of zinc sulfide concentrate has already been discussed. Several solvents are available for the resulting zinc oxide and zinc sulfate calcine, but only sulfuric acid is used at present. A chloride-leaching technique was used in England for several years, but was abandoned in 1924.

Leaching with sulfuric acid is comparatively simple, according to the reactions:

$$ZnO + H_2SO_4 = ZnSO_4 + H_2O$$

Details of zinc-leaching practice at some of the world's major electrolytic zinc plants appear in Chap. 7. As will be seen, leaching and electrolysis in all of these plants have the same basic structure, but differ in certain points of technique. These differences are the following:

Acid strengths for leaching range from 90 gpl sulfuric acid for a so-called "low-acid" plant to over 500 gpl for a "high-acid" plant. The high-acid leach is faster and has a higher capacity per unit but tends to take large amounts of impurities into solution. In any case, leaching proceeds rapidly and is usually complete in a few hours. Temperature of leach solution in a high-acid plant has to be higher than in the low-acid plant in order to hold in solution the larger quantities of zinc dissolved per unit of volume.

Current density for most electrolytic zinc plants runs about 30 to 40 amp per sq ft of cathode area. The Sullivan plant at Kellogg, Idaho, uses approximately 100 amp with good results. High current density goes with high acid strength. Each technique requires a whole series of special provisions, most of which are brought out in the detailed discussions of Chap. 7.

Leaching may be either continuous or batch. Continuous leaching, usually carried out in air-agitated tanks of the Pachuca type, is best suited to plants with large tonnages of a fairly uniform feed. It does not lend itself well to handling variations in content of impurities. Batch leaching, done in simple, mechanically agitated tanks, usually turns out a purer solution for electrolysis than the continuous system, because each batch can be held and treated until its content of impurities is known by analysis to be below the desired limits.

Single leaching, either continuous or batch, is used by some plants because it requires the minimum investment in equipment. Calcine is leached in an excess of acid until all the zinc is dissolved. Fresh calcine is then carefully added until the acid strength is down to about 0.4 per cent. A neutral solution is required in order to precipitate iron as a purifying agent. This cannot be done by adding fresh calcine because the excess of calcine needed would involve loss of undissolved zinc. Therefore, the remaining 0.4 per cent of acid is neutralized by adding lime. This system requires great care on the part of the operator in order to balance exactly the additions of fresh calcine and lime. Too much calcine means loss of zinc or use of extra acid and lime. Too much lime loads the system up with calcium sulfate, wastes acid, and increases filtering difficulties.

Double leaching is easier to control, but takes more equipment than single leaching. In the double-leach system, the main body of pulp is brought down to neutrality by adding excess calcine; then the residue containing some undissolved zinc is treated with dilute sulfuric acid in a separate leach. The small amount of solution from this second leach is mixed with the solution going to the first leach. The process, unlike single leaching, requires a second set of leach tanks and thickeners.

Purification of Solutions. Although leaching of zinc calcine is easy and rapid, difficulty arises because much of the original content of impurities in the ore goes through the roasting process and into solution along with the zinc. Impurities commonly found in zinc leach solutions include silica, alumina, iron, arsenic, antimony, copper, cadmium, cobalt, and some others. These have to be eliminated from the solution before electrolysis, or at least brought below certain permissible limits, or the zinc recovery becomes uneconomic or even impossible. Allowable quantities of some of these impurities are as follows:

Element	Grams per Liter
Germanium	0.00005
Antimony	0.00005
Arsenic	0.0001
Nickel	0.0005
Chlorine	0.001
Copper	0.01
Cobalt	0.01
Iron	0.03
Manganese	0.5–3.0

These impurities are removed in two groups by separate processes. The first group (iron, silica, alumina, arsenic, antimony, germanium, and tin or bismuth, if present) is removed along with the precipitate of ferric hydroxide that forms when the leach solution is neutralized. The second group (copper, cadmium, cobalt, and nickel) is removed by treating the neutral and filtered leach solution with zinc dust. Germanium, cobalt, and some others, if present in large quantities, require special methods for removal.

For successful removal of the impurities of the first group, two conditions must be met: (1) there must be at least 10 units of iron present for each unit of impurity to be removed; (2) all the iron must be oxidized to the ferric state. The first condition is met by adding ferrous or ferric sulfate in solution to the initial leach solution. The iron sulfate is usually obtained by leaching scrap iron with spent electrolyte. The second condition is met by adding enough MnO_2 to the first leach to oxidize any ferrous iron present to the ferric state. The reactions are:

$$2FeSO_4 + 2H_2SO_4 + MnO_2 = Fe_2(SO_4)_3 + MnSO_4 + 2H_2O$$
$$Fe_2(SO_4)_3 + 3ZnO + 3H_2O = 2Fe(OH)_3 + 3ZnSO_4$$

The MnO_2 added can be either pyrolusite concentrate or the manganese-bearing slime from the electrolytic cells. In the cell, manganese forms on the anode in a slime that continuously drops off and collects on the bottom of the tank.

Opinion varies as to the mechanism of purification with ferric hydroxide. One view holds that the iron precipitate simply carries arsenic and antimony out of the solution by adsorption; hence the use of the term "iron fall" to describe this step. Another view is that reactions between the iron hydroxide and the impurities are responsible. The following is typical:

$$4Fe(OH)_3 + H_3AsO_3 = Fe_4O_5(OH)_5As + 5H_2O$$

Impurities of the second group can be removed by agitation of the neutral solution (after filtering off the hydroxide precipitate) with zinc dust. The mechanism is simple interchange of the impurity with the zinc.

Copper usually replaces the zinc quite rapidly and is easily removed. Cadmium offers more difficulty and requires an excess of zinc dust over the theoretical amount to secure complete replacement. It is usually necessary to purify with zinc dust in two stages. The first agitation with zinc dust picks up the copper and most of the other impurities. After filtration, a second agitation with zinc dust catches all the cadmium and the other impurities. Elevated temperatures during agitation are needed to pick up nickel, if present. Any silica remaining is caught by zinc dust, but the result is a slimy residue that is hard to filter.

Further details of the zinc recovery process are brought out in the plant descriptions in Chap. 7.

Leaching of Lead.   Possible raw materials for leaching of lead include electrolytic zinc-plant tailings, lead sulfate flue dust, lead sulfate sludges from sulfuric acid chambers, lead sulfate from scrap storage batteries, lead sulfide concentrates high in silver sulfides, and complex or low-grade zinc–lead–iron sulfide ores.

As far as is known, little commercial use is being made at present of a leaching process on lead ore.   It seems probable, however, that this situation will change inasmuch as a leaching process is perfectly feasible and offers some economic advantage for handling low-grade lead ores that do not respond well to concentration by gravity or flotation.   If and when lead leaching comes into use, it will probably involve leaching with acidulated brine.

Generally speaking, oxidized lead compounds and lead sulfate are soluble in saturated brine that has been acidified with hydrochloric or sulfuric acid.   Precipitation of the lead can be based on the fact that at 90°C such a solution will hold about 9 per cent lead, but at 30°C it will hold only 1 per cent lead.   The lead can also be precipitated electrolytically.

Lead sulfide is not readily soluble in brine alone, but dissolution speeds up sufficiently if ferric iron is added to the solution.   The reaction leaves a residue of elemental sulfur.   Zinc sulfide is not affected significantly by this solvent.

If electrolytic precipitation of the lead is used, as in the Tainton process described in the following paragraphs, absence of ferric iron in the cell causes evolution of chlorine at the anode.   This complicates cell construction and operation because it requires scrubbing towers to recover the chlorine.   The problem can be avoided by providing sufficient ferric iron in the electrolyte.   If the solution in the tanks is agitated, complete depolarization results and no chlorine is evolved.   The iron is oxidized to the ferric form in proportion to the lead precipitated, but if the solutions are used cyclically on material carrying lead sulfide, the ferric iron readily reduces again to the ferrous state.   The method is analogous to the leaching and electrolytic cycle at Inspiration.   Practicality of the lead-leaching method has been proven on a test-plant scale.

The Tainton process for lead, operated on a semicommercial basis for a time by Bunker Hill at Kellogg, Idaho, treated slime residues from the zinc-leaching plant.[1]   The process involved roasting the galena to sulfate, removing soluble sulfates of manganese, magnesium, and other metals by a water wash, dissolution of lead sulfate in a saturated brine containing chlorine from the electrolytic cells, and recovery of lead and silver by

[1] D. M. Liddell, *Handbook of Nonferrous Metallurgy*, p. 154, McGraw-Hill Book Company, Inc., New York, 1945.

electrolysis at high current density and high acid strength in a cell with rotating sheet-iron cathodes and graphite anodes.

Leaching of Manganese. Sulfuric and sulfurous acids have proved most successful as solvents in the leaching of manganese ores. An impressive body of data has been built up from both laboratory and plant experience that should enable successful leaching plants for manganese ores to be designed when the need arises. All such work has used either sulfuric acid or sulfur dioxide as the solvent. The Bureau of Mines has done some work with nitrogen peroxide, NO_2, in water as the solvent, but large-scale tests have not been made. For detailed descriptions of plant experience with both sulfuric acid and sulfur dioxide for leaching of manganese ores, see Chap. 8.

The rate of dissolution in sulfurous acid of various manganese minerals has been studied by Davis.[1] His findings are as follows:

Dissolve rapidly: pyrolusite (MnO_2), psilomelane ($MnO_2 \cdot H_2O$), wad (earthy hydrous oxide), braunite ($3Mn_2O_3 \cdot MnSiO_3$).

Dissolves slowly: hausmannite (Mn_3O_4).

Dissolve very slowly: manganite ($Mn_2O_3 \cdot H_2O$), rhodochrosite ($MnCO_3$).

Virtually insoluble: rhodonite ($MnSiO_3$).

The rate of dissolution of hausmannite or rhodochrosite can be made comparable to that of pyrolusite by roasting at 650 to 900°C. Van Barneveld had previously reported braunite to be "not commercially soluble" in sulfurous acid. Davis attributes the difference in results to "different physical or chemical composition, as braunite is of variable composition."

The Bureau of Mines has made an extensive investigation of the solubility of low-grade manganese ores in the United States, and the results bear out Davis's findings.[2]

It is interesting to note that many manganese ores carry oxides of other metals that cannot be leached out by heating with dilute sulfuric acid, *e.g.*, zinc, copper, nickel, etc. However, some of these oxides, together with the manganese, can be dissolved by a combination of sulfur dioxide and sulfuric acid. For leaching with the latter, the various oxides must be reduced by roasting to manganous oxide, MnO, which is soluble in dilute sulfuric. This method is necessary for production by electrolysis of either manganese metal or manganese dioxide for dry-battery use.

Small-scale tests by the Bureau of Mines show that this reducing roast can be accomplished by using coal, coke, natural gas, butane, or oil as the

[1] C. W. Davis, Dissolution of Various Manganese Minerals, *U.S. Bureau of Mines Report of Investigation* 3024, 1930.

[2] W. T. Wyman and S. F. Ravitz, SO_2 Leaching Tests on Various Western Manganese Ores, *U.S. Bureau of Mines Report of Investigation* 4077.

reducing agent (see Chap. 8). Oil seemed to yield a better reduction with less weight of fuel required per ton of feed. In the Bureau's tests, oil was used at the rate of 6.48 per cent by weight of the total feed to the roaster.

Small-scale reduction tests preparing ore for leaching and electrolysis to produce pure manganese dioxide were made by the Dorr Co. Coal was mixed with the ore to reduce the manganese dioxide. It was necessary to add coal to make up about 10 to 20 per cent of the weight of the charge. This is about double the weight of reducing agent in the Bureau's tests with oil.

Leaching with sulfuric acid, after reduction by roasting, is done in batches, usually in mechanical agitators. Solution strength is about 25 to 30 gpl of sulfuric acid. Leaching takes about 1½ hr, and there is a rise in temperature of about 10°C during the leach. The solution must carry about 135 to 150 gpl of ammonium sulfate during leaching and electrolysis. This compound serves to buffer the solution, to ensure conductivity in the electrolytic cell (which is a diaphragm cell), and to prevent precipitation of manganese dioxide in the cell.

Leaching proceeds until manganese solution is complete. Sulfuric acid is added as needed to keep the pH at 2.5. At the end of the leach, the pH is brought up to about 6 by adding either fresh calcine or ammonia. Use of calcine cuts recovery of manganese from about 98 to about 93 per cent.

Manganese solution for electrolysis must contain no impurity in amounts greater than about 1 mg per l, except for some alkali- and alkaline-earth metals. The solution is purified in two or three stages: by adding iron, oxidizing it with manganese dioxide, then precipitating it as ferric hydroxide; by adding ammonium or hydrogen sulfide to precipitate the sulfides of iron, arsenic, copper, cobalt, nickel, lead, zinc, molybdenum, etc.; by cooling the solution to around 10°C, which throws out magnesium as a triple salt of magnesium, ammonium, and manganese. For details of the electrolytic process at the Bureau of Mines plant and at the Knoxville plant of Electro-Manganese Corp., see Chap. 8.

Sulfur dioxide leaching, which requires no preliminary roast, offers interesting possibilities for treating the low-grade manganese ores of the United States. Having been tested by the author during the First World War, the sulfur dioxide process reached plant scale during the Second World War at the Three Kids mine and plant of Manganese Ore Co., a subsidiary of M. A. Hanna Co. For details of the plant and comment on its operation, see Chap. 8.

Briefly, the process involved leaching the dry-ground ore in packed towers against incoming sulfur dioxide gas, thus converting the manganese dioxide of the ore to the sulfate plus some thionates. Leached pulp was washed in a countercurrent decantation circuit. Pregnant solution was neutralized by adding manganous oxide, prepared in a small rotary kiln, and the solution was purified by precipitation of iron hydroxide and by adding zinc dust to remove copper.

The pure solution was evaporated to yield a product containing manganese sulfate, manganese dithionate, and various alkali dithionates. This crystalline mixture was roasted in a rotary kiln to form Mn_3O_4 and sulfur dioxide, the latter going back to the leaching towers. The calcine went to a nodulizing kiln. Because the final nodular product still carried undue amounts of undecomposed Na_2SO_4, it was heap-leached with water. Final product carried about 65 per cent manganese, 0.25 per cent sulfur, 0.010 per cent phosphorus, and 2.82 per cent silica.

The many difficulties this plant ran into, some of which are summarized in Chap. 8, were not due to any inherent failure of the process itself. The plant was designed and built in a tremendous hurry, under wartime conditions, and too little time was given to study of the chemistry of the process on this particular ore. For example, the conditions of temperature and acid concentration under which the various manganese-sulphur-oxygen compounds are formed should have had longer study. Also, much more study should have been devoted to the formation of these compounds during evaporation. For instance, it was not known until the plant had run for some time that alkali salts, formed in the evaporator, made a low-melting eutectic mixture with manganese sulfate under the conditions met in the rotary kiln. The resulting ring formation in the kiln caused endless trouble. Given time to work out these problems, the process still has much to offer the research metallurgist.

Leaching of Nickel. About 90 per cent of the world's nickel has come from the sulfide ore bodies of the International Nickel Co. of Canada, Ltd. The metal is recovered by combined flotation and smelting processes. Rising interest has been shown, however, in use of hydrometallurgical processes to recover nickel from the ores where it occurs as the silicate, garnierite, whose composition is $H_2(NiMg)SiO_4 \cdot H_2O$.

One large-scale plant, the Nicaro Nickel Co. in Cuba, has already used a leaching process on this type of ore, and the method has been tested on other garnierite ores in North and South America. A continued high price for nickel will no doubt encourage wider use of recovery methods involving leaching. For a detailed description of the Nicaro process, see Chap. 8, page 270.

An ammonia-leaching technique was used at Nicaro quite similar to the ammonia-leaching process for copper used by Kennecott, Calumet, and Hecla. For nickel, the process is based on the fact that ammonia and ammonium salts react with metallic nickel in the presence of oxygen to form soluble nickel ammonium complexes.

At Nicaro, the ore was roasted with producer gas in multiple-hearth furnaces to a maximum temperature of 1350°F. Nickel and cobalt were reduced to metal, and iron was reduced to the magnetic oxide. It was found essential to balance carefully the composition of the roaster gases (as to H_2, CO, steam, and CO_2) and the temperature in order to get maximum reduction of nickel and to cut down production of a nonmagnetic iron. Some metallic iron was unavoidably produced.

A solution of ammonia and ammonium carbonate was used as the solvent, but in order to dissolve the nickel, oxygen must also be present to oxidize both the nickel and any metallic iron present. Turboaerators supplied this oxygen in the Nicaro plant. The reaction was probably as follows, according to Tobelmann and Morgan:[1]

$$2Ni + O_2 + 2(NH_4)_2CO_3 + 2NH_4OH = 2NiCO_3 \cdot 3NH_3 + 4H_2O$$

Iron was probably taken into solution as follows:

$$2Fe + O_2 + 2H_2O + 4(NH_4)_2CO_3 = 2FeCO_3 \cdot (NH_4)_2CO_3 + 4NH_4OH$$
$$4FeCO_3 \cdot (NH_4)_2CO_3 + O_2 + 2H_2O = 2Fe_2(CO_3)_3 \cdot (NH_4)_2CO_3 + NH_4OH$$
$$Fe_2(CO_3)_3 \cdot (NH_4)_2CO_3 + 6NH_4OH = 2Fe(OH)_3 + 4(NH_4)_2CO_3$$

The result was a solution carrying nickel as a nickel ammonium carbonate in which the iron precipitated as ferric hydroxide. It was found preferable to precipitate the iron in the ore pulp because the ore then carried down the gelatinous precipitate that otherwise would have been difficult to filter.

An interesting feature of the Nicaro operation was the use of magnetic flocculation, based on the presence of the magnetite produced in the roasters. By this means required thickener area for settling the leached pulp was about one-tenth of what otherwise might have been needed.

The clarified nickel solution was heated by steam in Semet-Solvay stills, the steam passing up as the solution descended in the towers. Ammonia vaporized during the descent, and when the ammonia content had decreased to about 2 per cent, green basic nickel carbonate began to precipitate. The solution leaving the stills at the bottom was stripped of nickel and contained less than 0.01 per cent of ammonia.

The basic nickel carbonate slurry was filtered and then calcined in an oil-fired rotary kiln. The nickel oxide produced carried 76.93 per cent

---

[1] H. A. Tobelmann and H. J. Morgan, "Review of the Nicaro Nickel Project," Report No. 97271, Plancor 690, U.S. Department of Commerce, Washington, D.C., p. 52.

nickel and 0.58 per cent cobalt.   Some of it was reduced to metal in a plant at Wilmington, Del., but most of it was sold as the oxide.

Caron on Nickel Leaching.   The method of ammonia leaching used at Nicaro is essentially the process developed by Prof. Caron of Delft University, Holland.   He has presented two papers to the AIME which deal with ammonia leaching of nickel and cobalt ores and the subsequent separation of the two metals.   The following notes are abstracted from these papers with the kind permission of Prof. Caron and the AIME.

The first paper deals with fundamental and practical aspects of leaching various ores of cobalt and nickel with ammonia solutions.   Other than copper, nickel, and cobalt, there are few ore constituents easily dissolved by ammonia.   Therefore, the precipitated basic nickel carbonate, as at Nicaro, contains only small amounts of iron, manganese, magnesium, silica, sulfates, or sulfides.

The cobalt content, however, may vary considerably, depending on the ore treated.   The metal from pure garnierite ores usually has less than 1 per cent cobalt.   The metal from medium-grade iron-rich nickel ores may have as much as 2 to 3 per cent cobalt.   That from laterite ores may run as high as 10 per cent.   Separation of cobalt and nickel, therefore, becomes important.[1]   Professor Caron's second paper deals with four methods of effecting this separation:

1. By treating precipitated basic nickel carbonate, which carries cobalt, with leach liquors having a low carbon dioxide to ammonia ratio, nickel can be dissolved preferentially to cobalt.   The separation is selective and is not complete, the bulk of the nickel being redissolved with a small amount of cobalt.   The residue carries most of the cobalt.   An example is given of a precipitate carrying 0.55 per cent cobalt that was treated with a liquor containing 7.12 per cent ammonia and 2.12 per cent carbon dioxide.   The residue was about 3 per cent of the original weight and contained 1.93 per cent iron, 6.01 per cent cobalt, and 34.87 per cent nickel.   The liquor was distilled and gave a precipitate carrying 0.008 per cent iron, 0.0146 per cent cobalt, and 42.37 per cent nickel.   Thus, 94 per cent of the cobalt in the original precipitate stayed in the residue that made up 3.5 per cent of the weight of the original sample.

An unfavorable factor in this method is that the residue filters badly owing to its slimy character, probably caused by silica.

2. Selective precipitation in stages was found to avoid the difficulty with filtration.   An example is:

[1] For details of the nickel-cobalt separation methods being developed by Chemical Construction Corp., see Is the Chemico Metals Technique Tomorrow's Metallurgy? *Engineering and Mining Journal*, Vol. 153, No. 6, June, 1952.

	Assay, %		Ratio of cobalt, %
	Ni	Co	
First precipitate...........	0.5631	0.0006	0.107
Second precipitate.........	5.6231	0.0062	0.111
Third precipitate..........	0.2810	0.0176	5.9
Fourth precipitate.........	0.1347	0.0481	26.3

The method of this test has concentrated more than 90 per cent of the total cobalt into the last two precipitates, which contain only 6.3 per cent of the total nickel. The first two precipitates contain less cobalt than is usually found in electrolytic nickel. This second method seems simpler and more economical than the first. The products filter easily.

3. The first two methods work well in separating nickel and cobalt, but other impurities have also to be considered. To eliminate iron, manganese, silica, etc., Prof. Caron has devised the following method:[1]

Solutions saturated with nickel may be obtained by partial distillation of pregnant liquors only to the point where nickel begins to precipitate. After cooling, these solutions are saturated with carbon dioxide, which precipitates the bulk of the nickel. Under these conditions, the impurities other than cobalt remain in solution while basic nickel carbonate precipitates. Analysis of a nickel precipitate formed in this way is as follows:

	Per Cent
Nickel....................	39.62
Cobalt...................	0.05
Iron.....................	Trace
Manganous oxide..........	0.006
Silica....................	0.004
SO_4.....................	0.005

4. Professor Caron also discusses the problem of separating alloys of nickel and cobalt. These can be separated under proper conditions by using them as soluble anodes in a suitable diaphragm cell. The exit solution must then be one that is substantially free of cobalt and from which the nickel may be recovered. The method is based on selective electrolytic deposition, under certain conditions, of cobalt in preference to nickel. The electrolyte is a modified ammonium carbonate solution. Details are too lengthy to be reproduced here and should be sought in Prof. Caron's paper.

Leaching of Vanadium. Vanadium occurs in several complex forms, each one of which serves as a source of the metal in the particular deposit

[1] See Dutch Patent 55,376–402.43, Sept. 16, 1943, and French Patent 931.765, Aug. 2, 1946.

in which it is found. There is little similarity, however, among the minerals themselves or the methods used to treat them. The minerals used as a source of vanadium are as follows:

Mineral	Composition	Principal deposits
Patronite.............	V_2S_9 (approx.)	Minasragra, Peru
Roscoelite............	$2H_2O \cdot K_2O \cdot Al_2O_3 \cdot 2V_2O_5 \cdot 6SiO_2$	Southwestern Colorado
Carnotite.............	$K_2O \cdot 2U_2O_3 \cdot V_2O_5 \cdot 2H_2O$	Colorado and Utah
Vanadinite...........	$(PbCl)Pb_4(VO_4)_3$	Spain, Mexico, and Arizona
Descloizite...........	$Zn_2V_2O_8 \cdot Zn(OH)_2$	Broken Hill, Rhodesia
Mottramite...........	$Cu_2V_2O_8 \cdot Cu(OH)_2$	Tsumeb, Southwest Africa

Patronite[1] has been treated by leaching, following an oxidizing roast to get rid of the sulfur. Solvents can be either sulfuric acid or a strong alkali, such as sodium carbonate or sodium hydroxide. With the acid, evaporation of the pregnant solution yields a low-grade vanadium oxide. With the alkali, sodium vanadate is formed in solution, from which a high-grade vanadium oxide can be recovered by acidifying with sulfuric acid. The roasted patronite can also be smelted directly to ferrovanadium in an electric furnace.

Roscoelite and *carnotite* are usually treated together in the mills of the Colorado Plateau region. Roscoelite alone can be treated by roasting with salt to convert the vanadium to a water-soluble vanadate. This is dissolved with hot water, and vanadic acid is precipitated from the acidified solution by boiling. This precipitate is filtered, dried, and fused.

For treatment of both minerals together, either a cold hydrochloric acid leach or a hot sodium carbonate leach is used. A chloridizing roast must precede either one.

In the acid-leach system, a preliminary water wash extracts about 75 per cent of the vanadium as sodium vanadate. The water-leach tailings are then releached with hydrochloric acid obtained by scrubbing the exit gases from the roaster. This dissolves about 90 per cent of the uranium and recovers another 15 per cent of the vanadium. The vanadium precipitates with sulfuric acid as "red cake." The method is feasible only where the lime content of the ore is less than 2.5 per cent.

In the carbonate leach, the ore is roasted with salt, then leached, either by percolation or agitation, with strong sodium carbonate solution (up to 10 per cent). About 85 to 90 per cent of both uranium and vanadium is recovered. Careful adjustment of pH with sulfuric acid then precipitates uranium as "yellow cake." More sulfuric acid precipitates vanadium as "red cake."

[1] H. A. Doerner in D. M. Liddell's *Handbook of Nonferrous Metallurgy*, p. 617, McGraw-Hill Book Company, Inc., New York, 1945.

Precipitation is easier with the carbonate process, but the circuit is harder to control. Lime has no ill effect on the carbonate process, but high lime can add materially to the cost of the acid method.

Vanadinite can be treated, according to Doerner, by a method devised by J. E. Conley. The mineral is fused with a mixture of soda ash and caustic soda. Lead is recovered as the metal, and vanadium is precipitated with slaked lime, yielding calcium vanadate. This can be dissolved in sulfuric acid, the calcium sulfate filtered off, and the vanadium recovered as the oxide.

Descloizite and *mottramite* could probably both be treated by the method used at Broken Hill, Rhodesia, for descloizite (zinc-lead vanadate) (see Chap. 8, page 307). The method involves grinding the ore in water with additions of manganese dioxide and superphosphate. The latter is added as an oxidizing agent to ensure the vanadium precipitating eventually as vanadium oxide and not as a lower oxide. The superphosphate increases the stability of the V_2O_5.

Leaching is by batch agitation with sulfuric acid in two stages. The first stage requires that the acid be added slowly, without much rise in temperature. This weak acid solution dissolves the zinc without affecting the vanadium. The second, or strong acid, leach dissolves the vanadium. The solution finishes with about 25 gpl of sulfuric acid and 25 gpl of vanadium oxide in solution. A conditioning period is provided to convert any silica gel that might form to a granular state, after which the solution is filtered. Vanadium is precipitated by adding sulfuric acid and boiling.

Leaching of Uranium. Uranium ores may be classified roughly into primary and secondary types. Pitchblende is the chief primary mineral. It is a massive, heavy, black mineral composed of uranium oxides carrying varying amounts of other elements such as lead, calcium, iron, and copper. Carnotite, composed of hydrated oxides of uranium, vanadium, potassium, etc., is typical of the secondary mineral group. For details of recovery methods for each, see Chap. 8.

Briefly, the method for pitchblende used at Port Hope, Ontario, consists in roasting the pitchblende concentrate received from the mines at 1100°C in order to decompose sulfides and carbonates, if present, and to volatilize arsenic and antimony. The roasted ore is then mixed with salt and roasted again to chloridize silver and uranium. The calcine is ground and leached with 50 per cent sulfuric acid. Barium chloride is added to collect the radium; hydrochloric acid precipitates the silver; sodium nitrate is added to oxidize the uranium. After further purification, the uranium is precipitated as sodium uranate by adding caustic soda. Uranium metal is finally produced by electrolysis.

The method for recovering uranium from carnotite ores has already been touched on under vanadium. Two methods are used: the hydrochloric acid leach, and the sodium carbonate leach. Of the two, the alkali leach seems more satisfactory because of easier filtration of precipitates, less trouble with lime in the ore, and lower cost. For details of the method as used in a Colorado Plateau mill, see Chap. 8, page 294.

Leaching of Antimony. Stibnite (Sb_2S_3) is the principal mineral of antimony, and because of the relative ease of treatment of stibnite by pyrometallurgical methods, a leaching process has never been applied to it commercially. Stibnite is soluble in alkali sulfides or hydroxides and a pure antimony sulfide can be recovered from the resulting solutions by precipitation with carbon dioxide or sulfur dioxide. The method has yet to be tested on a plant scale.

The scarcity of antimony during the Second World War brought about the development of two electrolytic plants in the Coeur d'Alene district of Idaho that offer interesting examples of leaching of antimony.

At one plant, that of Bunker Hill & Sullivan at Kellogg, Idaho, tetrahedrite concentrates ($3Cu_2S \cdot Sb_2S_3$) were mixed with sodium carbonate, sodium sulfate, and coal, and then fed to an electric furnace. Melt temperature was about 2,300°F. The matte that formed in the furnace was ground and leached with sodium sulfide to form the electrolyte for producing pure antimony. Sheet-steel cathodes were used in a diaphragm cell. Current density was 20 amp per sq ft. A weak solution was purified with barium sulfide and then recycled.

In the other plant, that of Sunshine Mining Co., near Kellogg, a somewhat similar process was used.[1] The antimony mineral was a silver-bearing tetrahedrite. The concentrate was leached with hot concentrated sodium sulfide. The solution carried about 250 gpl of sodium sulfide and 10 gpl of antimony. Leaching took about 9 hr at 95°C. Electrolysis was in diaphragm cells with an anolyte of caustic soda and barren catholyte, and a catholyte carrying 50 gpl of antimony and 250 gpl of sodium hydroxide. Copper and silver were insoluble in the leaching step.

The cycle produces sodium sulfates and sulfites, which build up and destroy the effectiveness of the solvent. The spent electrolyte was therefore regenerated by treatment with barium sulfide, forming sodium sulfide and barium sulfate, which was reduced again to barium sulfide by roasting in a rotary kiln with coal.

The process worked well as a wartime measure, but proved too expensive when former sources of antimony again became accessible.

[1] W. Church Holmes, How Electrolytic Antimony Is Made at Sunshine Plant, *Engineering and Mining Journal*, Vol. 145, No. 3, March, 1944.

CHAPTER 2

CRUSHING, GRINDING, CLASSIFICATION

The first mechanical requirement in the leaching of an ore is certainly the breaking down of the ore particles to a proper size so that the leach solutions can penetrate each particle and extract the soluble mineral. Some happily situated orebodies, like that of the old Ohio Copper Co., may not need to be mined at all for a satisfactory extraction. Others, more impervious, need fine grinding to unlock the desired mineral. In this chapter, some of the relationships that dictate the kind and extent of the size reduction required for leaching are examined, and examples drawn from practice are cited.

Most economical of all leaching processes, of course, are those in which ore can be leached in place. The classic example of this is the Ohio Copper Co., near Salt Lake City (for details, see page 71). This company, facing failure because of the high cost of mining a low-grade copper ore by standard underground methods, achieved success by simply eliminating the mining step altogether. The mine staff noted that water filtering down through the orebody was rich in soluble copper and that this water was collected by the impervious footwall of the orebody. It remained then only to spray water on the surface over the orebody and to let the solution drain down into a tunnel below the orebody. The copper was precipitated on tin cans.

The leaching was brought about by oxidation of pyrite and consequent dissolution of the copper sulfides by reaction with ferric sulfate. The essentials were a well-fractured orebody through which water and air could penetrate; presence of both copper and iron sulfides; presence of an impervious footwall to prevent loss of solution.

Similar techniques are followed in getting the last bit of copper out of some abandoned mine workings in the Southwest. Leaching is also being used in the Southwest to recover copper from rock that is so low in copper content as to be classed as waste under any other treatment method. It is rock that must be broken in any event to open up orebodies for surface mining. Water is sprayed over the rock, wherever it has been dumped, and the copper-bearing solution is collected by various means below the dump. Iron precipitation is standard.

30

CRUSHING

Crushing ore for leaching, assuming that the ore cannot be treated by the cheaper methods just mentioned, should not be dismissed lightly. Crushers have been used for hundreds of years, but it is becoming apparent that they have been taken for granted for far too many of these years. Proper design of a crushing plant is well worth considerable study, in view of the high rates that must be paid for labor and the steadily increasing burden of taxation and operating costs that mines must bear.

Hence, the trend is toward simplicity, toward elimination of the multistage crushing plants one used to see. These complex flow sheets simply take too many men to operate and maintain. Their materials cost for maintenance is too high. Modern crushing plants also tend to be built on a scale large enough to crush in one shift, or certainly no more than two shifts, enough ore to keep the rest of the mill going three shifts. Ease of operation is emphasized, as in the Magma Copper Co. mill, described later in this chapter, where one man takes care of the plant.

It is not within the scope of this book to discuss crushing-plant design at length, because several handbooks and textbooks have already covered this subject exhaustively.[1] However, it seems worth noting that great improvements in design of crushing, feeding, and screening equipment have done much in recent years to help achieve higher capacities, in simpler flow sheets, at lower cost. It is possible to obtain crushers as finely designed and built as a good watch, and quite economical in the use of power. New screening devices have been announced that should give better closed-circuit operation of crushers at lower cost. This should be of particular interest to plants doing crushing prior to leaching, inasmuch as the aim should be to crush as finely as needed, but not more so. This goal can be approached more closely by effective screening of crusher products than in any other way.

GRINDING

Grinding, like crushing, cannot be taken for granted despite the innumerable grinding plants now in existence or the decades during which "modern" techniques have been in use. The fact is that there is still much to be learned about grinding. To achieve lowest cost and desired metallurgical results, the grinding flow sheet should be tailor-made for the specific installation. It should not be bought in package form, nor chosen simply because it worked well somewhere else.

J. F. Myers, mill superintendent at Tennessee Copper Co., has advanced

[1] For example, A. F. Taggart, *Handbook of Mineral Dressing*, John Wiley & Sons, Inc., New York, 1945.

on numerous occasions a philosophy that ought to govern design of all grinding flow sheets. In essence, his idea is that a grinding circuit cannot be regarded simply as a means of producing daily a certain amount of a product ground to a given size. A grinding circuit is rather a means of conditioning a mineral product so that it will yield optimum metallurgical results under the final treatment process. This approach balances increased fineness of grind against increased recovery, or increased cost of grinding against increased loss in mill tailing. It takes into account possible chemical reactions in the grinding mill, and possible overgrinding of softer but more valuable minerals in the ore. Only in this way can optimum results be achieved.

The literature on the grinding process is voluminous, and no attempt is being made here to examine grinding in detail. However, there are certain trends that can be noted in today's grinding plants that will be reviewed briefly.

Dry grinding is becoming more widely used outside its original home in the cement industry. Where it can be applied, it offers certain advantages in simplicity of operation. A dry-grinding plant for zinc calcine is described in this chapter on page 47. Another for dry grinding of manganese ore is described on page 48.

To illustrate the possibilities in certain dry-grinding apparatus, one may cite a device called the Fluid Energy mill. Although used mainly for extremely fine grinding, as for pigments, this mechanism could be used to grind calcine or concentrate in a reducing atmosphere to an extremely fine size. The resulting leaching process would be almost instantaneous. As far as is known, no one has made use of this technique, but it offers interesting possibilities.

The device mentioned uses a strong current of air or other gas to sweep around in an annular tube a suspension of the material to be ground. A form of air classifier removes fine material. The grinding is by abrasion of particles colliding among themselves, and must be done dry.

Two-stage grinding is being more widely adopted, although the term needs some explanation. It is used here to refer to a combination of rod mill and ball mill, which in many mills has replaced fine crushers (or rolls) and ball mills. If a product to be leached needs grinding to 10 mesh or so, use of a rod mill is probably the most satisfactory way to do it.

As an example of the cost savings and increased production that can be obtained by a switch from rolls to rod mills, note the experience at the Anaconda Copper Mining Co. mill at Anaconda, Mont. For years this plant crushed and ground the Butte ores in rolls and ball mills. Later rod mills were used in place of the rolls and screens. A 9 by 12 rod mill under test has ground 2,000 tons daily of 40 per cent plus-$\frac{3}{4}$-in. ore in one pass to minus 10 mesh. The rolls that were formerly used crushed the ball-mill feed to only minus $\frac{3}{8}$ in. The result is that the ball-mill capacity has been increased from 600 to about 1,000 tons per mill. This use of rod mills cuts the manpower requirement, cuts ball wear, and eliminates troublesome belts and clutches.

Grinding media furnish a topic for debate at every operators' meeting. One school holds to the use of alloy-steel balls, fed to the mill in carefully apportioned quantities and sizes. Another makes its grinding balls out of scrap steel and tosses them into the mill whenever the charge gets low. Still another uses the ore itself as the grinding medium. At Lake Shore, for example, plus-2-in. lumps of the ore are screened out at the shaft collar and added to the grinding mills instead of balls. Grinding capacity is cut considerably, but a cost saving of 25 cents per ton milled results. The saving is in ball wear. Pebbles for grinding have long been in use on the Rand in Africa.

Later, a similar idea was developed into the Aerofall mill, a large diameter unit in which the ore helps grind itself. Action in this mill is somewhat complex, ore particles breaking themselves against steel plates, against other fragments, and by rubbing about in the central mass. Impressive results have been obtained in a number of tests on non-metallic minerals.

Liners have come in for much study of late. It is clear by now that liners can greatly affect the economics of a grinding operation. In several recent rod-mill installations, wrong choice of liner threatened at first to hold up the operations of the whole plant. It was found that shape of liner must be suited to speed of mill, that adequate lifter bars must be provided to "key" the charge to the mill shell, that lifter bars must not be too high, that properly fitted liner bolts and plates can do much to cut down liner wear and expense. Some operators zinc-in their liners with excellent results, in that there are no bolts to work loose and the plates can be worn down much thinner than bolted plates.

There is no certainty that liner composition is as important in controlling liner wear as are the factors outlined above. Any alloy steel will wear out rapidly if forced to work under extremely corrosive or abrasive conditions.

Control of grinding circuits has received considerable attention because of the possibilities such circuits offer for automatic control. Pulp density meters can be bought or made.[1] Electric ears can register ball-mill conditions by the sound and adjust the feeder accordingly. The

[1] Carl Marquardt, An Accurate Reliable Pulp Density Meter, *Engineering and Mining Journal*, Vol. 152, No. 1.

load on classifier motors, or the sand load itself, can be measured and controlled automatically.[1] All these factors can be utilized to furnish a means of continuously adjusting conditions in the grinding circuit to provide optimum performance, as with the Massco Circuitron. However, until operators generally are able to count on a uniform feed to their mills, conditions will always arise with which automatic instruments of this kind cannot cope.

CLASSIFICATION

There need be no attempt made here to discuss the theory and practice of classification in general. The reader is referred to any standard handbook or textbook on ore dressing.[2] The purpose here is to show the possible importance of classification to the leaching process and to indicate how classification may best be carried out.

The Andes Copper and the Inspiration plants offer striking examples of the usefulness of classification in leaching. Both plants were built without provision for classification of ore before leaching, and both eventually had to turn to it. Metallurgical results were materially improved by classification. The reason for installation of classification systems at these plants was that percolation was being inhibited or prevented by fine ore particles in the leach tanks.

It should be understood, however, that fine sizes are not necessarily an unmixed evil in percolation. Fine particles that are granular, not colloidal, and that do not flocculate may actually aid percolation by helping to form minute channels or pores through which the solution may easily pass. The substance "Filteraid" is an example. On the other hand, fine particles may tend to flocculate, or to collect on the surfaces of larger fragments of ore, in such a way as to prevent dissolution of the contained soluble mineral.

It might be possible to avoid the ill effects of this type of slime particle if conditions in the leach tanks could be controlled to prevent flocculation. It is rarely possible to do this, and the only sure way of avoiding difficulty with slimes in percolation leaching is to remove the slime particles altogether and treat them in a separate circuit by agitation leaching.

At Inspiration, before the slimes were removed by classification, the total loss of copper in the tailing averaged 3.88 lb per ton. For the two

[1] Phelan McShane, Automatic Control of Pulverizers, *Engineering and Mining Journal*, September, 1948.

[2] For example, see A. F. Taggart, *Handbook of Mineral Dressing*, Sec. 8, John Wiley & Sons, Inc., New York, 1945; A. M. Gaudin, *Principles of Mineral Dressing*, McGraw-Hill Book Company, Inc., New York, 1939; or A. F. Taggart, *Elements of Ore Dressing*, John Wiley & Sons, Inc., New York, 1951.

years after classifiers were installed, the tailing loss averaged 2.66 lb per ton, a saving of 1.22 lb of copper per ton of feed.

On the basis of 9,000 tons of feed per day, this saving made possible the amortization in a reasonable time of the cost of classifiers and a separate slimes-treatment plant. Obviously, for percolation leaching the possible removal and separate treatment of fines are matters of major importance.

Equipment for classification falls into two categories: the horizontal or mechanical type of classifier, and the vertical or hydraulic type. The latter finds its chief usefulness in close sizing of feed to tables or in similar work requiring accurate splitting of a product into various fractions, according to size or specific gravity.

The first category, the mechanical classifier, is of greatest interest in leaching. Machines of the rake or spiral type are widely used and can be adjusted conveniently to yield any size separation desired, within their operating range. For separations at very fine sizes, or for work in acid solutions, the Esperanza-type classifier has been utilized in several plants. It consists of a belt, equipped with metal scrapers or flights, that drags the coarse sand up out of the classifier pool. To cut down wear and power consumption, the newer versions of this ancient classifier are built with bottoms conforming to the catenary of the belt. For examples of rake classifiers used in leaching plants, see the flow sheets described in the following pages.

CRUSHING-PLANT PRACTICE

The following crushing and grinding plants are representative of good modern design and of designs that are still serviceable, although somewhat outdated. Examples are presented of leaching-plant practice in the major metals so treated.

Morenci, large Arizona copper property of Phelps Dodge Corp., represents modern design of large-scale crushing and grinding plants. Side-dump cars carrying 80 tons of run-of-mine ore dump directly into a 60-in. gyratory over a 9-in. grizzly. Largest blocks of ore may run up to 8 ft in one dimension. Grizzly undersize and gyratory discharge are screened at 3 in., and oversize is crushed in two 7-ft standard cones. Screen undersize and cone discharge join to be screened at 3/4 in., with the oversize going to four 7-ft short-head cones. The second screen undersize and short-head discharge go to the grinding-plant bins. Capacity of this plant was designed for 27,000 tons in two shifts.

Grinding to 65 mesh is done in sixteen 10-by 10-ft grate ball mills, running at 17.9 rpm, with a 50-ton ball charge. Circuit is closed by 32 duplex, submerged-spiral classifiers. Throughout both crushing and grinding plants, the designers' aim was to supply ample headroom, ease of access to all machinery, and simplicity in making repairs or replacements.[1]

It might be mentioned that the same staff that designed the Morenci plant has modified its views in designing the new sulfide copper mill at Chuquicamata, to the extent of using rod mills instead of the second stage of fine crushing. It is believed that a saving in cost will result from crushing to about 1 in., grinding in rod mills to about 10 mesh, then finishing the job in the ball mills.

Magma Copper Co. has a mill that represents good modern practice in a medium-sized plant.[2] Plenty of headroom is provided for easy access to all units, and good housekeeping is assured by use of grating floors throughout the plant. A vacuum-cleaning system is provided to clean up accumulations of dust.

The crushing plant uses three-stage crushing, as follows: the primary stage is an 18- by 36-in. Traylor jaw crusher; secondary, a Symons 4-ft standard; tertiary, two Allis-Chalmers type R crushers. Screens include one Ty-Rock double-deck for scalping, and two Ripl-flo single-deck screens for finishing. Capacity of the plant is 200 tons per hour to minus $\frac{1}{2}$ in.

Dings tramp iron detectors protect the crushers and an electrical inter-lock system controls conveyor-belt motors. Crushers, screens, and belt-transfer points are hooded for dust collection.

Finished rock is scalped off by the Ty-Rock screen after the primary stage; the tertiary crushers are run in closed circuit with the finer screens. All units are on one floor to provide simpler operation. From the central control point, the operator can see all units and can start and stop all motors.

Crushing Practice in Leaching Plants

The following descriptions are of crushing plants actually in operation in leaching plants recovering various metals. They are presented as examples of what has been done, but are by no means offered as models. In many instances progress in equipment and in technique has gone well beyond some of the practices indicated here. These are presented, nevertheless, to give a foundation of methods which have worked successfully, as a basis for future design improvement.

Inspiration Consolidated Copper Co. Table 5 shows the effect of installing classification at the Inspiration plant. Note the substantial

[1] For a full description, see the entire issue of *Mining and Metallurgy*, March, 1942.
[2] Halder J. Rex, A Mill Designed for Easier Operation, *Engineering and Mining Journal*, p. 68, December, 1948.

increase in recovery of both sulfide and oxide copper when the slimes were removed and treated separately. The following is an outline of the plant as it operated after classification was provided.

The coarse-crushing plant consists of gyratory crushers and horizontal-shaft Symons disk crushers, which reduce mine-run ore to $1\frac{1}{2}$ in. Crushed ore goes to the leaching-plant ore bins, which hold 10,000 tons of which 8,000 is available. The ore then moves to eight Hum-mer vibrating screens with $\frac{1}{2}$-in. opening. Undersize goes to the washing

TABLE 5. EFFECT OF DESLIMING ON PERFORMANCE OF INSPIRATION LEACHING PLANT

(Separate slime-treatment plant operated after 1928)

	1927	1928	1929	1930	1931
Feed:					
Oxide copper...............	0.718	0.632	0.663	0.658	0.625
Sulfide copper..............	0.338	0.387	0.504	0.550	0.681
Total copper...............	1.056	1.019	1.167	1.208	1.306
Tailing:					
Oxide copper...............	0.048	0.053	0.023	0.020	0.020
Water-soluble copper..........	0.011	0.012	0.001	Trace	Trace
Sulfide copper..............	0.129	0.135	0.103	0.092	0.142
Total copper...............	0.188	0.200	0.127	0.112	0.162
Extraction:					
Oxide copper...............	91.78	89.72	96.38	96.96	96.80
Sulfide copper..............	61.83	65.12	79.56	83.27	79.15
Total copper...............	82.20	80.37	89.12	90.73	87.60

plant, where slimes are removed, the resulting sands going directly to the leaching tanks. Oversize is sent to a pocket bin over coarse rolls.

There are four sets of 78- by 24-in. Traylor rolls with 9-in. shells. Two sets are operated as fine rolls and one set as a coarse roll, leaving one as a spare. The discharge from all rolls goes to 16 Hum-mer screens equipped with $\frac{3}{8}$-in. Ton-Cap screen cloth. The undersize from these joins the sand product from the washing plant and goes to the leaching tanks. Oversize goes to pocket bins over the fine rolls. The coarse rolls are set at $\frac{5}{8}$ in., and the fine at $\frac{5}{16}$ in. The rolls operate at 110 rpm and each set uses 275 hp. Roll-shell data are given in Table 6.

The crushing of 9,000 tons (the leaching-plant capacity) requires about 10 hr, but rates better than 1,100 tons per hr have been maintained for several hours.

The washing unit consists of two Dorr bowl classifiers, 16 by 33 ft. The bowls are 25 ft in diameter and the arms revolve at 2 rpm. Rake speed is 26 strokes per min; slope of bed, 2 in. per ft. The bowl overflow runs to a sump, from which it is pumped by an 8-in. Wilfley sand pump through a 12-in. wood-stave pipe to the concentrator. Here the pulp is floated to recover sulfides. It then receives an acid-agitation treatment to recover the oxide copper. Leach solution cannot be used in the washing process because it would prevent subsequent flotation of the slime product.

TABLE 6.   ROLL-SHELL DATA AT INSPIRATION

Date	Dry tons crushed	Pounds steel per ton ore crushed
Sept. 27, 1926 to Dec. 31, 1927.....	3,469,384	0.06501
1928.............................	3,040,171	0.06427
1929.............................	3,052,268	0.09159
1930.............................	2,518,974	0.09804
1931.............................	2,402,479	0.06938

In 1931, 5.75 per cent of the ore received from the mine overflowed the classifiers and went to the concentrator and slime-leaching plant for treatment. The classifier sands contained an average of 20.2 per cent moisture and 3.3 per cent minus-200-mesh material. Water used per ton of slime amounted to 1,045 gal. Overflow data were as follows:

> Dry tons overflow........... 146,468
> Overflow, per cent:
>   Oxide copper............. 1.156
>   Sulfide copper........... 0.398
>   Total copper............. 1.545

Andes Copper Co.   The crushing plant of the Andes Copper Co. includes five cylindrical steel ore bins, five No. 9-K Gates gyratory crushers, and auxiliary equipment such as apron feeders, conveyors, magnets, etc.

The coarse-crushing plant is made up of five identical parallel units, the three northern units handling sulfide ore and the two southern units handling oxide ore. Each crushing unit is provided with a steel cylindrical storage bin, 40 ft in diameter and 60 ft high, which receives run-of-mine ore through mine grizzlies with 10-in. spacing. Crushers are set to a 3½-in. maximum size of discharge.

At capacity, power consumption in the coarse-crushing plant is as follows: crushing, 0.0779 kwhr per ton ore through plant; conveying, 0.0348; lighting, 0.0144; total, 0.1271 kwhr.

The oxide fine-crushing plant crushes broken ore from the coarse crushers to minus ½ in. maximum size in two stages. There are four parallel crushing sections, each consisting of one primary and two secondary Symons disk crushers and auxiliary equipment.

Ore to be crushed passes over 4- by 5-ft Hum-mer screens with ⅜-in. square openings. The undersize, which varies from 33 to 40 per cent of the total ore, goes to the washing plant. The screen oversize forms the feed to the primary Symons crushers. These are set to crush to approximately 1⅛ in. Half of the discharge from each of these crushers furnishes the feed to a type-39, 4-ft Hum-mer screen equipped with woven-wire screen having ½- by ⅞-in. rectangular openings. The oversize of each screen forms the feed to a secondary Symons crusher, and the undersize joins the secondary crusher product.

The secondary Symons crushers are set to give a product with a maximum size of ½ in., which goes to the sample tower, passing over a Merrick Weightometer. A conveyor from the sample tower runs 1,120 ft along the east side of the leaching vats.

Power consumption from coarse crushing and ending with ore delivered in vats is as follows: crushing, 0.643 kwhr per ton of ore; conveying, 0.286; washing plant, 0.242; sample tower, 0.019; loading bridge, 0.029; lighting, 0.031; total 1.250 kwhr.

The primary Hum-mer screen undersize (minus ⅜ in.) from the fine-crushing plant goes to three washing and dewatering units, each made up of two Dorr classifiers, two Oliver filters, and auxiliary equipment. Splitters permit delivery to any one or to all of the washing units.

The two Dorr classifiers of each unit are 11 ft wide by 20 ft long, and operate in tandem. The cut from the feed belt at each unit is sluiced into a drum distributor which feeds the rougher classifier. The sand from the rougher classifier is advanced into the finishing classifier. The washed sand from the finishing classifier is discharged to an Oliver filter. The overflow from the rougher classifier is laundered to the slimes-leaching plant. The overflow from the finishing classifier is elevated by an air lift and used for sluicing sands into the rougher classifier. The washed sand that forms the feed to the Oliver filter contains approximately 2 per cent minus-200-mesh material.

Two Oliver filters are provided for each unit but only one is used, the other being a spare. The filters are 14 ft in diameter by 12 ft long. Vacuum is about 2 in. of mercury and under normal conditions the cake averages about 3 in. in thickness. The discharge from the filters contains about 11 per cent moisture.

Representative fine-crushing- and washing-plant data for a 7,500 ton vat charge are given in Table 7.

TABLE 7.   TYPICAL WASHING-PLANT DATA, ANDES COPPER CO.

Ore through fine-crushing plant, tons............... 7,908
Ore washed, tons.................................. 1,802
Fines to slime leaching plant, tons............... ...   408
Washed sand to vats, tons......................... 1,394
Unwashed ore to vats, tons........................ 6,106
All ore to vats, tons............................. 7,500
Ore washed, % of total crushed................. ....   22.79
Ore to slimes leaching, % of total crushed.... ......   5.16
Washed sands, % of vat charge.................... 18.59
Washed sands, % moisture......................... 11.52
Total charge to vat, % moisture.................. 6.25

TABLE 8.   CUMULATIVE SCREEN ANALYSES OF SLIMES AND VAT CHARGE, ANDES
COPPER CO.

Screen size	Slimes	Vat charge
−0.525 in.............	.....	2.96
+0.371 in.............	.....	19.33
+4 mesh....	.....	51.60
+8 mesh..............	.....	67.09
+20 mesh.............	.....	80.08
+48 mesh.............	0.30	87.91
+65 mesh.............	1.43	
+100 mesh...........	6.36	
+150 mesh...........	14.34	
+200 mesh...........	27.40	93.99
−200 mesh...........	72.60	6.01

Chile Exploration Co., Chuquicamata, Chile.   In the leaching plant at Chuquicamata, Chile, fines are not removed and treated separately by agitation.   Dust from crushing is collected by cyclones and a Cottrell plant.   All dust is moistened in a pug mill and is discharged to the ore conveyors from either of the two secondary plants.   A screen analysis of the crushed ore is as follows:

Screen Size	Weight, %
+⅜ in.............	10
+8 mesh...........	56
+28 mesh..........	19
+100 mesh.........	10
+200 mesh.........	5
−200 mesh.........	2

Power consumption for primary and secondary crushing is 0.30 and 1.25 kwhr per short ton, respectively.

Ore from the mine is dumped by a rotary car-dumper over a manganese steel grizzly with 4-in. openings at top and 8-in. at bottom, set at an angle of 33 deg.   The oversize ore goes directly into two 60-in. Superior McCully double-discharge gyratories.   The crushed ore (9 in.) and the undersize from the grizzlies go to three bins, which are served by three 72-in. pan feeders, 34 ft long.   These are of the enclosed type and each has a capacity of delivering 2,000 tons per hr to two 60-in. conveyors that carry the ore to the ground level.   Here the drive end of these conveyors terminates in two junction houses, where the ore is picked up by conveyors that carry it to the three silo-type bins of the new and old secondary plants.

There are three crushing sections in the secondary plant, each serviced by a separate bin, and composed of one No. 10 McCully gyratory crusher or one No. 7 cone crusher, two 48-in. vertical-disk coarse crushers, and four 48-in. vertical-disk fine crushers.

Three 72-in. pan feeders are located under the bins and deliver ore directly to the secondary breakers.   Each pan feeder discharges into one 11- by 6-ft grizzly with manganese steel bars spaced $1\frac{1}{2}$ in. at the top and $2\frac{1}{2}$ in. at the bottom.

The undersize from each grizzly and the gyratory discharge (3 in.) drop to a 36-in. inclined conveyor, which carries the ore to the disk-crusher building.   Each conveyor discharges to a splitter box from which the ore is taken by two chutes equipped with stationary cast-manganese steel screens with 1-in. openings.   The oversize from each chute passes to a 48-in. vertical-disk coarse crusher, which makes a 1-in. product.

The discharge from each crusher, plus the screen undersize, passes by gravity chutes to a splitter box.   Two chutes equipped with manganese steel screens with $1\frac{3}{16}$-in. diameter openings take the ore from each splitter box and deliver the oversize to the 48-in. vertical-disk final fine crushers.

The $\frac{3}{8}$-in. product of these machines is joined by the screen undersize and drops to a 48-in. underground conveyor.   This conveyor carries the ore to an underground junction station, where it is transferred to another conveyor, leading to the top of the sample tower.

The ore, after leaving the sampling tower, is deposited on a 60-in. conveyor, 1,257 ft long from center to center, which parallels the seven east leaching vats.   This conveyor runs over the head pulley of a traveling loading bridge, which spans the vats and distributes the ore in each one.   Similar sampling tower, conveyors, and loading bridges serve the old crushing plant and six leaching vats to the west.   The towers are connected by a 48-in. conveyor so that ore from the old plant may be routed to the east vats (see Fig. 1, plant layout).

TABLE 9. CRUSHING, GRINDING, AND CLASSIFICATION EQUIPMENT, COPPER-LEACHING PLANTS

Operation	Insp. Cons. Copper Co.	Andes Copper Co.	Chile Explo. Co.	Un. Min. du H. Katanga*
Primary crushing	Gyratory crushers and horizontal-shaft Symons disk crushers	Five No. 9-K Gates gyratory crushers: 3 sulfide ore, 2 oxide ore	Two 60-in. Superior McCully gyratory breakers; seven No. 10 McCully gyratories	One 48- by 36-in. jaw crusher
Duty	Mine run to 1½ in.	Mine run to about 3.5 in. max size	Mine run to 3 in.	Mine run to 4 in.
Secondary crushing	Second stage: 78- by 24-in. Traylor roll Third stage: two 78- by 24-in. Traylor rolls	End stage: Symons disk crushers Third stage: Symons disk crushers	Third stage: 14 disk crushers. Fourth stage: 36 disk crushers	Two to five gyratories, set 2 in. Two sets 54- by 16-in. rolls Five 6- by 12-ft rod mills
Duty	Second stage: 1½-⅝ in. Third stage: set ⁵⁄₁₆ in.	Second stage: 3.5-1⅛ in. Third stage: 1⅛ to max ½ in.	Third stage: 3-1 in. Fourth stage: 1-⅜ in.	4 in. to 20 mesh in three stages
Classification . . .	Two Dorr bowl classifiers, 16 ft by 33 ft 4 in. by 25 ft bowl, 26 spm, not acidproof	Three washing units; two Dorr classifiers, each 11 by 20 ft, not acidproof		One 6-ft duplex Dorr classifier; Six 4-ft-6 in. Dorr bowl classifiers, acidproof
Plant capacity, tons per day	Classification, percolation, agitation	Classification, percolation, and agitation	No classification, percolation only	No percolation, agitation only
Percolation	9,000	7,500	1,400,000 short tons per month	Concentrates (1939–1940) 23,418 short tons per month
Agitation	*ca.* 500	*ca.* 400		
Washing plant . .	. . . .	*ca.* 1,800	*ca.* 46,000 per day	*ca.* 769 tons concentrate per day

* Original plant treated *ca.* 41,450 tons ore per month.

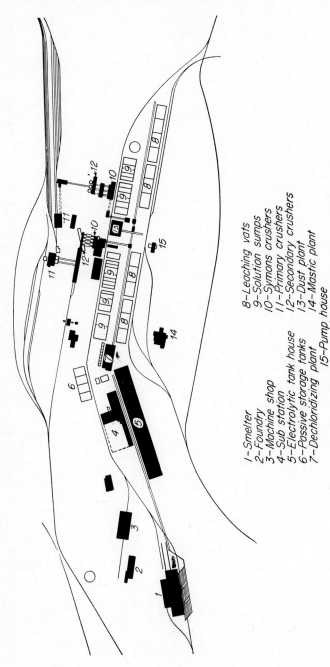

1—Smelter
2—Foundry
3—Machine shop
4—Sub station
5—Electrolytic tank house
6—Passive storage tanks
7—Dechloridizing plant
15—Pump house

8—Leaching vats
9—Solution sumps
10—Symons crushers
11—Primary crushers
12—Secondary crushers
13—Dust plant
14—Mastic plant

FIG. 1. Plant layout, Chile Exploration Co., Chuquicamata, Chile.

TABLE 10. CLASSIFICATION EQUIPMENT, ZINC-LEACHING PLANTS

Anaconda, Great Falls, Mont.	A. S. & R. Co., Corpus Christi, Tex.	Amer. Zinc Co., Monsanto, Ill.	Cons. M. & Sm. Co. Trail, British Columbia	Electr. Zinc Co., Risdon, Tasmania	Sullivan Min. Co., Kellogg, Idaho	H. B. M. & S. Co., Flin Flon, Manitoba	Norske Zinkompani, Eitrheim, Norway
Two SSCAP Dorr classifiers, 2 ft 3 in. Seven SSCAP Dorr classifiers, 2 ft 3 in. by 14 ft 8 in. Two DSFHA Dorr classifiers, 4 by 20 ft	Classification not used	Dorr-duplex DSFGH classifier, stainless steel, ca. overflow, 94%, −200 mesh	Three Dorr duplex classifiers, wood tanks, iron rakes; rakes, 16 ft 23 in. wide; speed, 8 spm	Six Dorr duplex classifiers, 16 ft long, slope line; 39 bronze rakes; each ladder 22-ft long; speed, 10 spm; mesh of separation, 100 to 150	Classification not used	Dorr duplex classifier, acidproof (two SWCAP, 2 ft 3 in. by 14 ft 8 in.)	Two Dorr classifiers, 2 ft 3 in. by 18 ft, AP

Union Miniere du Haut Katanga. Agitation only is used at the copper-leaching plant of the Union Miniere du Haut Katanga in the Belgian Congo. Figure 2 shows the flow sheet (1944) of the primary and secondary crushing and intermediate storage at Katanga. Figure 3 shows the

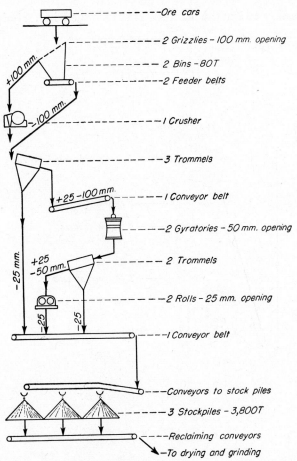

Fig. 2. Flow sheet of primary and secondary crushing plant, Union Miniere du Haut Katanga, Belgian Congo, Africa.

flow sheet of the drying and grinding section. These have been redrawn and titles translated from the article in French by E. Roger.[1]

The flow sheets are clear and self-explanatory so that no description is needed. Because leaching is all done by agitation, fine crushing and

[1] E. Roger, *Min. Inst. Roy. Col. Belge,* Tome 4, 1948.

grinding are required.   A screen analysis of leach plant feed is as follows:

Size Fraction	Weight %
+35 mesh (+0.417 mm).............	21.45
+100 mesh (+0.147 mm)............	42.35
+200 mesh (+0.074 mm)............	52.30

It is necessary to dry the plant feed because the 1-in. material has to be

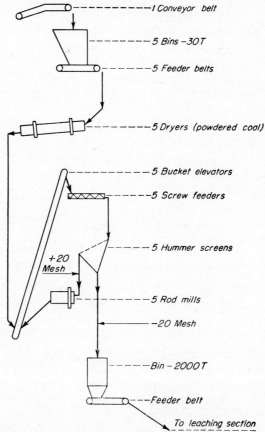

FIG. 3.   Flow sheet of drying and grinding plant, Union Miniere du Haut Katanga, Belgian Congo, Africa.

ground to a nominal 20 mesh.   The ore cannot be ground directly from the storage piles because of its moisture content and its sticky character. Wet grinding cannot be used because it would unbalance the leach solutions.

The moisture in the ore as mined, plus rain water on the exposed piles, make up an unacceptable total of 5 to 12 per cent, depending on the season. Inasmuch as wet grinding followed by drying would be too expensive, preliminary drying and dry grinding were accordingly adopted. The drying is done in a division comprising five Ruggles-Coles double-shell dryers, 2.3 m in diameter by 16.7 m.

American Smelting & Refining Co., Corpus Christi, Tex. Leaching for zinc is confined to handling flotation concentrates; therefore crushing is not a problem in zinc plants. However, the concentrates usually require grinding, either before or after roasting; the electrolytic zinc plant of American Smelting & Refining Co. at Corpus Christi, Tex., furnishes a good example of how this may be done.

Sphalerite concentrate arrives at the Corpus Christi plant from a number of mines. It has been ground to varying degrees of fineness, but the average size is not fine enough for optimum leaching (see Chap. 7, page 228, for a description of the entire plant).

Reclaimed from storage bins, the wet concentrate is discharged into 100-ton bins over either one of two 20-ft-diameter Skinner suspension-type roasters. The two upper hearths of these roasters are for drying. The concentrate is rabbled across these two hearths, then falls down a chute to a ball-mill feed bin. The average moisture content at this point is 0.5 per cent or less.

Dried concentrate is ground in two 7- by 3-ft Hardinge air-swept ball mills. Classification, in closed circuit, is by air. The ground product, 98 per cent minus 200 mesh, is caught in a 9-ft. cyclone dust collector, which discharges into an 80-ton dry-feed bin.

The bin discharges through a 24-in. gate valve and a closed-type rotary feeder to a 24-in. belt feeding the concentrate burner. Air at 15,000 cfm is supplied to the burner by a fan, which also draws a controlled quantity of hot gas from the roasting chamber into and across the second drying hearth. This hot gas goes through the drying hearth and back into the concentrate burner, picking up a regulated amount of atmospheric air on the way. After roasting, the calcine is denodulized in a 5-ft- by 22-in. ball mill. Capacity of the roaster-grinding installation is 70 to 120 tons of concentrate per day for each roaster.

Nicaro Nickel Co., Cuba. The Nicaro Nickel Co. treated a nickel-iron-cobalt ore by ammonia leaching. Crushing and grinding the ore presented no particular problem except for its extremely high moisture content. Carrying up to 35 per cent moisture, the ore had to be dried to less than 2 per cent before it was ground. The drying and grinding procedures were as follows:

Wet mine ore came in at the rate of 5,600 tons daily. From the plant stockpile, ore was carried on a 36-in. belt through a set of 30- by 48-in. crushing rolls set at 4 in. Crushed ore went over four 42-in. pan feeders to four rotary kilns used as dryers, which were 11½ ft in diameter and 130 ft long. Dried ore went through a hammer mill, then to a 16-ft Sturtevant air separator in closed circuit with a 9- by 3-ft Hardinge dry-grinding ball mill. Material was ground through 80 mesh.

Manganese Ore Co., Henderson, Nev. Designed to treat 1,000 tons of manganese ore daily, the crushing plant of the Manganese Ore Co., working on the Three Kids orebody in Nevada, operated satisfactorily although the rest of the plant met a good deal of trouble.

The ore, neither very hard nor abrasive, was crushed to minus 4 in. in a 30- by 42-in. Traylor jaw crusher, then crushed to minus ¾ in. in a Traylor 4-ft gyratory in closed circuit with a Symons rod-deck screen. Grinding was done dry in two 10- by 3-ft Hardinge ball mills in closed circuit with two Hardinge No. 126 loop-air classifiers. Two Clarage fans supplied 23,000 cfm of air. Hot air came from two 7- by 16-ft oil-fired air heaters (see also Chap. 8).

CHAPTER 3

ROASTING PRACTICE

The objectives and the chemistry of the various roasting processes have been discussed in Chap. 1. In this chapter, the principal equipment and techniques for roasting are described and some examples cited from practice. It is interesting in glancing over the development of the roasting process in recent years to trace the steady progress in efficiency of method and accuracy of control.

The earliest roasting technique consisted in burning the ore in heaps or stalls. It is probably still used in remote areas. The ore has to be in lumps about 2 in. in size, fines must be removed, enough sulfur must be present (about 20 per cent) to carry the combustion after a layer of fuel has started it. The method is slow, inefficient, hard to control, dangerous to its operators, and ruinous to the surrounding countryside.

Some improvement was gained by putting a roof over the heap and forming a crude reverberatory furnace. It was discovered that a measure of control and increased speed of roasting could be gained by stirring the heap of ore so that air could get at the hot sulfides. Hand rabbling was thus instituted but these furnaces were still hot, gassy places in which to work, and were wasteful of time and floor space.

The mechanically rabbled furnaces of the multiple-hearth type were then gradually developed and still hold a place in the industry. They gave greater control of the roasting process, stepped up efficiency, and vastly improved the tonnage treated per square foot of floor space. However, it was observed that the speed of roasting sharply increased whenever material was turned over by a rabble arm or when it dropped from one hearth to the next. Nevertheless, it took years to make the logical step that these observations indicated.

Roasting went fastest when the burning sulfide, for example, had full access to a supply of oxygen. Similarly reduction, chloridizing, or sulfidizing would proceed faster with more intimate contact between calcine and gas. The flash roaster took advantage of these facts by eliminating the hearths formerly used and dropping the burning sulfide particles down through the hot air of the open furnace. A further step was to blow fine sulfide into the furnace through a nozzle, burning it as one would coal.

The method was ideally suited to fine flotation concentrates, which make up the greater part of material to be roasted. It could not, however be so easily applied to coarser raw materials. Rotary kilns, in which the ore was constantly lifted and dropped through the kiln atmosphere, supplied an answer for coarser ores. Sintering machines of the Dwight-Lloyd type gave enormous capacity per square foot of hearth area, but were suited for the formation of blast-furnace feed rather than for leaching-plant feed.

The latest step in this progression was the development of the Dorrco FluoSolids[1] roasting process in which air-solid contact is at a maximum, heat transfer is also at a maximum, and a hitherto unheard-of precision of control is established. Floor space, in turn, is reduced to a point that certainly must approach the minimum.

More details are given on these roasting methods in this chapter. The reader will note the marked progress from point to point, as various mechanical devices were worked out to speed up and to control the simple basic reactions of the roasting process.

Heap-roasting or hand-rabbled furnaces require no further discussion, and one may also dismiss the earlier mechanical types which are now mainly of historical interest, although tremendous tonnages were handled by them. Names such as Ropp, Wethey, Allen-O'Hara, Keller, Brown, Pearce, Bruchner, and Douglas will long be remembered. The following, however, are the only roasters still used.

MODERN ROASTING FURNACES

Edwards Roaster. Although the Edwards roaster and similar types are typical of the straight-line roaster developed a great many years ago, they have survived to the present day. Developed in Australia, the Edwards roaster was also used in the United States and Canada until recently, for example, in roasting gold ores in the Golden Cycle mill in Colorado Springs.

A typical Edwards roaster has a straight hearth 76 ft long by $6\frac{1}{2}$ ft wide, with a slope from feed to discharge end of $\frac{1}{2}$ in. per ft. The roaster can be fired by gas or oil from one end and from ports along the side.

The rabble arms are short and are attached to vertical shafts projecting through the roof and spaced in the furnace so that, when the arms revolve, each rabble arm cuts the circle of rotation of its neighbors almost to the center. This action throws the calcine back and forth across the width of the furnace as it travels down the length of it. There are, of course, dead spaces between rabble arms that go untouched.

Proponents of the Edwards and the similar Merton furnaces claimed

---

[1] A trade-mark of the Dorr Company.

economy of power in operation, ease of maintenance, and improved roasting performance. More modern designs have, however, surpassed them so far as these advantages are concerned.

Herreshoff Roaster. The first successful multiple-hearth air-cooled furnace for the roasting of ores was designed in 1889 by Dr. J. B. F. Herreshoff, engineer of the Nichols Chemical Co., and was installed at Laurel Hill, N.Y.

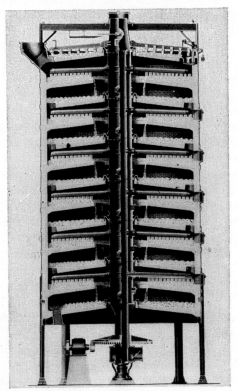

FIG. 4. Section through Nichols-Herreshoff hearth roaster for zinc concentrates; 12 hearths, top hearth as dryer.

Experience has proved that sulfur elimination per square foot of hearth area increases with the number of drops between hearths. Accordingly, the trend in furnace construction has been to provide furnaces with a larger number of hearths. Recent Herreshoff furnaces for desulfurizing ores have had 10 or 12 hearths, and a few have had as many as 14 or 16 hearths. Illustrating this, Fig. 4 shows a Nichols-Herreshoff furnace for zinc roasting with 12 roasting hearths plus a top-drying hearth.

The following is a description of various features incorporated in the design of the Nichols-Herreshoff furnaces:

Cooling-air flow is designed to cool and thus to protect the rotating central shaft and the rabble arms. Air is delivered, in regulated quantity and pressure, from a low-pressure fan or blower discharging into an air housing at the bottom of the shaft.

The central shaft is a vertical cast-iron column built in sections. The portion enclosed by the furnace hearths has two compartments. One, an inner central tube of cast iron or steel, is called the "cold-air tube." The other, an outer annular compartment surrounding the cold-air tube, with its outer wall exposed to the furnace temperature, is called the "hot-air compartment." Two or more rabble arms are attached to the shaft at each hearth and ample air passages are provided from the cold-air tubes to the rabble arms.

Each rabble arm is built with a central steel tube to conduct cold air to the extreme end of the rabble arm. Air then goes through the outer air space in the arm back to the hot-air compartment in the shaft, from which it may be discharged into the air or used for combustion purposes.

Air from the hot-air compartment usually has a temperature of 400 to 500°F and may be discharged to waste either from the top or the bottom of the shaft through controlling dampers.

The air flow is then as follows: from the fan through damper and air housing to shaft cold-air tube, thence back to the hot-air compartment, discharging at top or bottom of shaft to waste or for combustion purposes.

Hot air may be discharged into the furnace on one or more hearths through hot-air arms attached to the central shaft. It can also pass through hot-air return pipes projecting down the outside of the furnace from the top of the shaft to one or more hearths.

Gas flow, in normal furnace design, carries the products of combustion from the bottom to the top of the furnace.

The present philosophy of hearth roasting provides for a large number of clear drops from hearth to hearth. Designers employ large port openings and comparatively narrow hearths to allow for the time element. Gas velocities are kept down to a minimum, even on large capacities.

The central ports are circular and leave a large clear opening between the edge of the hearth and the wall of the shaft on the "in-feed" hearths. The "out-feed" hearths, which are supported from the shell by special brick designed to take the thrust of the hearth, are constructed so that a series of openings is provided all around the hearth.

Ore flow starts from the top of the furnace. Ore is usually delivered from a storage hopper into a feeding plate located upon the upper framework of the furnace. An adjustable feeding knife or cutter revolves with the shaft and scrapes off a regulated amount of ore from the feed plate. The ore then falls to the top dryer hearth, which is open to the air. It acts as a mixing, warming, and drying area. This hearth, like the lower ones, is provided with rabble arms to move the material across at the desired rate of speed.

From the top of the dryer hearth the ore drops through openings to a feed plate similar to the dryer hearth feed, which seals any gas leakage from the interior of the furnace or air leakage from the outside. A cutter or feed knife attached to the rabble arm scrapes off a regulated amount of ore to the floor of the first hearth. The revolving rabble arms and "in" rabble teeth move the ore across the hearth and it drops through a large circular port to hearth 2, where it is moved by "out" rabble teeth to the peripheral ports through which it drops to hearth 3. Similarly, ore moves down through other hearths until it is discharged from the furnace through the sealed calcine opening located on the lowest hearth.

Retention time in the furnace may be varied by changing the rabble-tooth design and the shaft speed. Changing the angularity of the rabble teeth permits a constant shaft speed and at the same time a varying ore bed on the hearths, as desired.

TABLE 11. HEARTH AREAS OF HERRESHOFF ROASTERS

Shell diameter	4-hearth	6-hearth	8-hearth	10-hearth	12-hearth
6 ft 6 in. OD...........	70	104	138		
8 ft 6 in. OD...........	130	193	256		
10 ft OD..............	188	276	364		
13 ft 6 in. OD..........	390	575	760	944	
16 ft OD..............	573	845	1,117	1,305	1,550
18 ft OD..............	727	1,068	1,410	1,752	2,090
19 ft 6 in. OD..........	863	1,268	1,660	2,060	2,464
21 ft 6 in. OD..........	1,077	1,580	2,084	2,570	3,046

The shaft is revolved by a large split-bevel gear keyed to it and driven by a bevel pinion, which is part of a spur-geared reduction set driven by pulley and belt or by direct connected motor. With this arrangement speeds may be adjusted from one turn in several minutes to several turns per minute, as required.

Rabble-arm design permits replacement from outside the furnace without materially reducing furnace temperature. The arms are made with a longitudinal dovetail groove along the underside of the arm which receives the rabble teeth.   The tooth construction is such as to allow any combination of tooth angle desired.

A *conical hearth* is recommended.   Hearths constructed of special refractory shapes are considered desirable because of reduction of joints, less total hearth weight, and longer life.

Table 11 gives hearth areas for various diameters of shell and number of hearths, based on a 9-in. wall lining and standard shaft diameter. When 13-in. wall linings are used for insulation, the nominal outside diameters are increased accordingly.

Bethlehem Wedge Type.   The Bethlehem Wedge roaster consists essentially of a rotating central shaft, its bearings, and its driving mechanism, and arms and rabble blades to move the ore charge continuously over a series of superimposed hearths.   The whole is surrounded by a suitable wall and shell having the necessary openings for operation and control.

In operation the charge is fed to an open dryer hearth and thence to the first roasting hearth.   Rabbled alternately inward and outward on succeeding hearths, the material is finally discharged from the bottom hearth.   In most units the gases travel upward countercurrent to the charge, and are removed through a gas outlet or a stack, depending upon whether or not the gases are to be utilized.

The most important single feature of the Bethlehem roaster is the central shaft which may be either an accessible, insulated steel-plate shaft, or an inaccessible, uninsulated cast shaft.   Certain advantages are inherent in either type of construction.

The accessible and insulated shaft permits an operator to enter the shaft for adjustments or replacement of parts, without cooling the roaster. Positive arm locks and controls for cooling and oxidizing are located in the shaft, and provision is made for admission to selected hearths of preheated oxidizing air.   When required, water may be used for cooling the arms.   Where conservation of heat is necessary, the insulated shaft is desirable.   Beyond certain height limitations, the cast shaft is preferable.

Inaccessible cast shafts, generally not insulated, have the advantage of assisting in the dissipation of heat.   When this is necessary, larger volumes of cooling air may be used.   Certain disadvantages include the necessity of locking the arms from outside the roaster, and inconvenience and loss of time caused when arms are to be removed or replaced.   Lack of positive control of arm cooling and the difficulty of providing for water cooling, if necessary, are also factors.   Rabble blades may be removed singly without the necessity of removing more than one at a time from any arm.

Effective roasting hearth areas are shown in Table 12.

TABLE 12. BETHLEHEM WEDGE ROASTERS, EFFECTIVE ROASTING HEARTH AREA*
(In square feet, exclusive of drop holes)

Number of roasting hearths	9-ft-9-in. shell diam		12-ft shell diam		14-ft shell diam			16-ft shell diam		
	2-ft-6-in. diam steel shaft	C. I. shaft	C. I. central shaft		C. I. central shaft			Accessible steel central shaft		
	9-in. wall	7-in. wall	9-in. wall	7-in. wall	11½-in. wall	9-in. wall	7-in. wall	13½-in. wall	11½-in. wall	9-in. wall
3	115	130	220	235	300	324	340	334	357	385
4	155	180	290	310	395	425	450	442	472	510
5	190	230	360	385	490	528	560	548	586	633
6	...	280	430	460	585	630	668	656	701	758
7	...	330	500	535	680	735	777	762	815	881
8	...	...	570	610	775	837	886	870	930	1006
9	...	...	640	685	870	940	995	976	1044	1129
10	...	...	710	760	965	1043	1104	1084	1159	1254
11	...	...	780	835	1060	1146	1213	1190	1273	1377
12	...	...	...	...	....	....	....	1298	1388	1502
13	...	...	...	...	....	....	....	1404	1502	1625

Number of roasting hearths	18-ft shell diam				20-ft shell diam				21-ft-6-in. shell diam			
	Accessible steel central shaft			C. I. shaft	Accessible steel central shaft			C. I. shaft	Accessible steel central shaft			C. I. shaft
	13½-in. wall	11½-in. wall	9-in. wall	9-in. wall	13½-in. wall	11½-in. wall	9-in. wall	9-in. wall	13½-in. wall	11½-in. wall	9-in. wall	9-in. wall
3	474	498	528	565	624	654	690	727	732	771	801	846
4	630	661	701	756	830	870	918	972	972	1024	1064	1122
5	782	821	871	934	1030	1080	1140	1204	1204	1269	1319	1390
6	937	984	1044	1125	1236	1296	1368	1499	1444	1522	1582	1666
7	1090	1144	1214	1303	1436	1506	1590	1681	1676	1767	1837	1934
8	1245	1307	1387	1494	1642	1722	1818	1926	1916	2020	2100	2210
9	1395	1467	1557	1672	1842	1932	2040	2158	2148	2265	2355	2478
10	1550	1630	1730	1863	2048	2148	2268	2403	2388	2518	2618	2754
11	1702	1790	1900	2041	2248	2358	2490	2635	2620	2763	2873	3022
12	1857	1953	2073	2232	2454	2574	2718	2880	2860	3016	3136	3298
13	2010	2113	2243	2410	2654	2784	2940	3122	3092	3261	3391	3566

Number of roasting hearths	22-ft-6-in. shell diam					25-ft shell diam								
	Accessible steel central shaft				C. I. shaft	Accessible steel-plate central shaft							C. I. cent. shaft	
	18-in. wall	13½-in. wall	11½-in. wall	9-in. wall	9-in. wall	24-in. wall	21-in. wall	18-in. wall	13½-in. wall	11½-in. wall*	11½-in. wall*	9-in. wall	13½-in. wall	9-in. wall
3	735	805	835	880	932	880	923	975	1053	1095	1128	1140	997	1078
4	975	1066	1115	1175	1242	1170	1226	1295	1398	1455	1501	1515	1318	1426
5	1205	1320	1375	1450	1544	1450	1518	1605	1733	1805	1867	1880	1633	1768
6	1445	1581	1655	1745	1854	1740	1821	1925	2078	2165	2240	2255	1954	2116
7	1675	1835	1915	2020	2156	2020	2113	2235	2413	2515	2606	2620	2269	2458
8	1915	2096	2195	2315	2466	2310	2416	2555	2758	2875	2979	2995	2590	2806
9	2145	2350	2455	2590	2768	2590	2708	2865	3093	3225	3345	3360	2905	3148
10	2385	2611	2735	2885	3078	2870	3011	3185	3438	3585	3718	3735	3226	3496
11	2615	2865	2995	3160	3380	3160	3303	3495	3773	3935	4084	4100	3541	3838
12	2855	3126	3275	3455	3690	3440	3606	3815	4118	4295	4457	4475	3862	4186
13	3085	3380	3535	3730	3992	3730	3898	4125	4453	4645	4823	4840	4177	4528

* Differences in hearth areas are due to differences in drop-hole or gas-port areas.

Skinner Type (Colorado Iron Works Co.).   Hearths in the Skinner furnace are constructed from standard shapes of fire brick, *i.e.*, standard straights, side arch, and special wedges.   The skewback blocks that support the hearths are molded.   The bricks used in the hearths are all made by standard brick machines.

The central shaft of the furnace is cast iron, having a cross section with four compartments.   The two compartments opposite each other are closed at the top of the central shaft, and the other two are closed at the bottom.   The rabble-arm sockets are cast integrally with the central shaft.   The rabble arms are cast with an inside vertical partition extending from the open end of the arm to approximately 8 in. from the other or closed end.   This type of construction gives positive circulation of the cooling air through the central shaft and rabble arms.   The vertical rib in the rabble arm acts as a beam and gives additional support to the arm to prevent sagging.

A bayonet lock fastens the rabble arm to a socket on the central shaft. The hub or socket end of the rabble arm is tapered and very small tolerance is maintained between the socket and the rabble arm.   This makes it possible to remove a broken rabble-arm stub or the arm itself by simply turning it 90 deg to the right.   All work is performed from the outside of the furnace.

Rabbling.   For sticky material that is hard to rabble, long narrow rabble blades are provided so that the material is cut through by the rabble tooth instead of being pushed.

In the lower hearths of the Skinner furnace, the rabble blades are made T-shaped in order to allow the part of the material being rabbled to pass over the top of the blade.   This rabble blade exposes more of the surface area of the material per revolution of the central shaft than do conventional blades.

Furnace Drive.   The central shaft of the large-size Skinner furnace is driven by machine-cut tooth spur gear and pinion.   The pinion is mounted directly on the low speed shaft of a vertical speed reducer. The face of the driving pinion is made wider than the gear it drives to permit raising or lowering the central shaft.   The central shaft is raised or lowered by means of heavy jackscrews attached to the main step bearing of the furnace.

The Skinner multiple-hearth muffled furnace is used where the combustion gases have to be kept separate from the material being calcined or roasted.

Carborundum is usually used to build the hearths of the muffled furnace because of its larger radiating capacity as compared with regular fire brick.

Flash Roasters. Flash roasters were developed from the observation that the liveliest roasting action took place in the drop holes from hearth to hearth of the common multiple-hearth furnace. This logical deduction was hampered by the fear, in handling zinc concentrate, that such high-speed and perhaps high-temperature roasting would lead to excessive ferrite formation. A number of plants now use the flash-roasting system, however, and experience no difficulty with ferrite.

Nichols Engineering & Research worked out one flash-roasting system in the 1920's. Known as the Nichols-Freeman process, it was adopted at several plants throughout the world. Dry, fine flotation concentrate, carrying at least 40 per cent sulfur, is fed through a special burner nozzle at the top of the roasting chamber. Most of the air needed for combustion comes in at the burner; the remainder comes in at the bottom of the roasting chamber. The fine burning sulfides settle very slowly in the furnace and are oxidized to less than 0.5 per cent sulfur by the time they reach the furnace bottom. Waste gases, at a temperature of around 1000°C, leave the furnace at the top.

At Consolidated Mining & Smelting Co. of Canada, and at the American Smelting & Refining Co. zinc plant, Corpus Christi, a flash-roasting system is used that incorporates part of a multiple-hearth roaster. Wet concentrate is dried on the upper hearths, then dry-ground in a ball mill. Dry concentrate is fed into the open central part of the roaster through a burner. All the combustion air comes through the burner and waste gases leave through the bottom of the furnace. This gas flow reverses the practice in the Nichols-Freeman furnace. Burning concentrate falls through a space of about 20 ft, is then collected by the rabble arms, passed through one or two more hearths, and discharged from the furnace. Final sulfur elimination, to about 1 per cent, takes place on the two lower hearths.

The illustration, Fig. 5, shows the roasting equipment and auxiliaries used at Consolidated Mining & Smelting Co. of Canada, Trail, British Columbia. A brief description of the equipment follows:

No. 1 is the furnace proper, which contains the combustion chamber 2, the drying hearths 3 and 4, the collecting and sulfide-control hearths 5 and 6, and, when required, the sulfate-control hearth 7; each hearth has arms and rabbles rotating with the central column 8. The auxiliary equipment consists of the circulating and secondary combustion air fan 9, the burner 10, the gas-circulating conduits 11, 12, and 13, the wet-concentrate hopper 14, and the dried-concentrate hopper and feeding device 15. The ball mill 16 has a feed chute and feeder 17, and an elevator 18, at the discharge end. Chute 19 conveys the low-sulfate calcine to the Jacoby rotary conveyors 20, and chute 21 receives the

product from the sulfating chamber. The main gas outlet is 22, and
23 is the gas outlet from the sulfating chamber. By means of valves,
either or both of these outlets may be used. The waste-heat exchanger
is usually by-passed through conduit 25, unless concentrate very low in
thermal value is being treated. For such concentrate, air is passed
through the heat-exchanger tubes by means of the fan 34, and is delivered to the secondary air fan 9. The boiler 26 is preferably of the vertical
water-tube type, although fire-tube boilers are also in use. From the

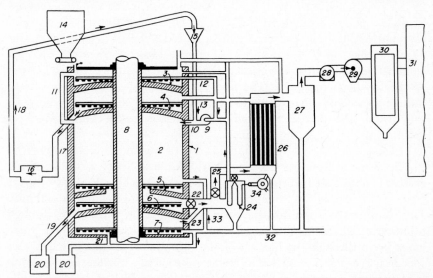

Fig. 5. Flash-roasting equipment at Consolidated Mining & Smelting Co. of Canada
Ltd., Trail, British Columbia.

boiler, the gases are drawn through the cyclone dust collector 27 by the
fan 28 and are passed into the balloon flue 29 and thence, through the
Cottrell precipitator 30, to the acid plant 31. The screw conveyor 32
can return the dust products either to the base of the combustion chamber
5 through the elevator 33, or to the sulfating chamber 7, or to the finished
product conveyor 20.

Results from this roaster type are given later in this chapter.

FluoSolids Roasting. In the flash, or suspension-type, roaster the
particles of ore are in contact with gas at roasting temperature only for
the few seconds that it takes them to fall through the roasting chamber.
To complete the process in this time, the material must first be finely
ground and temperatures must be quite high.

The FluoSolids equipment goes a step further in that it provides
complete contact between all particles and gas, at roasting temperature,

for as long as may be necessary to complete the reaction. There is no
need for grinding beyond about 14 mesh, nor for carrying a roasting
temperature higher than the minimum required. And a most important
factor is that the process is under complete control, within quite narrow
limits, at all times.

The reactor is shown in Fig. 6, together with its accessory equipment.
It consists essentially of a roasting chamber with inlets for gas and ore

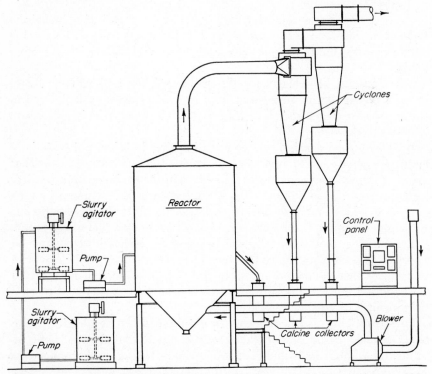

FIG. 6. FluoSolids reactor with accessory equipment, as used for roasting a sulfide
concentrate fed as a slurry.

and outlets for gas and calcine. The bottom of the chamber is formed
by a perforated plate through which the gas or air enters the roasting
chamber.

Material to be roasted must, in most cases, be crushed to minus 14
mesh. Fed to the reactor to make a bed about 1 to 6 ft or more in depth,
the ore particles are kept in suspension by the air forced up through the
perforated bottom or "constriction plate."

Fuel, if needed, is introduced with the air. An auxiliary burner starts
the combustion. Ore is fed by a screw feeder, and the calcine simply

overflows by displacement into quench tanks or into other roasting hearths.

Dust, carried out by the flow of gas, is caught in one or more cyclones. Because this dust has been roasted to the same degree as the solids left in the roaster, it is simply dropped into the calcine quench tanks along with coarse material. Dust carry-over with FluoSolids seems to amount to somewhat less than in flash roasting and somewhat more than in multiple-hearth roasting.

The bed of ore in the operating reactor behaves as a fluid; *i.e.*, it exhibits hydrostatic head, flows through pipes and over weirs, has a density much lighter than the individual particles, and churns and bubbles like a boiling liquid.

Therefore, the bed being roasted possesses substantially uniform chemical and physical properties throughout its volume, except for the hydrostatic pressure which increases with depth. Temperature is uniform in all parts of the bed.

Increase of bed depth increases retention time but does not materially increase capacity. The area of the bed plus the quantity of sulfur that must be burned away are the chief factors in determining capacity. A higher percentage of sulfur in the ore means a larger volume of air to burn it off, which in turn means reduced capacity for that type of material. Each particle in the bed is surrounded at all times by a film of gas or air.

The gas flow to the reactor, which keeps the bed fluidized, must be supplied at a pressure that overcomes the pressure drop in the constriction plate, plus the pressure drop in the bed, plus the resistance of the cyclones and ducts. Pressure in an average single-compartment reactor runs about 3 to 4 psi.

Fuel, consisting of either oil, coal, or natural gas, can be added with the air, if needed. If the product being roasted has at least about 12 per cent sulfur, the combustion will be self-supporting. Owing to the tremendous surface area exposed to the action of the fuel, the heat transfer is extremely fast, and the temperature remains remarkably uniform throughout the bed.

It has been found possible to shut down a FluoSolids reactor by simply shutting off the gas flow and the ore feed, and restart it as much as 3 days later without difficulty and without reheating. This assumes, of course, that there is no tendency for the ore particles to fuse and sinter into a solid mass. Also, during operation the temperature must be held below the sintering point or the bed will gradually freeze. Freezing can also be caused by formation of low-melting-point products or by excessive formation of sticky sulfates.

Ore feed should be finer than 14 mesh for best results, but there is no need to grind finer than any flotation concentrate is ground.

A screw feeder is satisfactory for dry or crumbly material. If sticky damp material must be fed, it is better to repulp it and pump it into the reactor at the thickest mixture that can be pumped. For such slurry feeding, more sulfur is required to make the charge self-burning; about 16 to 18 per cent sulfur is the minimum in this case. However, filter cake containing as little as 12 per cent sulfur and 12 to 15 per cent moisture has been successfully self-roasted.

Power used by the FluoSolids process may be greater than for other types of roasting equipment. The blower furnishing the air takes most of the power required. For a single-compartment reactor, taking a 35 per cent sulfur concentrate to a dead roast, the power requirement is about 20 kwhr per ton roasted.

Control is obtained through the following means:

1. Water injection controls temperature within limits of 10 to 20°F. Water contained in slurry, if this feed method is used, also affects temperature.

2. Ore-feed rate affects temperature as well as composition of calcine, which is discharged by displacement.

3. Gas composition is controlled by the nature and quantity of the elements admitted. Close control of this factor makes it possible to obtain an exit gas, *e.g.*, in roasting pyrite, as high as 15 per cent sulfur, dry basis. Older roasting processes yield gases no higher than 8 per cent sulfur.

These are some of the elements in roasting processes over which the FluoSolids technique gives precise control:

1. Formation of ferrites in zinc roasting.
2. Formation of soluble iron in copper sulfating.
3. Formation of ferrites in copper roasting.
4. Incipient fusion that might halt roasting.
5. Formation of zinc or copper sulfates.

Applications of FluoSolids. Introduction of the FluoSolids technique is so recent that there has been no time to explore all its possible applications. Originally developed during the Second World War as the fluid-catalyst process for cracking petroleum fractions, the method was licensed by the Standard Oil Development Co. to the Dorr Co. for use in the roasting and calcining fields. Plants are now in operation for burning lime and for roasting arsenical gold ores. Tests are under way on a wide variety of ores and concentrates.

On gold ores, FluoSolids has been found particularly useful in removing arsenic and sulfur prior to cyanidation. Capacities are of the order of magnitude of 2 to 3 sq ft of reactor area per dry ton of concentrate (20 per cent sulfur) per day.[1]

In pyrite roasting, the primary objective is production of sulfur dioxide gas for making sulfuric acid. The residue should be suitable for sale as iron ore.

The greater sulfur content of pyrite concentrates, around 50 per cent as against 20 to 30 per cent for gold concentrates, results in reduced

TABLE 13. FLUOSOLIDS ROASTING OF A CUPRIFEROUS PYRITE

Feed, % Cu	13.3	Overflow, % wt	47.7
Feed, % Fe	34.6	Carry-over, % wt	52.3
Total % S	40.0	Gas strength, % SO_2	7.0
Soluble S %	0.3	Gas strength, % O_2	3.0
Roasting temperature, °C	700		

	Water-soluble			5 % H_2SO_4-soluble		
	Calcine	Residue	% Soluble	Calcine	Residue	% Soluble
Overflow, % Cu	29.2	2.6	91.5	31.1	0.9	97.3
Overflow, % Fe	0.6	58.2	1.0	1.4	61.2	2.3
Carry-over % Cu	19.6	2.2	87.2	20.8	1.3	92.7
Carry-over, % Fe	0.35	62.3	0.4	1.2	63.6	1.5

Over-all solubilities: Water-soluble Cu.......... 90.2%
Acid-soluble Cu............ 95.2%

capacity. Massive pyrite ores must be crushed to about 10 to 14 mesh to fluidize readily.

On concentrate carrying 45.6 per cent iron and 49.4 per cent sulfur, crushed to 14 mesh, about equal portions of overflow calcine and dust carry-over were produced. Roasting temperature was 900°C; exit gas ran 16.2 per cent SO_2, with a trace of SO_3. The overflow calcine ran 70.6 per cent iron, 0.75 per cent total sulfur, 0.25 per cent sulfide sulfur, 0.71 per cent insoluble. The dust carry-over ran 69.4 per cent iron, 1.1 per cent total sulfur, 0.33 per cent sulfide sulfur, 0.58 per cent insoluble.

Table 13 shows some results of roasting a cupriferous pyrite, where the objectives were to render copper soluble, to keep iron insoluble, and to recover sulfur.

[1] For more details, see T. B. Counselman, FluoSolids Roasting of Sulphides, *Mining Congress Journal,* March, 1951.

In zinc roasting, the objectives in preparing calcine for leaching are to get maximum solubility of zinc and cadmium with a minimum of zinc sulfate production. These objectives can be largely attained by means of the precise control available in FluoSolids.

In roasting for retort zinc, the calcine is usually sintered. It is therefore desirable to leave 2 or 3 per cent sulfur in the calcine to serve as sinter fuel. Here again, FluoSolids control gives the desired results.

In either method, sulfate sulfur is controlled by removing the calcine from the roaster atmosphere of sulfur dioxide while the gas temperature is above 850°C. Cooling calcine beyond 850°, under a partial pressure of sulfur dioxide, causes formation of sulfates.

Capacities for zinc roasting by FluoSolids are of the order of magnitude of 2.5 to 3 sq ft of reactor per ton of dry feed per day.

In copper roasting, the particular advantage of FluoSolids lies in production of water-soluble and weak-acid-soluble copper. The method is not as advantageous where it is desired merely to reduce sulfur content in order to meet a desired matte analysis.

By careful control of the reactor, however, it is possible to treat sulfide copper flotation concentrates in such a way as to render 95 per cent of the copper water-soluble, and 99.5 per cent of the copper soluble in weak sulfuric acid. This makes it economically possible to consider roasting, leaching, and electrolysis as an alternative method for handling sulfide copper concentrates, as against the conventional smelting processes.

ROASTING FOR COPPER LEACHING

Practically all types of roasting have been tried out in pilot-plant installations for copper leaching, but with the exception of chloridizing as applied to copper extraction, and sulfur reduction on pyrites cinders (Henderson process), no ore roasting is now done as part of large-scale processes for copper leaching. This has been due principally to economic factors. It is perfectly practicable to roast copper sulfide ores or concentrates so as to obtain satisfactory solubility of the copper. However copper sulfides are easily and completely recovered by flotation, and installation and operating costs for flotation are usually considerably less than for the corresponding costs for conventional roasters.

Gold and silver values in present operations follow the copper and are recovered at comparatively low cost in the process of refining, but are difficult to recover in a leaching process. It is probable that recovery of these precious-metal values by cyanidation of residues would cost more and give less complete extractions than by present practice.

However, when copper concentrates carry low or negligible precious-metal values, or when such concentrates have to be shipped considerable distances to a smelter, it is theoretically possible that roasting and leaching of such concentrates may be economical. In considering such a plant, the scale of operation is an important factor because an electrolytic plant is expensive and it must produce considerable copper per day in order to have reasonable operating costs. Furthermore, power for electrolysis at a reasonable cost may not be available.

Recent developments in roasting have changed this picture. It is now possible by the application of the FluoSolids technique to roast copper concentrates so as to obtain a very high percentage of the copper in water-soluble form. Obviously, this brings up the possibility of treating copper concentrates by sulfate roasting, leaching, precipitation, and recovery of the metal on a comparatively small scale by other than electrolytic methods, the latter being indicated for sufficient tonnages.

ROASTING FOR ZINC LEACHING

Conditions for roasting for zinc leaching are quite different from those for copper. Because practically all raw material for zinc leaching carries the metal in the form of the sulfide which is insoluble in any practicable commercial solvent, roasting is obviously required as a preliminary to leaching. The object of roasting is to make as large a percentage as possible of the zinc soluble in sulfuric acid. Complete solubility, while desirable, is not always necessary, since the residues after leaching are usually smelted for the recovery of lead. Lead slags, when they carry sufficient zinc, are treated for its recovery. Zinc concentrate carrying iron will, on roasting, often give considerable amounts of acid-insoluble zinc in the form of ferrite or ferrate, but the fuming operation recovers zinc in this form from slags after smelting the leach residues for the recovery of lead.

In some of the early zinc-leaching processes, the roasting aimed at forming as much water-soluble zinc as possible. In modern practice this is not necessary for the reason given, and also because too much water-soluble zinc builds up free acid in the solutions, which must then either be neutralized or discarded. If the concentrate carries lead, barium, calcium, etc., a small amount of water-soluble zinc is necessary in the calcine in order to yield enough acid to take care of these impurities. Usually from 2 to 5 per cent of sulfate in the calcine is sufficient.

The following notes on the conditions for zinc roasting are from a description by Laist and others of early operations at Great Falls.[1] Ore or concentrates must be finely pulverized in order to get maximum solubility. Purchased material, when appreciably coarser than flotation concentrate, was sent through ball mills.

[1] F. Laist *et al.*, Electrolytic Zinc Plant of Anaconda Copper Mining Co. at Great Falls, Mont., *Trans. AIME*, Vol. 64, p. 699, 1921.

Low initial-roasting temperatures give better solubilities on concentrates containing appreciable amounts of lead and iron sulfides. With 5 per cent lead or more, the concentrate tends to sinter and ball up, causing insufficient roasting, low solubility, and a large amount of classifier sand in the leaching plant.

The aim is to prevent the simultaneous oxidation of the iron and zinc sulfides by keeping the temperature of the two top roasting hearths below the active breakup temperature of ZnS and yet high enough to permit FeS and FeS_2 to oxidize in the time allowed. Perfection is never achieved because ZnS begins to oxidize at the temperatures of the top hearths and a small amount of ferrite is accordingly formed. Zinc dross with a large amount of metallics fed into the top hearths greatly increases ferrite formation, but if charged below where there is little or no iron sulfide, it causes little ferrite formation.

Apparently the amount of sulfate formed is largely influenced by the amount of Fe_2O_3 present, and the reactions that take place in sulfate roasting are essentially those of the contact sulfuric acid process when freshly prepared ferric oxide is used as catalyzer. The iron sulfide burnt to Fe_2O_3 on the top hearths acts as a catalyst on the SO_2 from the roasting ZnS, converting the SO_2 to SO_3 which in turn combines with the freshly forming ZnO to produce $ZnSO_4$.

The amount of sulfate in the finished calcine is dependent on the end temperature, which when raised results in a decrease of the sulfate content. While this lowers solubility somewhat, it is still better than having ferrites, instead of Fe_2O_3, formed on the top hearth.

More time is required for sulfate as compared with oxide roasting, indicating less capacity per roaster and higher fuel consumption. Gas volume is greater for sulfate roasting and this involves greater flue-dust losses. The excess air required for cooling is responsible for the increased gas volume.

Auxiliary heat from fireboxes is required for maintaining temperatures of the lower hearth and also for heating air for the upper hearths. The volume must be great enough to keep temperatures sufficiently low to prevent breakup of sulfate. Sulfur dioxide in the gas from the furnace intake must be 2 per cent or less for maximum solubility when running at capacity.

In the United States, zinc-concentrate roasting is usually done either in the ordinary type of multiple-hearth roaster (*e.g.*, Wedge, Herreshoff, etc.) or by the recently developed flash or suspension roasting, which has considerable advantages over the multiple-hearth type. For details, see individual plant data that follow.

Roasting at Corpus Christi. Tables 14 and 15 give typical roaster data and analyses at the Corpus Christi, Tex., plant of A. S. & R. Co., in which concentrates are flash-roasted. The furnaces are 20 ft ID, with two upper drying hearths, a combustion chamber 24 ft high, a third hearth (the bottom of the combustion chamber), and a lower or fourth hearth from which gases and calcine leave the furnace.

The roasted feed contains 6.5 to 7 per cent water. Dried concentrate contains 0.5 per cent or less. The dry concentrate is ground, blown back into the furnace through burners, and roasted in suspension. Gas from the lower hearth is passed to a waste heat boiler.

TABLE 14. TYPICAL ROASTER DATA, A. S. & R. Co., CORPUS CHRISTI, TEX., PLANT

Tons roasted per 30-day period...................... 4,444
Tons concentrate per furnace per day................. 80.1
Weight concentrate, −200 mesh..................... 98%
SO$_2$ gas at Cottrell inlet............................. 9.0%
Temperature roaster combustion chamber, °C.......... 930

TABLE 15. ROASTER PRODUCT ASSAYS, AMERICAN SMELTING & REFINING CO. PLANT, CORPUS CHRISTI, TEX.

	Concentrate feed, %	Calcine, %	Cottrell dust, %	Residue, %
Total Zn.............	56.7	66.0	52.7	18.4
Acid-soluble Zn.......	......	64.5	.....	9.5
Water-soluble Zn.....	......	0.3	.....	2.8
Pb...................	1.3	1.0	2.15	
Cu..................	0.57	0.65	0.52	
Cd..................	0.71	0.82	1.40	
Fe..................	4.60	5.5	4.30	24
Total S.............	31.5	0.83	6.25	
Sulfate S.............	......	0.73	5.70	
Sulfide S.............	......	0.1	0.5	
Insoluble............	2.3			
As...................	0.11			
Sb...................	0.04			
Mn..................	0.40			
CaO.................	0.51			
MgO.................	0.11			
Moisture.............	6.8			
Au, oz per ton........	0.007	0.009	0.01	
Ag, oz per ton........	5.2	5.2	14.0	

Roasting at the Sullivan Plant. Eight Wedge roasters, 25 ft in diameter, are in use at the Sullivan plant, Kellogg, Idaho. Gas is taken from two uptakes on the top of the roaster hearths to a 1,100-ft balloon flue and thence to the Cottrell plant. The flue dust recovered averages about 20 per cent of the raw concentrate, and Cottrell dust about 5 per cent.

Analyses of these products are as follows:

	Zn %	Acid-soluble % Zn	Water-soluble % Zn	% Fe	% S
Flue dust............	43–49	25–40	7–12	6–9	1–12
Cottrell.............	20–45	15–25	9–20	2–7	2–12

TABLE 16. ANALYSES OF CONCENTRATE AND CALCINE, SULLIVAN ROASTER PLANT

	Concentrate, %	Calcine, %
Total Zn...................	50.6	56
Acid-soluble Zn.............	....	50.7
Water-soluble Zn............	....	3.4
Pb........................	3.3	
Fe........................	9.4	9.2
Cu........................	0.2	
Total S....................	31.0	3.1
Sulfide S..................	....	0.05
Sulfate S..................	....	2.63

All flue dust and Cottrell dust are returned to the roasters. Sulfuric acid as a by-product is not made at this plant. Sullivan uses the Tainton process (see Chap. 7). The roaster operation must provide for necessary replacement of soluble-sulfate losses from the plant in leach residues, purification residues, and other unavoidable solution losses. It is therefore necessary to roast to a low sulfide sulfur, to a sufficiently high water-soluble zinc, and to as low a ferrite formation as possible. For the latter, a maximum temperature of 750°C on any roaster floor has been set. As to furnace capacity, the most economical rate for the grade and type of concentrate given appears to be betweeen 40 and 50 ton of wet concentrate per 24 hrs.

Roasting at Trail, British Columbia (C. M. & S. Co.). The suspension roasting system is used at Trail. The original installation consisted of 25 standard multiple-hearth Wedge roasters, 25 ft in diameter. These were converted to the suspension type, and eight converted suspension roasters gave sufficient capacity. Construction and operation are similar to the Corpus Christi plant. A difference is found at Trail, where the concentrate is already 95 per cent minus 200 mesh and therefore the ball mill is used only for breaking up any agglomerations.

In the combustion chamber of the furnace, the burning concentrate holds the temperature between 1650 and 1750°F. Air adjustment is made as required to keep the temperature within these limits.

Gas circulation is provided between the combustion chamber and the two drying chambers. Temperatures in these are: lower, 450 to 500°F and upper, 250 to 350°F. This circulation performs two functions: drying concentrate and control of temperature in the combustion chamber.

About 60 per cent of the charge is deposited on the floor of the combustion chamber. Between 30 and 40 per cent passes out with the gases and is recovered in cyclones. About 4 per cent is recovered in Cottrells. All the products from the roast are leached directly without further treatment.

Each furnace unit can treat, without extraneous fuel, zinc concentrate containing up to 11 per cent moisture at any rate between 50 and 130 tons per day, maintaining definite control of calcine quality with respect to sulfide and sulfate-sulfur content. Analyses of concentrates, products, and leaching-plant feed are shown in Table 17.

TABLE 17. ANALYSES OF ROASTER PRODUCTS AND LEACH RESIDUE, CONSOLIDATED M. & S. CO. OF CANADA, LTD., TRAIL, BRITISH COLUMBIA

	Concentrate, %	Hearth product, %	Cyclone dust, %	Cottrell dust, %	Leach feed, %	Residues, %	
						Leaching	Oxide plant
Ag, oz per ton.....	2.2	....	....	....	....	6.0	
Total Zn.........	51.0	60.1	54.3	42.2	57.3	20.9	9.3
Soluble Zn........	.....	86.7	88.5	90.0	87.5	2.42	
Pb..............	3.5	2.3	5.3	9.8	3.7	11.2	33.5
Fe..............	11.4	13.7	11.5	10.2	12.8	32.2	13.0
Total S..........	32.8	0.8	4.0	7.8	2.3		
Sulfate S.........	.....	0.5	3.0	7.5	1.7		
Cu..............	0.14	....	....	....	....	0.32	0.24
SiO$_2$..............	0.6	....	....	....	....	.....	3.3
Mn.............	0.52	....	....	....	....	1.05	0.79
CaO............	0.2	....	....	....	....	0.40	0.7
Cd.............	0.16	....	....	....	....	0.20	0.12
Moisture.........	9–10						
As..............	.....	....	....	....	....	.....	0.30
Sb..............	.....	....	....	....	....	.....	0.31

It is interesting that, although the Trail concentrate contains zinc mainly as marmatite, the ferritization ratio, or units of zinc combined with units of iron, is less with suspension roasting than it was with the original multiple-hearth furnaces, being 0.46 and 0.522, respectively.

Roasting at Anaconda and Great Falls. The following notes are abstracted from the article by Laist *et al.*,[1] describing the electrolytic

---

[1] For complete details, see the original article, *Trans. AIME*, Vol. 64, p. 699, 1921.

zinc plant of the Anaconda Copper Mining Co. Inasmuch as it was published in 1921, it may not describe present practice, but there is sufficient discussion of theory to make the article of value for similar problems.

Two furnace types were used in the Anaconda plants: 20-ft McDougall furnaces at Anaconda, and 25-ft Wedge furnaces at Great Falls. The material to be roasted consisted of zinc concentrates, shipped from Butte and Anaconda. Great Falls was started on the oxide roast, as developed at Anaconda. However, when the plant reached full capacity, additional acid had to be purchased and therefore sulfate roasting was started to

TABLE 18.   COMPARISON OF RESULTS ON LOW-GRADE ZINC CONCENTRATES AT ANACONDA AND GREAT FALLS, MONT.

	Anaconda (McDougall roasters)		Great Falls (Wedge roasters)	
	Concentrate	Calcine	Concentrate	Calcine
Zn...............	31.9	34.5	30.5	33.0
Cu...............	1.6	1.7	1.8	1.9
Pb...............	9.0	10.0	9.5	10.3
Ag, oz...........	16.0	17.6	16.5	17.8
Au, oz...........	0.06	0.07	0.06	0.07
Insoluble........	6.0	7.0	6.5	7.4
FeO.............	19.0	21.0	20.0	22.3
Total S.........	34.0	4.1	34.5	4.5
SO_4S............	.....	3.5	.....	3.7
Soluble Zn.......	.....	85.67	.....	82.7

provide enough water-soluble zinc sulfate to render the purchase of acid unnecessary. With a concentrate of 33 per cent zinc to 20 per cent iron, total soluble zinc amounts to 82 to 85 per cent. With a concentrate of 50 per cent zinc and less than 5 per cent iron, total soluble zinc is about 94 per cent. Very high temperatures must be avoided, and in general roasting was held at 600 to 625°C. These temperatures were greatly increased when the concentrate did not sinter, as happens if the percentage of lead is high.

The 1918 extension required more roaster capacity than was available at Great Falls, and accordingly 14 of the 20-ft six-hearth McDougall furnaces in the copper-leaching plant at Anaconda were converted to zinc roasters. These furnaces gave better and more consistent results than the larger Wedge furnaces.

Table 18 is a comparison of results on low-grade concentrates during June, 1919, at Anaconda, and during September, 1918, at Great Falls, in the two types of furnaces.

CHAPTER 4

LEACHING AND SOLUTION SEPARATION

It would seem logical to consider leaching by beginning with the ore in the ground and working outward, so to speak. Therefore this discussion will take up the following techniques in the order named:—

1. Leaching in place.
2. Heap leaching.
3. Leaching by percolation.
4. Leaching by agitation.

Of these methods, the first three are generally used for copper. The fourth is used for copper only at Katanga (see page 145), but is widely used for zinc, manganese, antimony, vanadium, uranium, nickel, etc.

Choice of one of the three varieties of percolation, rather than agitation, for copper leaching, has certainly not been made arbitrarily. It seems to indicate that unit operating costs are less for percolation than for agitation. Actually, the decision is quite clear-cut in each case.

If the mineral, like a copper oxide or sulfide, can be liberated at a coarse size and can be dissolved in an easily handled solvent, there is no reason why it should be processed expensively by fine grinding and agitation leaching. Most copper ore that is ground fine requires fineness for liberation and, once ground, it is cheaper to float the ore, if it is amenable to flotation.

Ores of most other meals, however, do not leach readily at a coarse size. Sphalerite, of course, is already finely ground and roasted when it comes up for leaching. Percolation will not work on material as fine as flotation concentrate.

In general, percolation requires huge tonnages of ore to treat; large capital investments in massive tanks, loading and unloading bridges, etc.; long operating life to amortize this investment; ore that leaches readily at a coarse size.

Agitation leaching is suited to small high-grade orebodies; fast-moving leach reactions; ores that require roasting; ores that must be, or have been, finely ground; or ores in which formation of slimes or gelatinous precipitates would block percolation.

LEACHING IN PLACE

Any discussion of "leaching in place" has to begin with an admission and a warning. The admission is that there is probably no such thing as real leaching in place, if by "leaching" one means a well-controlled process in which a fairly complete recovery is made of the metal available in the ore. The warning is that only under the most fortunate circumstances imaginable could leaching be economically successful on an unbroken, undeveloped orebody. Lack of appreciation of this fact has led to several unsuccessful attempts to leach unbroken ore underground.

The reason for failure is clear in the nature of the leaching process. A piece of rock containing copper, for example, can be leached only if it is sufficiently porous to let the solution get to the mineral, act upon it, and return to the surface of the piece of rock, carrying the dissolved copper with it. The time required for completion of this process obviously depends on the size of the piece of rock. This is true regardless of the minerals involved or the chemistry of their dissolution.

Thus, as an approximation, it can be said that an Arizona porphyry ore, ground to minus 60 mesh, can be leached by agitation in 4 to 8 hr. The same ore, crushed to minus $\frac{1}{4}$ in., can be leached in about 5 days. However, when the same ore is crushed to 6 in. size and piled in heaps, it will take 4 to 6 years of heap leaching to get a reasonable extraction.

This rapid increase of leaching time, as particle size increases, makes it practically impossible to consider leaching unbroken ore in place. How, then, was the Ohio Copper ore handled? It has been cited for years as the best example of "leaching in place." The fact is that the ore had been fractured by caving and the average particle size of the ore leached was probably about 4 in. The Ohio Copper operations have been described by Anderson and Cameron,[1] and the following is abstracted from their paper.

The area leached was a caved zone of broken rock surrounded on the sides, bottom, and most of the top by largely unbroken rock. The area was roughly an inverted, distorted, truncated cone, standing at an angle of about 40 deg from the vertical. The estimated quantity of broken rock was 38,000,000 tons, probably averaging 0.88 per cent copper. The ore was a porous quartzite with sulfides of copper, or copper and iron, irregularly distributed. There was some copper sulfate on broken surfaces, and some malachite and azurite. The solvent was a mixture of about two-thirds Bingham mine water and one-third tailing solution from the precipitation plant. The precipitation plant was located in

---

[1] Arvid E. Anderson and F. K. Cameron, Recovery of Copper by Leaching, Ohio Copper Co. *Trans. AIME*, Vol. 63, p. 31.

the Mascotte tunnel under the orebody.   For details of precipitation, see Chap. 5, page 133.   Anderson and Cameron give the following data:

Total launder capacity, cu ft.......................... 22,755
Average flow, gpm..................................... 1,348
Cu ft launder per gpm................................ 16.8
Average Cu in pregnant solution, %.................... 0.204
Average Cu in pregnant solution, lb per 1,000 gal........ 16.93
Average Cu in barren solution, %...................... 0.0058
Average Cu in barren solution, lb per 1,000 gal........... 0.481
Average recovery, %.................................. 97
Cu recovered from solution, %......................... 0.198
Cu recovered per day, lb.............................. 31,898
Cu ft launder per lb Cu per day....................... 0.71

The precipitated cement copper was washed from the residual iron in a by-passed section of launder, and as shipped contained about 30 per cent water.   About 75 per cent of the product graded 90 per cent copper or better, the remainder from 60 to 70 per cent.

Costs per lb of copper were

Operating................ $0.03847
Smelting charges.......... 0.02477
Total.................... $0.06324

The figure for operating included all labor and materials in leaching, precipitation, mining and exploration, office, laboratory, and salaries. The cost of iron per lb copper produced was about $1\frac{1}{4}$ cents.   More than half the labor was expended in handling the iron.

The recovery was low.   The authors estimate that only 0.3 per cent copper was recovered out of 0.88 per cent in the broken ore.

HEAP LEACHING

Both percolation and agitation leaching require crushing and grinding, and actual leaching in vats or agitation apparatus.   Installation and operating costs for these steps are sufficiently high to be prohibitive for very low-grade ores.   There were and still are large amounts of low-grade and waste material, especially that stripped from open-cut operations, for which a method decidedly lower in operating and installation cost is necessary.

These considerations led to an adaptation in the Southwestern United States of the Rio Tinto leaching method,[1] modified for American conditions.   It had been used for years at Rio Tinto in Spain to extract copper from heavy pyritic ore.   The success of this process was supposed

[1] Courtney deKalb, Metallurgical Methods at Rio Tinto, *Mining and Scientific Press*, February, 1921.

to be due to some obscure and mysterious quality either of the Rio Tinto ore or of the Spanish climate. Its application to our low-grade Southwestern ores was therefore overlooked for many years.

The method will be described here in some detail because it has important possibilities for treating low-grade stripping ore, etc., at very low costs both for installation and operation. This is evident from the fact that the Phelps Dodge 10,000-ton experimental heap at Bisbee paid all its own operating costs. Later, large-scale work on rock stripped from the Sacramento Hill deposit produced copper from this low-grade material at a lower cost than other conventional Phelps Dodge operations. A part of the following is abstracted from an article describing the work.[1]

An early small-scale heap-leaching test at Bisbee was a failure, due to lack of knowledge of proper operating methods. Later, these methods were determined by laboratory investigation, followed by a 35-ton test at Douglas, Ariz., on sand tailings from Tyrone, N. M., and by pilot-plant work on a 20,000-ton pile at Tyrone and a 10,000-ton pile at Bisbee. Results were sufficiently encouraging to recommend treatment of low-grade ore from Sacramento Hill at Bisbee by this method.

The material mined was classified as follows:

1. Waste, 0.0 to 0.5 per cent copper.
2. Low-grade, 0.5 to 1.0 per cent.
3. Concentrating, 1.0 to 3.0 per cent.
4. Smelting, 3.0 per cent and over.

The second grade was classified as leaching ore, with an estimated 8,500,000 tons available, averaging 0.73 per cent copper. Plans called for delivery of 400,000 tons yearly.

Preparation of Site. Before ore was piled, the site was cleared of cactus and brush. The need for some form of waterproofing was evident from experience with the two large test heaps. However, the site selected was largely underlaid with "caliche," which is supposed to have some waterproofing character derived from the formation of a crust of calcium sulfate upon contact with the leach liquors. The site was therefore assumed to be waterproof.

A site not naturally waterproof must be made so, for which ground having a gentle slope is best suited. It should be cleared of all vegetation, then covered with a blanket of rolled and tamped clay or slime tailing. When the ore heaps are built, a layer of coarse fragments should be put down first to assist later drainage. Culverts must also be built,

[1] A. W. Hudson and G. D. Van Arsdale, Heap Leaching at Bisbee, Arizona, *Trans. AIME*, Vol. 69, p. 137, 1923.

as mentioned in the following paragraphs.   The first layers of the pile must be put down carefully to avoid breaking up the waterproof layer of clay.   The potential economies of the process are vitiated if any great amount of solution is lost into the soil.

Ore Delivery.   The diagrams, Figs. 7 and 8, illustrate the site and plant location selected for the first 2,000,000 tons of ore, about 1,800 by 750 ft, the slope of which was between 3.5 and 4 per cent, thus allowing

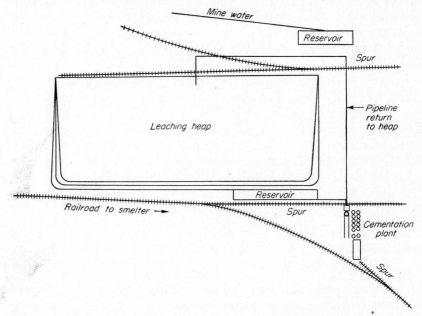

Fig. 7.   Plant arrangement, heap leaching project of Phelps-Dodge Corp., Bisbee, Ariz.

easy drainage.   Before operations started, a track was built along the north side of the site and dumping began on the ground sloping to the south.   Cars of 20 to 25 cu yd capacity, dumping to either side were used, and were loaded at the mine by steam shovels.   Trains consisted of six cars, and a grab sample was taken from each trainload after dumping.   As dumping progressed, the track was moved to the edge of the dump.   Large lumps were broken with powder into pieces 8 to 12 in.

Culverts.   Rough culverts were built ahead of the ore being dumped. Cross culverts were continuous across the site, and those at right angles were staggered so that the drainage system was an interlaced network. Culvert openings were about 12 in. in the clear.   These culverts drained into the main launder leading to the reservoir below the heap.

Rio Tinto practice requires the construction of vertical ventilating flues for preventing overheating of the piles. These were not necessary for the Sacramento ore because of its low sulfur content. Fines were used on the heap surface for covering and for constructing leaching basins.

Plant. Two reservoirs were provided, one above and the other below the heap. The upper reservoir was for settling suspended matter from the mine water, which was a part of the liquor going to the heap. The

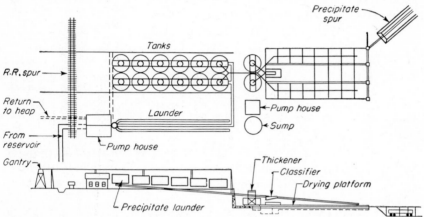

Fig. 8. Cementation plant, heap leaching project of Phelps-Dodge Corp., Bisbee, Ariz.

lower one was to act as a surge tank for holding drainage liquor from the heap before going to the cementation plant.

The cementation plant, Fig. 8, was built for the use of scrap iron as precipitant. It was planned to use 12 Irving-Dorr precipitating vats, 24 ft in diameter by 10 ft deep. These were connected in two series with parallel launders to permit cutting out any tank for cleaning or repairs. Iron was distributed into the tanks by a gantry crane. A precipitation launder was provided to remove the last traces of copper. A Dorr thickener, a Dorr classifier, and a drying floor for cement copper were provided for handling the product.

Results were satisfactory from the cost standpoint. Aside from the low cost of preparing the site, it is no more expensive to pile waste ore in a heap than to dispose of it otherwise. Because this is waste which has to be moved in any case, value of the material is charged against the ore mined for concentration. Accordingly, while the operation continued for about 6 years or more, interest charges per ton of ore were low, involving only the investment for site preparation and for the cementation plant. The only operating costs per ton of ore are for pumping and for the small amount of labor connected with irrigating the heaps.

Solution Balance. For the Sacramento leaching ore, the following solution balance was established. Delivery of 300,000 gal of mine water per day, which had to be treated in any case, was assumed. The pumping capacity of solution to the heap was based on $1\frac{1}{4}$ gal per ton per day. Accordingly, when treating 400,000 tons during the first year, 500,000 gal per day were eventually needed. Soakage, evaporation, and other losses were estimated at 50,000 gal per day. These assumptions gave the following balance, in gallons per day:

Year	Ore, tons	Mine water, gal	Loss, gal	Solution off heap, gal	Return to heap, gal	Waste, gal
First........	400,000	300,000	50,000	500,000	250,000	250,000
Second......	800,000	300,000	75,000	1,000,000	775,000	225,000
Third.......	1,200,000	300,000	100,000	1,500,000	1,300,000	200,000

The discard or waste was required by reason of the use of mine water. Without this, the operating solution volumes would be in balance except for evaporation, leakage, and other losses, which would require make-up water.

Acid Requirements. For the Bisbee work no acid was added. For the Tyrone experimental pile, acid was required. Acid may be formed by oxidation of pyrite and therefore extra acid may or may not be required, depending on the amount of pyrite and the acid-consuming constituents present in the ore.

Precipitation. All precipitation of copper from mine waters, heap-leaching liquors, and other weak copper solutions has been by replacement of the copper by iron, a process usually called cementation. Electrolysis is impracticable because of large solution volumes and their very low copper content. A modern plant in the Southwest would probably use shredded, baled tin cans from Los Angeles, handled in the same way as the Inspiration cementation plant.

Iron precipitation is not ideal because of the delivered cost of the iron and because the cement copper produced is not a desirable product for further treatment. An improved precipitation process doing away with these difficulties would probably increase the use of heap-leaching in the Southwest.

Mechanism of the Process. Run-of-mine rock is used for heap leaching, with larger pieces reduced to, say, 4 to 8 in. Dissolution and removal of copper from the interior of pieces of rock of this size evidently depend on two main physical factors, namely porosity of the rock and capillary action. Most rocks have more or less porosity and this is true of the Southwestern porphyry ores, most of which carry copper partly as originally present and partly as resulting from secondary deposition. The secondary copper obviously was the result of the presence of microscopic channels, pores, or fractures permitting access of solutions carrying copper from which the metal was deposited, either as sulfide or "oxide" compounds.

Accordingly, material carrying secondary copper is probably amenable to heap leaching, while rock carrying primary copper may only be amenable if sufficient porosity is lacking. In this respect another factor is of importance, namely the fact that many rocks disintegrate when exposed to alternate wetting and drying and this disintegration, which may be greatly accelerated by the action of solution carrying dissolved salts, may or may not be favorable to heap leaching. It is favorable to the extent that it permits solution access to minerals, but may be mechanically unfavorable if the rock breaks up to very fine or claylike particles.

It seems certain that the only way leach solutions can contact copper minerals enclosed in any large-size rock is by reason of its porosity. It is equally certain that solutions cannot be removed after contact by ordinary washing. However, what may be called "reversed capillarity" may be counted on to bring the solutions to the surface.

At Morenci years ago, appreciable amounts of bluestone formed on the more or less dry walls of old drifts. At this mine the action was sufficiently marked to bring about attempts at "leaching in place," which were of course unsuccessful. The same condition can sometimes be seen in old dumps at cyanide plants.

The foregoing, if correct, indicates that heap leaching, properly carried on, should include the following steps:

1. Add sufficient precipitation-plant tailing liquor to wet the ore thoroughly.

2. Allow sufficient time for drying and migration of the solutions to the ore surfaces by "reverse capillarity," bringing dissolved copper with these solutions.

3. Wash the pile with plant tailing liquor.

4. Pass the drained liquor from the heaps through cementation launders to a storage tank from which the iron solution is pumped to a dried section of the heap and the cycle repeated indefinitely.

This gives an idea of the amount of solution theoretically necessary for application at each cycle. Assume that a section of a pile or an individual of rock is dry. All that can be accomplished by a single application of solution or water is to wash off the soluble salts on the surface. No greater amount than is needed for this purpose need be used; a larger volume simply means more dilute effluent liquors. As the volume of the pores is comparatively very small, no large amount of solution is needed for refilling, the amount of solution remaining on the surfaces after the washing step probably being ample. It is certain that complete immersion of the ore, or the use of an excessive amount of solution, is unnecessary and undesirable.

Chemistry of the Process. In heap leaching, it is probable that carbonates, cupric oxide, cuprous oxide, metallic copper, and sulfides are attacked in the order named. It also seems certain that if an ore carries any considerable amount of its copper as oxides, a certain amount of added sulfuric acid is required, some or all of which may come from the ore if it has sufficient readily oxidizable pyrite. Assuming that ferric iron is the main leaching reagent, chalcocite among the sulfides is attacked first, bornite next, and chalcopyrite last and probably very incompletely.

Regarding chemical reactions, it is believed a number of the following probably take place, but their relative importance cannot be decided:

$$CuO + H_2SO_4 = CuSO_4 + H_2O \tag{1}$$
$$Cu_2O + Fe_2(SO_4)_3 + H_2SO_4 = 2FeSO_4 + 2CuSO_4 + H_2O \tag{2}$$
$$3CuO + Fe_2(SO_4)_3 + 3H_2O = 3CuSO_4 + 2Fe(OH)_3 \tag{3}$$
$$4CuO + 4FeSO_4 + 6H_2O + O_2 = 4CuSO_4 + 4Fe(OH)_3 \tag{4}$$

Reduction of acidity, as by (3) and (4) above, or by action of soluble basic ore constituents other than copper, results in precipitation of iron compounds. Maintaining the iron balance is of course important. Theoretically, so far as iron is concerned, reaction (3) is more or less balanced by the cementation reaction (5):

$$CuSO_4 + Fe + FeSO_4 = Cu + 2FeSO_4 \tag{5}$$

As a matter of fact, in the above equations (3) requires only 2 Fe for 3 Cu, while in (5) 1 Fe to 1 Cu is returned to the circuit. However, iron is usually precipitated in the cementation reaction. Both free acid and soluble iron salts may be produced in the heaps from the oxidation of pyrite, and maintaining an iron balance is in theory quite complicated. Practically, it is a matter of adjustment of conditions.

Copper sulfides are probably dissolved according to the well-known equations:

$$Cu_2S + 2Fe_2(SO_4)_3 = 2CuSO_4 + 4FeSO_4 + S \tag{6}$$
$$Cu_2S + Fe_2(SO_4)_3 = CuSO_4 + 2FeSO_4 + CuS \tag{7}$$

Direct oxidation of copper sulfides by air is also possible.

Ferrous iron has very little solvent action on copper compounds, and therefore its oxidation to the ferric form is necessary, one reaction for which may be written:

$$4FeSO_4 + 2H_2SO_4 + O_2 = 2Fe_2(SO_4)_3 + 2H_2O$$

The production of iron salts and free acid from the oxidation of pyrite has to be accounted for. The direct oxidation of the FeS_2 to produce SO_2 and iron oxides may be written:

$$4FeS_2 + 11O_2 = 2Fe_2O_3 + 8SO_2$$

This reaction starts at comparatively low temperatures and may have a measurable velocity at ordinary ambient temperatures. At any rate, the reaction being strongly exothermic, a heap of pyrite, if not properly ventilated, heats up. If not controlled, this pyrite eventually burns. Precautions to prevent this have to be taken at Rio Tinto, where the ore is mainly pyrite, but with the porphyry ores of the Southwest accumulation of heat and large temperature rise are not possible, although the same pyrite oxidation may take place slowly.

PERCOLATION LEACHING

Certain of the factors involved in choice of percolation as a leaching method have already been mentioned. This process was selected to handle copper leaching at four large properties: Ajo (shut down), Chuquicamata, Andes, and Inspiration. It may again be called upon to treat copper orebodies as yet undeveloped.

Briefly, percolation should be considered for ores of higher grade than those already mentioned as suitable for heap leaching. It should be possible to leach the ore completely in a reasonable time at a coarse size. There should be enough tonnage available to allow amortization of the large investment necessary to provide the great "holding" capacity that percolation leaching requires. There should be no slimes, or claylike constituents, present that could block percolation in the vats.

Because of the presence of a good deal of soluble copper, most copper ores treated by leaching are crushed dry. Dry crushing becomes uneconomical below about $\frac{1}{4}$ in. Fine grinding in water, as for agitation, is likewise not usually permissible in leach plants because it upsets solution balance. Grinding in copper leach solution could probably be done, but the problems of preventing corrosion would be enormous. Hence, percolation has been favored for copper ores.

Percolation leaching and washing are somewhat more efficient than agitation. Solution volumes are greater for agitation than for percolation, because ore crushed to minus $\frac{1}{4}$ in. can be drained to less than

TABLE 19. LEACHING EQUIPMENT, COPPER PLANTS

	Inspiration	Andes	Chuquicamata
Number of tanks.	13	9	13
Capacity, tons ore per tank.......	9,000	7,500	11,500
Tank dimensions.	Length, 175 ft Width, 67.5 ft Depth, 18 ft	Length, 105 ft Width, 115 ft Depth, 19 ft 6 in.	Length, 150 ft Width, 110 ft Depth, 16 ft 6 in. to 18 ft 5 in. to top of filter bottom
Construction.....	Reinforced concrete, single row	Reinforced concrete, single row, four sets of two and one single; concrete piers, 6 ft 3 in. high	Reinforced concrete, tanks in blocks of three or four, set on piers for bottom inspection
Lining...........	7-lb chemical lead; wall protection, 2-in. planks and vertical posts	Floors, 1½-in. mastic Walls, 8½-in. acid-proof brick, mastic mortar, no wall protection	Reinforced mastic, walls and bottoms, cast in place, 4 in. thick, no wall protection
Filter bottoms...	Filter boards 2 in., fifteen ⅜-in. holes per sq ft countersunk underneath to ¾ in., filter protected by 4- by 6-ft timbers parallel to long side of tank, on 3-ft centers; 6-in. layer of ore left	Inspiration type; 6-by 6-ft sills, 16-in. centers on mastic bottom above sills, 2- by 3-in. boards, 12-in. centers; filter boards, 2- by 12-in. planks, 36 ⅜-in. hole per sq ft, countersunk below to ¾ in.; stringers, 4 by 6 in., 30-in. centers rest on filter boards	Special Chuquicamata type, 6- by 6-in. pine sills, 6 ft long, end to end, 18 in. apart. Across these, 2- by 6-in. planks, ¼-in. apart. Leave eight spaces 10-ft square for drainage. In these, place filler units containing cocoa matting. Bottoms last 8 years
Slime leaching....	One Dorr thickener. Three Dorr slurry mixers, 36 ft diam by 20 ft deep Three Dorr agitators, 20 by 14 ft Four Dorr CCD Trac. thickeners 150-ft diam Eight triple Dorrco pumps, AP Repulpers	Two Dorr 150-ft diam trac. thickeners. Three Dorr slurry mixers (spec.) 36 by 20 ft deep Three Dorr leaching agitators 24 ft diam. by 16 ft deep Two rows, three each, Dorr CCD thickeners, 150 ft diam.	

15 per cent moisture, but thickener underflows, such as might be found in an agitation leach plant, are usually not denser than 50 per cent solids.

Contact time, however, is much greater for percolation than for agitation. As already pointed out, required contact time is a function of particle size, the time increasing enormously as particle size increases beyond 6 in., at least for the Southwestern porphyry coppers. It is also true that contact time is a function of solution strength. As in cyanidation, at a given particle size the product of the time of contact and the solution strength is a constant. In percolation leach, for example, leaching for 5 days with 1 per cent acid gives the same extraction as leaching for ten days with 0.5 per cent acid. The only difference is that the weaker solution dissolves fewer impurities, which might well be a deciding factor.

In crushing for a percolation leach, the objective should be to crush no finer than necessary, a point to be settled in the laboratory, and to try to get as much as possible of the crushed product within a narrow size range. The fewer fines, the better. This objective is becoming easier to attain as both efficiency and effectiveness of screens are improved from year to year. It is a widely held opinion that certain types of crusher, such as disks, provide a closely sized discharge with a minimum of fines. It is much more likely, however, that adequate and efficient screening does more than anything else to minimize fines.

Percolation is carried on in vats so arranged that loading and unloading are made as easy as possible, and with filter bottoms built so that the solution can be pumped in under the charge (for details, see Chap. 6). Percolation can be either upward or downward, the former usually preferred. No special precautions need be observed in loading the vats beyond the obvious one of spreading the charge evenly to avoid segregation of fine material, as such segregation would result in channeling of solution.

Because of the relatively few number of percolation leaching plants, and because of the marked differences in the leaching reactions in them, detailed descriptions of those now operating on copper ores are provided, and will be found in Chap. 6.

AGITATION LEACHING

In general, agitation leaching has been selected for high-grade ores or concentrates where smallness of tonnage or the need for speed in reaction prevents use of slow-paced percolation. Agitation also takes care of ores in which the desired mineral is so fine-grained, or so well disseminated, as to be beyond the reach of percolation.

Contact time is usually a matter of hours for agitation processes, against days for percolation. In this connection, a good field for investigation is that of leaching material ground extremely fine.   Enough tests have been run to indicate that reactions change radically as between fairly coarse and extremely fine material.   Apparatus is available for economical fine grinding, and a good research project is indicated.   For example, tests actually run on one ore that was given only a 48-mesh grind showed that leaching could be reduced to a matter of seconds under proper conditions.

Agitation has always been thought of as a kind of egg-beater operation in a pulp of ore and solvent, but this idea is beginning to change.   Radically new methods of speeding up leaching reactions by new approaches to the old agitation concept are appearing on the horizon.

Katanga.   The only large-scale copper-leaching plant using agitation is that of Union Miniere du Haut Katanga in the Belgian Congo.   The process was chosen there not because of a fondness for it, but because the nature of the ore required it.   The copper at Katanga is found in veinlets, in very fine, isolated grains, and in masses impregnating blocks $\frac{1}{2}$ cu m in size.   A great deal of primary slime, some of it colloidal in character, is present.   All this precluded not only percolation as the major process, but any combination of percolation and agitation as well.   Because a great deal of copper carbonate was present, the carbon dioxide evolved in percolation would also have interfered with leaching.

The ore is crushed, dried, and ground to minus 20 mesh, then leached in agitators for about 48 hr.   The solution is separated, purified, and clarified in much the same manner as the solution in a zinc plant.   Copper recovery is by electrolysis.   The plant was built to handle 1,500 tons daily of ore carrying 6 to 9 per cent copper.   Extraction of copper is about 95 per cent or better but actual copper recovery runs between 85 per cent for leached ore and 93 per cent for leached concentrates.   The high loss is due to solution entrained in the residues.   Details of the process are given in Chap. 6.

Zinc Leaching.   Agitation leaching of zinc sulfide calcines and direct leaching of zinc ores as a preliminary to electrolysis are more complicated than the same operation for copper leaching.   There are two reasons for this: (1) the well-known fact that practically all soluble metal constituents other than zinc must be almost completely removed from the solutions before electrolysis; (2) many zinc concentrates and ores carry silica in a form soluble in acid.   The result of this solubility, unless properly controlled, may be a gel of the dissolved silica, rendering settling or filtration impossible.   Ralston[1] stated that "as little as 0.5 per cent of

[1] O. C. Ralston, *Electrolytic Deposition and Hydrometallurgy of Zinc*, McGraw-Hill Book Company, Inc., New York, 1921.

TABLE 20. AGITATION EQUIPMENT, ZINC-LEACHING PLANTS

Anaconda	A. S. & R. Co., Corpus Christi, Tex.	Amer. Zinc Co., Monsanto, Ill.	Cons. M. & Sm. Co., Trail, B.C.	Electr. Zinc Co., Risdon, Tasm.	Sullivan M. Co., Kellogg, Idaho	H. B. M. & Sm. Co., Flin Flon, Man.
Pachucas	Tanks, wood-stave construction, 20 ft diam by 10 ft deep; lining, 10-lb lead and 4.5-in. acidproof brick; Dorrco type AW special Mechanism, horizontal wood arms attached to wood shaft 10 ft above tank bottom, 8 rpm Charge, 18,000 g spent electrolyte	40-volume-ton lead and acid-proof brick-lined slurry tanks; wooden paddle mixer, 30 rpm Five leach tanks, same as slurry tank	Acid section, seven Pachucas in series Neutral section, eight Pachucas in two series, four each, 10 ft diam; 30 staves, 10-in. wooden central column Continuous operation	Nine 12-ft-diam by 34-ft stave Pachucas, 20-in. wooden column, 60° cone bottom Air pressure: normal 30 lb per sq in., during charging—90 lb per sq in. Working charge, 16,000 g solution, 17,000–20,000 lb calcine wet weight Cycle, total, 3½ hr	20-ft-diam by 13-ft stave, lead-lined tanks Mechanism, iron shaft and radial arm, lead-covered, vertical iron pipes joined at bottom Cycle, 3 to 4 hr	Surge mixing tanks Pachucas, 16-in. wooden central columns, 40 lb air Cycle, 2 to 4 hr

Purification Agitators

	A. S. & R. Co., Corpus Christi, Tex.	Amer. Zinc Co., Monsanto, Ill.	Cons. M. & Sm. Co., Trail, B.C.	Electr. Zinc Co., Risdon, Tasm.	Sullivan M. Co., Kellogg, Idaho	H. B. M. & Sm. Co., Flin Flon, Man.
	Two-stage, four tanks in parallel; stage tanks, wood stave unlined; 20-ft diam by 10-ft 5-in. deep lid; cap., 22,000 g steam coils, 2-in. Cu pipe; agitator of 6-in. Cu pipe, 12 rpm Dorrco type AW special	10-volume-ton surge tank Five 49-volume-ton stave tanks, wood paddled, 35 rpm	Sixteen mixers, each 10-ft diam by 18-ft stave; cap. 38.5 water tons each Wooden impellers on 8- by 8-in. wood-stem overhead drive Stem supported by bronze step bearing Speed, 40 rpm	Four agitators in series, 28-ft diam by 12-ft stave Two 9-ft wooden impellers, 16 rpm, plus 30 lb air through Cu tubes	Lead-lined agitators, 22 ft diam by 15 ft high; paddle-type agitators; lead-pipe steam coils for heating	Six 31-ton agitator tanks

silica in a neutral zinc sulfate solution will cause it to set to a gel on standing overnight, and higher percentages of silica will act more quickly."

Bretherton[1] described pilot-plant work for studying this effect and for devising practical means to avoid it. It was found that slight alkalinity, or more properly "basicity," brought about by adding comparatively small amounts of zinc oxide, resulted in the precipitation of most of the silica in a filterable and washable form. A laboratory test illustrating this is given in Table 21.

TABLE 21. PRECIPITATION OF SILICA FROM ZINC SULFATE SOLUTIONS TO AVOID SILICA GEL*

Time interval, min	Basicity, ZnO, gpl	SiO₂, gpl in solution
0	0.000	15.00
7	0.402	0.370
14	0.462	0.336
21	0.476	0.320
28	0.476	0.312
35	0.496	0.320
42	.....	0.272
49	.....	0.312
55	.....	0.284

* Zinc 5.96%, SiO_2 1.81%, acidity neutral; 2,000-cc solution heated to 90°C, and 5 g ZnO stirred in.

On a pilot-plant scale, the silica is precipitated in less than 1 hr when heated to 90 to 100°C, 5 lb zinc oxide in excess being added to 2 tons of solution containing 1 per cent silica and 5 to 6 per cent zinc. The silica is not completely removed under these conditions, 1 or 2 per cent of the total coming down later in the zinc-dust purification.

It should be noted that this difficulty with soluble silica is not serious with the usual zinc calcine, but is met in treating carbonate and silicate zinc ores. An example is furnished by Rhodesia-Broken Hill Development Co., Northern Rhodesia, which treats an ore high in silica. By the use of principles similar to the foregoing, and control of temperature and basicity, this company is able to precipitate dissolved silica in a form sufficiently granular to be washed.

For other details on agitation leaching as used in zinc plants, see Chap. 7. Agitation leaching as it is applied to other metals is discussed in Chap. 8.

[1] J. O. Bretherton, Soluble Silica in the Preparation of Zinc-sulphate Solutions for Electrolysis, *Trans. AIME*, Vol. 69, p. 159, 1923.

HANDLING THE CORROSION PROBLEM

Corrosion of equipment in contact with leach solution can be prevented by choosing suitable acid-resisting materials. Copper leach solutions generally speaking, are much more corrosive than those from zinc leaching. Copper solutions normally contain copper sulfate, ferrous and ferric iron, varying amounts of free sulfuric acid, small amounts of chlorine, plus nitric acid at Chuquicamata, all of which are corrosive. Aluminum, calcium, magnesium, and sodium sulfates may also be present, but with the exception of aluminum they are not usually corrosive in effect. In special cases, other heavy metals may be present, *e.g.*, cobalt in the solutions at Katanga.

Experience at Katanga is summarized in the following quotation from an article by Wheeler and Eagle.[1]

"The solutions proved to be extremely corrosive and copper, brass, and bronze in contact with them went into solution with unbelievable rapidity. The bronze bolts in the leaching mechanisms, scrapers, and valves of the filters, bronze filtrate pumps, etc., all failed in quick succession and had to be replaced by lead parts or steel parts covered with lead. The work developed the fact that only lead, Duriron, rubber, asphalt, mastic, glass, and porcelain could safely be used in contact with the solutions."

This quotation refers to the preliminary pilot-plant work. Probably the Katanga staff tested copper, bronze, and brass because these materials worked well at the Anaconda zinc-leaching plant. The cobalt in the Katanga solutions probably contributed to the serious corrosion noted. It could not be accounted for by the small amounts of ferric iron present.

Theoretically, wood (Oregon pine and Douglas fir) is resistant to copper leach solutions, *e.g.*, wood-stave pipes are used at Chuquicamata. However, it should be noted that even quite dilute leach solutions containing small amounts of free sulfuric acid eventually char wood, due to evaporation. This action stops at the solution level. For instance, the tops of wood staves in copper-leaching tanks may become badly charred, although they may be quite durable below the solution level. It may be said that for copper-leaching plants carefully selected acid-proof materials should be used throughout.

Conditions in zinc-leaching plants are somewhat less severe, in that purified neutral zinc sulfate solutions are not strongly corrosive. Therefore, in zinc plants only equipment carrying free acid and copper requires acidproof materials.

Lead linings, for example in agitation tanks in zinc leaching, are

[1] A. E. Wheeler and H. Y. Eagle, *Trans. AIME*, Vol. 106, p. 609, 1932.

chemically resistant but are subject to erosion. Therefore they are usually protected by wood or brick linings over the lead. A serious disadvantage of lead is its "creeping" characteristic, that is, its habit of expanding under heat and failing to retract on cooling. This results eventually in cracks and leakage. It seems probable that the use of tellurium lead may diminish this difficulty.

Mastic for lining is entirely satisfactory so far as the corrosion problem is concerned. It is cheaper than lead and is readily repaired. Of course, it cannot be used where solution temperatures are above the softening point of the mastic, which usually rules it out for zinc-leaching equipment.

Duriron is satisfactory in that it resists corrosion, but has the disadvantage of brittleness. Copper and bronze cannot be used in copper leaching, but they are both used in some sections of zinc-leaching plants.

Special corrosion problems are met in ammonia leaching for copper and nickel. Copper equipment cannot be used because it is readily soluble in ammonia solution. At Kennecott, it was stated that the hot concentrated ammonia from the evaporators corroded iron and caused some trouble. This was overcome by using aluminum tubes and sheets in the condensers and by a concrete lining in the storage tank.

At the Nicaro nickel plant in Cuba, using the Caron process,[1] serious trouble with corrosion arose only in certain pieces of equipment handling strong liquor from the ammonia distillation operation. All-iron pumps, ordinarily satisfactory for strong ammonia solutions, failed after a few weeks of service. Cast-iron pumps, fitted with stainless steel shafts, gland rings, and other parts, gave better service but the life of such units was still not satisfactory.

The pump problem was completely corrected by replacing the cast-iron pumps with units constructed of a 24-20 nickel-chrome alloy. After more than a year's service, the wetted parts of the alloy pumps showed no signs of corrosion.

Localized failure of pipe lines and valves in the strong liquor service, as the result of cavitation and corrosion at points of high liquor velocity, were frequent in early operation. The reduction of velocities, when practicable, and the use of resistant alloys or rubber covering where high velocities were required reduced failures of this type to a negligible amount.

Corrosion of the tubes in the heat-exchanger equipment handling strong ammonia solutions was the most serious corrosion problem. Welded steel tubes are entirely unsatisfactory for this purpose because they rapidly failed along the welds. Stainless steel tubing gave some-

---

[1] M. F. Dufour and N. C. Hills, Nickel from Cuba, *Chemical Industries*, p. 621, October, 1945.

what better service, but lasted only a few months. Stainless steel tubes of the 304 type proved disappointing in practice. The use of aluminum tube bundles was a satisfactory answer.

SOLUTION SEPARATION AND WASHING

Solution separation in heap leaching, or leaching in place, presents no problem because in the very nature of the material leached the problem is solved. In other words, the solution separates itself.

Washing is usually impossible in leaching in place because of the difficulty in controlling progress of solution through the orebody. One has only the roughest sort of check on the efficacy of the leaching technique chosen, and a very long period of percolation through the orebody is the best assurance of adequate washing.

Washing could be done in heap leaching, but as already pointed out it seems unnecessary. All that can be done in heap leaching is to remove the soluble salts carried to the surface of each particle by the solvent. This is adequately accomplished by flow of remaining solvent. No additional wash is needed.

Discussion of solution separation and washing of residues must therefore be confined to the other two leaching processes, percolation and agitation. For both these procedures, countercurrent washing methods are used. That is, the fresh wash water is added to the circuit as the final wash before the leached solids are discarded. The wash water progresses up through the circuit, collecting soluble values as it goes, while the residue travels down through the circuit, countercurrently to the wash water, becoming more barren of soluble values as it travels. The ideal state, of course, would be to discharge a residue containing no soluble metal at all. The attainment of this ideal is not practicable and all leaching plants suffer in varying degree from a "soluble loss."

Theoretically, countercurrent washing is the same for both percolation and agitation leaching. In percolation vats a system of "advancing washes" is used which greatly resembles the "overflows" from the thickeners of the conventional countercurrent decantation plant usually used following agitation leaching. (Countercurrent decantation, by the way, is usually abbreviated as CCD and will be referred to in that manner hereafter.)

One obvious difference between percolation and CCD is that in the former process the ore remains stationary, with the washes advancing from tank to tank. In CCD washing, both the washes and the ore move, but in opposite directions.

"Circulation" in percolation is a term employed when the same solution is pumped over and through the same ore charge several times. This is a means of gaining uniformity in washing. In agitation systems, a similar uniformity can be gained by repulping the charge between each stage of CCD.

Another important difference between the two systems is that in percolation washing, *e.g.*, of copper ores, these can be drained to a moisture content of perhaps 7 to 12 per cent. After agitation leaching, settling is seldom better than 1:1 or 50 per cent moisture. This residual moisture can usually be reduced to perhaps 25 per cent by the use of filtration, but generally speaking total wash volumes for agitation and volume of wash discharged with tailing will be larger per unit of product than for percolation washing. Accordingly, metallurgical results may be slightly better for percolation systems. At Inspiration, for instance, tailing from the percolation vats carries only a trace of water-soluble copper, while the tailing from the slime-treatment plant carried 0.035 per cent. The same holds true for the Andes Copper plant, published figures (1931) being 0.015 and 0.047 per cent water-soluble copper for tailing from percolation and agitation respectively.

There are several general principles of washing:

1. In any balanced cyclic system of leaching, the amount of wash water that can be used is limited to the amount discharged as moisture in the final tailing, plus the amount of evaporation per cycle, and minus the amount of moisture entering the system with the ore. If more than that amount of wash water is needed to obtain a satisfactory tailing, either evaporation or a solution discard is required.

2. With any quantity of solution and any number of washes, the maximum extraction is obtained if equal quantities of solution are decanted at each operation.[1]

3. A given total wash volume gives the highest extraction when divided into the largest practicable number of separate washes.

Washing after Percolation. In copper leaching by percolation, washing methods differ considerably, variables being direction of percolation, drainage time, amount of residual moisture after drainage, and circulation of wash. In any given plant, quantities of wash water, efficiencies, and other conditions are usually established by tests and may vary from time to time. Accordingly, theoretical calculations of washing efficiencies and recoveries in percolation washing cannot usually be made. This differs from CCD washing after agitation, for which quite precise efficiency and recovery figures can be predicted by calculation.

The flow sheets given in plant descriptions usually show only the complete operation. It is difficult to visualize from these the sequence of

[1] Julian and Smart, *Cyaniding Gold and Silver Ores*, 3d ed., p. 149, Charles Griffin & Co., Ltd., London.

events in an individual tank. Therefore the accompanying diagram (Fig. 9) has been drawn to show individual tank operations at the Andes Copper Co. plant. The vats there are provided with means for either upward or downward percolation, for circulation without advancing,

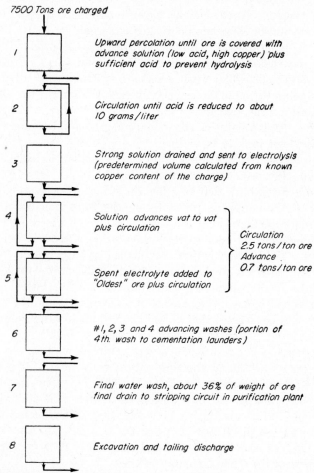

7500 Tons ore charged

1 — Upward percolation until ore is covered with advance solution (low acid, high copper) plus sufficient acid to prevent hydrolysis

2 — Circulation until acid is reduced to about 10 grams/liter

3 — Strong solution drained and sent to electrolysis (predetermined volume calculated from known copper content of the charge)

4 — Solution advances vat to vat plus circulation

5 — Spent electrolyte added to "Oldest" ore plus circulation

Circulation 2.5 tons/ton ore
Advance 0.7 tons/ton ore

6 — #1, 2, 3 and 4 advancing washes (portion of 4th. wash to cementation launders)

7 — Final water wash, about 36% of weight of ore final drain to stripping circuit in purification plant

8 — Excavation and tailing discharge

FIG. 9. Example of leaching-vat operation, showing flow of solutions in one vat, Andes Copper Co., Potrerillos, Chile.

and for advancing from vat to vat. There are eight main steps shown. In the washing steps, this is done by displacement washing. The ore drains to about 11.5 per cent moisture. The final wash is stated as about 36 per cent of the weight of the charge. Therefore a discard must obviously be made in order to maintain balance of solution volumes.

This is done by eliminating from the circuit all of the last water wash, together with a part of the fourth wash.

The following discussion of the washing schedule at the Inspiration plant is abstracted from the article by Aldrich and Scott.[1]

"A tank of 9,000 dry tons when discharged as tailing will carry 10.3 or 927 tons moisture. As the final acid solution drain averages 21.6 g copper per l, the amount of copper to be washed out would be 40,046 lb per tank per day. This represents 19.45 per cent of the daily production.

"Three days are used for washing. Ten washes in all are used. The first five are called regular washes and are systematically advanced, the first wash going to the main solution system, the second wash becoming the first wash on the next tank to be washed and so on. The fifth wash is taken from the cementation stock-solution tank and becomes the fourth wash on the next tank to be washed.

"Four cementation solution washes follow, and these washes likewise come from the cementation stock-solution tank. The washes are drained to a surge tank that supplies the cementation launders. Practically all of the copper is precipitated, the total iron content of the solution is increased, and acid and ferric iron are consumed. The cementation tailing solution goes to the cementation stock-solution tank for further use. Fresh water is used for the last or tenth wash.

"Normally a batch wash is used; that is the entire wash water is pumped into the ore, circulated, and drained. At times when a leaching tank has a short tonnage, the amount of wash water to fill the tank to its overflow would be so great that an unbalanced wash water volume would result, therefore a piston or displacement wash is used."

This system has two results: (1) a very complete washing out of water-soluble copper, the tailing showing only a trace of it; (2) a means of maintaining the iron balance in the main solutions. The ore yields only about $\frac{1}{3}$ lb of iron per ton of ore leached, whereas it is desired to carry about 20 gpl total iron in the leaching solutions. The amount of cement copper made has a direct bearing upon the iron put into solution.

Table 22 gives leaching-solution and wash-water data for the Chuquicamata plant of the Chile Exploration Co.

The statement is made that about 3,500 cu m of solution are required to submerge 10,000 metric tons of average ore containing 1.5 per cent moisture. Of this volume 750 cu m is adsorbed and 27 cu m is drainable. This is equivalent to about $7\frac{1}{2}$ per cent moisture in the ore after draining.

Washing after Agitation. Only one large-scale copper-leaching plant, that of the Union Miniere du Haut Katanga, uses agitation leaching.

[1] H. W. Aldrich and W. G. Scott, The Inspiration Leaching Plant, *Trans. AIME*, Vol. 106, p. 661.

TABLE 22. LEACHING AND WASH-WATER DATA, CHUQUICAMATA

	First strong solution	Second strong solution	First advance	Second advance	Covering or treating solution	Spent electrolyte	First wash	Second wash	Third wash	Fourth wash	Fifth wash	Volume discard	Sixth wash	Water
Volume.........	5,000	5,000	3,500	3,500	3,500	8,800	3,000	2,000	2,000	2,000	2,000	300	3,000	2,350
Temperature, °C...	15	22												
Cu, gpl.........	42.0	32.0	22.0	19.0	17.0	15.0	9.0	7.0	5.5	4.0	2.5	1.5	1.0	
H_2SO_4, gpl.........	25.0	32.0	......	......	......	58.0								
Fe, gpl.........	2.5	2.5	......	......	......	2.5								
Ferric iron, gpl...	1.7	1.0	......	......	......	2.0								
Ferrous iron, gpl...	1.8	1.5	......	......	......	0.5								
HNO_3, gpl.........	1.5	1.5	......	......	......	1.5								

Sands and slimes are separated by classification and leached separately by agitation.   For both, CCD washing is used.

In general, the efficiency of a CCD system is dependent (1) on settling to maximum possible density of underflow of each thickener, and (2) on obtaining thorough mixing of the diluting liquor and the sludge prior to each settlement.   The number of thickeners in series is also an important factor.

In washing by CCD, theoretical extractions can be calculated, assuming (1) a given number of thickeners and settling operations; (2) the solution composition or quantity of material to be washed out; (3) the final settling ratio; (4) the permissible amount of wash water; (5) the permissible amount of solution that may be discharged with the tailing. In practice, results very close to the theoretical are obtainable, provided that the several mixings of sludge and solution are complete and provided that the ratios of solution and solids in each settler are uniform.   Irregularities or variations in the above assumptions result in corresponding differences between actual and theoretical results.

The methods of calculation for CCD washing are well known and have frequently been tested in practice.   Briefly, the method consists of equating the dissolved material in and out of each thickener and making a series of simultaneous equations, one for each thickener.   Because the amount of dissolved material going into the first thickener is known, and because the wash water to the last thickener carries zero dissolved material, the equations can readily be solved, giving the quantity of dissolved metal recovered per thickener, the strength of solution for each thickener, and the final total recovery.   Calculations for various flow sheets, including filters, can be made and such calculations, after small-scale tests to determine the basic factors, are important for plant design. The following are simple examples:

CCD Calculations.   For preliminary purposes, the following formula may be used for determining washing efficiency where the flow sheet is straight CCD, with all water introduced to the system as wash to the last thickener, and with the second thickener overflow used as make-up and returned to the system in the first thickener feed:

$$R = 1 - \frac{D^N}{W}$$

where R = washing efficiency or recovery
$\quad\quad D$ = tons of water in the thickener underflow
$\quad\quad W$ = tons of wash water
$\quad\quad N$ = number of thickeners

Wherever the flow sheet is not straight CCD, the washing efficiency must be calculated mathematically.

The method of calculating CCD flow sheets can be best illustrated by going through a typical case. Figure 10 is a typical straight CCD layout. Figure 11 (page 95) is a little more complicated in that there are two dissolution steps and a filter is added to the end of the washing series.

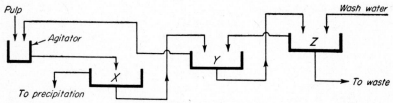

FIG. 10. Flow sheet showing straight CCD to explain thickener calculations.

Data for Fig. 10

Assumptions:

1. Pulp from agitation to be washed free of dissolved salts.
2. 15 tons of insoluble salts per 24 hr.
3. 10 tons of dissolved salts per 24 hr.
4. Strong solution overflowing first thickener to contain approximately 9 per cent dissolved salts.
5. Insoluble settle to 2:1 (water to solids).
6. Maximum soluble loss to be no more than 2 per cent of the dissolved salts, *i.e*, recovery of 98+ per cent.

Calculations for flow tonnages:

1. Overflow from first thickener: 98 per cent of 10 = 9.8 tons of solubles = 9 per cent, or 9.8/0.09 = 109 tons of total solution or 109 − 9.8 = 99.2, say 100 tons of water.
2. Underflow from all thickeners: 15 × 2 = 30 tons of water.
3. Feed to first thickener = 100 + 30 = 130 tons of water. Overflow from the other thickeners will then be 130 tons of water.
4. From the formula $R = 1 - \dfrac{(D)^N}{(W)}$, the number of thickeners is determined:

$$R = 1 - (^{30}/_{130})^N$$
$$= 1 - 0.23^N$$

Recovery with $N = 2$ will be $1 - 0.052 \times 100 = 94.71$ per cent.
Recovery with $N = 3$ will be $1 - 0.0121 \times 100 = 98.79$ per cent.
∴ $N = 3$

5. If 100 tons of water overflow first thickener and 30 tons of water leave system in final sludge, 130 tons of wash water will have to be added.

Calculations for solution strengths and recoveries:

1. Let X, Y, and Z equal the pounts of dissolved salts per ton of water in the respective thickeners.
2. Equating dissolved salts out of and into each unit:

$$100X + 30X = 130Y + 20,000$$
$$130Y + 30Y = 130Z + 30X$$
$$130Z + 30Z = 30Y$$

3. Solve by substitution:

$$160Z = 30Y$$
$$Z = 0.1875Y$$
$$160Y = 24.38Y + 30X$$
$$Y = 0.2212X$$
$$130X = 28.73X + 20,000$$
$$X = 197.54$$
$$Y = 43.696$$
$$Z = 8.18$$

4. Recovery equals tons of X thickener overflow times the value X, or $197.54 \times 100 = 19,754$ lb.
5. Loss equals tons (T) of Z thickener underflow times the value of Z, or $8.18 \times 30 = 245.7$ lb.

Total accounted for $= 19,999.7$ lb.

Error due to neglected decimals $= 0.3$ lb.

Feed to system $= 20,000$ lb.

6. Washing efficiency $= \dfrac{19,754}{20,000} = 98.77$ per cent.

Another method of calculating flow sheets in which all of the soluble salts are present in the first thickener feed, *i.e.*, there are no additional steps between washings, is used by a number of engineers and claimed by them to be much simpler. It follows.

Using the assumptions in Flow Sheet No. 1, let X equal pounds of soluble salts in underflow of thickener Z.

Then, by the ratio of volumes in overflow to underflow, or $130:30$, $4.33X =$ the overflow from Z.

Therefore $X + 4.33X$ or $5.33X =$ the total that came from underflow Y.

Again by ratio in Y, $130:30$ or $4.33 \times 5.33 = 23.08X$, the value of overflow Y.

The total dissolved salts in Y are $23.08X + 5.33X$, or $28.41Z$, and since $4.33X$ came from the Z overflow, the underflow from X must have been $24.08X$.

Again by ratio in X, $\frac{100}{30} \times 24.08X = 80.19X$, the overflow from the first thickener.

The feed to the first thickener $= \frac{130}{30} \times 24.08 = 104.27X$.

Therefore $80.19X + X = 20,000$ lb, or $X = 246.3$ lb in underflow Z and $20,000 - 246.3 = 19,753.7$ lb. in overflow X.

Two checks can be made on the calculations.

1. The underflow from each thickener is always greater than the overflow from the succeeding thickener by X.
2. As an over-all check, leaving the system is $80.19X + X$ or $81.19X$, the weak liquor having picked up $23.08X$ and this, plus $18.19X$, comes back to $104.27X$, which was calculated to be the content of the first thickener.

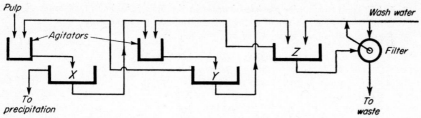

FIG. 11. Flow sheet for thickener calculations including two-stage agitation, CCD and filtration.

Data for Fig. 11

Two-stage Agitation, CCD, and Filtration

Assumptions:

1. Agitation in strong and weak liquor required to dissolve solubles.
2. 25 tons solids to be treated, of which 8 tons dissolve in A agitators and 2 tons in B agitators.
3. Strong solution overflowing first thickener to contain approximately 9 per cent dissolved salts.
4. Insolubles settle to 1.75:1 (water to solids) in strong liquor and 2:1 in weak liquor.
5. Maximum loss must be no more than 2 per cent of the dissolved salts.
6. With a 2:1 wash (2 tons of wash to 1 ton of moisture in cake) on a filter, the displacement of solubles is 80 per cent.
7. Filter cake moisture is 40 per cent.

Calculations for flow tonnages:

1. Overflow from first thickener, 98 per cent of 10 = 9.8 tons of dissolved salts = 9 per cent or $9.8/0.09 = 109$ tons total or $109 - 9.8 = 99.2$, say 100 tons of water.
2. Underflow from first thickener, $17 \times 1.75 = 30$ tons of water; underflow from other thickener, $15 \times 2 = 30$ tons of water.
3. Feed to first thickener, $100 + 30 = 130$ tons of water; overflow from second and third thickeners is the same.
4. If 100 tons of water overflows first thickener and 10 tons of water leaves system with filter cake, 110 tons of wash water has to be added.
5. Water in filter cake $15 \times {}^{40}\!/_{60} = 10$ tons.
6. Filtrate $30 - 10 = 20$ tons, wash water $2:1 = 10 \times 2 = 20$ tons; remainder of wash water, $110 - 20 = 90$, must be added to the last thickener feed.
7. Approximate the number of thickeners required.

Calculations for solution strengths and recoveries:

1. Let X, Y, and Z equal the pounds of dissolved salts per ton of water in the respective thickeners.
2. Consider filter as two machines, F and G, *i.e.*, the first machine corresponds to the action of the filter during the cake-formation period, and the second the portion of the cycle when washing is taking place.

3. Let F equal lb solubles per ton of water in the filter cake before washing.   Let G equal lb solubles per ton of water in the filter cake after washing.

4. Equating dissolved salts out of and into each unit:

$$100X + 30X = 130Y + 16,000$$
$$130Y + 30Y = 130Z + 4,000 + 30X$$
$$130Z + 30Z + 30Y + 20Z = (10)(0.8F)$$
$$10F + 20F = 30Z$$
$$10G + (10)(0.8F) = 10F$$

5. Simplifying the last two equations:

$$10G = 2F$$
$$G = 0.2F$$
$$30F = 30Z$$
$$F = Z$$

6. Solve by substitution:

$$G = 0.2Z$$
$$160Z = 30Y + 20Z + 8Z$$
$$132Z = 30Y$$
$$Z = 0.2273Y$$
$$160Y = 29.53Y + 4,000 + 30X$$
$$130.47Y = 4,000 + 30X$$
$$Y = 30.66 + 0.23X$$
$$100.1X = 19,985.8$$
$$X = 199.66$$
$$Y = 76.58$$
$$Z = 17.85$$
$$G = 3.57$$

7. Recovery equals tons of X thickener overflow times value X, or $199.60 \times 100 = 19,996$ lb.

8. Loss equals tons of water in filter cake times value G, or $3.57 \times 10 = 36$ lb.
   Total accounted for $= 20,002$ lb.
   Error due to decimals $= 2$ lb.
   Feed to system $= 20,000$ lb.

9. Washing efficiency $= \dfrac{19,966}{20,000} = 99.83$ per cent.

In calculations for CCD washing efficiencies, it is assumed that the liquor in the sludge and the wash liquor are perfectly mixed before the repulped sludge enters the next thickener.   If this is not accomplished the solids may settle *en masse* in the next thickener, carrying along large amounts of the original strong liquor.   Washing efficiency is thereby reduced.   Some materials, because of their porous structure, actually absorb solution and it requires long and thorough mixing for the wash solution to mix with the absorbed strong solution.

This lack of thorough mixing accounts for most cases in which actual operation falls short of theoretical efficiency.   Where thickeners are operated to give a uniformly thick sludge and mixing is sufficient, theoretical washing efficiencies can be obtained. In case of difficulty in repulping, the Dorrco repulper should be used between every thickener of a CCD series.

Absorbed salts in chemical precipitates can often be rendered soluble by additional treatment, such as agitation of the partially washed solids in an alkaline or acid liquor. If, however, these methods are unsuccessful, the washing efficiency of a CCD system can only be based on the readily soluble salts.

By referring again to Fig. 10, it will be seen that flow of liquor is maintained entirely by gravity. The only pumps required are those used to control the rate of discharge from the various thickeners. This is a very desirable feature where corrosive or hot solutions are being handled.

A straight countercurrent flow is the most efficient method of washing by decantation. Any other flow sheet employing successive water washes or partial counterflow requires larger quantities of wash water and results in weaker liquors, or for the same amount of wash water more decantations are required to give equal washing.

The CCD flow sheets are not always as simple as the ones shown. Very often a larger number of thickeners are used. In some cases agitators are inserted between the first and second thickeners, for instance in cyanide plants in order to obtain the additional extraction possible with a weak liquor, or in a caustic plant to consume the excess lime left over from the first reaction. With such a flow sheet, the first thickener is usually called the primary thickener and those following the agitators are the washing thickeners. In other cases a filter is added to the end of CCD series and by means of the moisture reduction and by washing on the filter, the soluble loss is cut down.

Washing in Ammonia Leach Plants. The methods for leaching and washing for the ammonia process, used some years ago at the Kennecott plant in Alaska and by the Calumet and Hecla Co. for treating sand tailing, differ radically from the usual procedures for copper and zinc treatment. The following is taken from a description of the Kennecott plant:[1]

"After the tanks are filled with ore, the charge is allowed to drain for about 24 hr. The drain cocks are then closed and the first leach solution is pumped in through the bottom. This first leach is pumped directly from the preceding charge and the ammonia contained therein is approximately 60 per cent saturated with copper. As this solution rises through the ore bed some of the residual water from the charge collects at the top of the rising column of solution. The first of this, containing only traces of copper and ammonia, is siphoned off to waste

[1] E. J. Duggan, Ammonia Leaching at Kennecott, *Trans. AIME*, Vol. 106, p. 547.

and the next few inches, containing more copper and ammonia, is sent to the wash storage.

"The first leach is allowed to stand on the ore for about 12 hr without circulation. The solution will then be enriched with copper to about three-fourths of the saturation point, or a ratio of NH_3 to Cu of about 1.3 to 1, which is the practical limit for good extraction. A portion of the solution is then pumped from the charge, and this portion becomes the rich or pregnant solution and is withdrawn from the leaching circuit for evaporation.

"This rich solution is then replaced by an equal volume of a mixture of low-grade make-up solution and enough concentrated ammonia from the evaporators to complete the extraction of the copper. Fresh ammonia is added if required. The solution or second leach is then circulated for 36 to 48 hr by downward percolation, then it is pumped to the leaching tank containing the next charge of ore, on which it becomes the first leach."

As the second leach is pumped off, it is followed immediately by 24 to 30 tons of wash solution. When the solution leach is within a few feet of the bottom of the tank, low-pressure live steam is admitted to the top. Most of the steam condenses on contact with the ore and virtually constitutes a hot-water wash, which probably accounts for the fact that apparently no copper is precipitated during the steam wash. Pumping is continued until the charge is heated to the bottom, when the effluent is turned to a water-cooled surface condenser on which is maintained a low vacuum. Steaming is continued until the effluent has the desired ammonia content; then the steam is turned off and the tailing is discharged to the waste dump. Automatic devices are installed to prevent too high or too low pressures in the tanks. Table 23 gives a typical operating cycle for one charge.

Washing—Miscellaneous. Washing for the Caron ammonia process for the extraction of nickel at the Nicaro Nickel Co. plant in Cuba was done in a series of four Dorr torque type S thickeners, provided with gas-tight covers to prevent loss of ammonia. For details of this operation, see description of the Nicaro plant, Chap. 8.

Comparing zinc and copper leaching, it is obvious that both extraction and washing of zinc are less efficient than the same operations for copper. In practice, however, tailing from copper leaching is usually a final product on which further treatment is impossible. Zinc tailing is always re-treated so that high efficiencies in zinc leaching and washing are less important.

Filters are generally used in washing zinc leach tailing. At Trail, British Columbia, acid thickener underflow at 40 per cent solids is delivered to Moore filters for preliminary washing.   The Moore cake is re-treated on seven American filters.   These are split into two sections of three each, with one spare, and the sections operate in series.   The discharge from the first section is pugged with water.

The final cake containing 30 per cent moisture is discharged to V-bottom cars for delivery to the smelter, where the lead and silver are recov-

TABLE 23.   TYPICAL OPERATING CYCLE IN AMMONIA-LEACHING PLANT, KENNECOTT COPPER CO.

Hours	Operations	Amount of solution, tons	% NH_3	% Cu	% CO_2
0–12	Charge 575 tons ore at 0.94% carbonate copper, 5% H_2O				
12–24	Draining				
24–32	Pump to bottom first leach solution	192	10.50	6.30	12.40
30–31	Siphon from top to waste	10	Trace	Trace	
31–32	Siphon from top to waste storage	6	2.00	1.40	
32–44	Still leach				
44–46	Pump from bottom to rich solution storage	59	10.32	7.85	12.20
44–46	Pump to top concentrated ammonia	23	26.00	.....	22.00
44–46	Pump to top make-up	36	4.00	2.50	4.30
46–94	Circulation leach				
94–102	Pump from bottom to next charge	192	10.50	6.30	12.40
94–96	Pump to top wash	30	1.50	1.00	
98–108	Steam, 28-ton steam to top				
102–104	Pump from bottom to make-up storage	36	4.00	2.50	4.30
104–108	Pump from bottom to wash storage	24	1.40	0.65	
108–120	Discharge tailing, 0.14% carbonate copper				

ered.   Zinc, in the form of oxide, is extracted from the slag and delivered to the oxide-leaching plant.   A varying percentage of this cake is dried in rotary dryers to about 10 per cent moisture before delivery to the smelter.   Average assay of this product for 1935 was: gold, trace; silver, 6 oz per ton; copper, 0.32 per cent; lead, 11.2 per cent; zinc, 20.9 per cent; total sulfur, 4.7 per cent; sulfate sulfur, 2.6 per cent; insoluble, 3.2 per cent; iron, 32.2 per cent; manganese, 1.05 per cent; calcium oxide, 0.40 per cent; cadmium, 0.20 per cent; acid-soluble zinc, 1.50 per cent; water-soluble zinc, 0.92 per cent.

At Risdon, Tasmania, the prepared residue pulp is filtered in a Moore vacuum unit.   The filter consists of 22 leaves of 80 sq ft filtering area, at

TABLE 24. SOLUTION REMOVAL AND WASHING EQUIPMENT, ZINC-LEACHING PLANTS

Anaconda, Great Falls	A. S. & R. Co., Corpus Christi, Tex.	Amer. Zinc Co., Monsanto, Ill.	Cons. M. & Sm. Co., Trail, B.C.	Electr. Zinc Co., Risdon, Tasm.	Sullivan M. Co., Kellogg, Idaho	H. B. M. & Sm. Co., Flin Flon, Man.
Fifteen Dorr thickeners, 50-ft AP Three 28-ft N thickeners Fifteen 50-ft AP thickeners Eleven 50-ft AP thickeners	Seven Burt filters, 5-ft diam by 40-ft copper-lined steel shell Pulp to two Dorr thickeners in series, 30 ft diam by 8-ft standard arms, 0.2 rpm, u'f to two Oliver vacuum filters 8 ft diam by 12 ft	Three Dorr thickeners, 50 ft by 15 ft, type ARG, o'f from first Two Dorr thickeners in parallel Three 16- by 10-ft diam Eimco rotary-drum vacuum filters	Eight Dorr thickeners, 50-ft diam by 12-ft stave tank; stem and arms, Douglas fir; rakes, maple Two Moore filter baskets Seven Amer. filters Six disk, 8 ft 6 in. diam Neutral side: Dorr thickeners, three 50 ft, nine 40 ft, five 32 ft	Five Dorr thickeners, 50- by 15-ft staves, lead-lined bottom, bitumen jointed concrete, aluminum-bronze plow arms, copper tie rods, 4-in. lead-covered steel shaft Moore filter unit	Six Burt filters, 5 ft diam by 40 ft Pulp to two Dorr thickeners, u'f to 10- by 12-ft Oliver filters	Neutral side: Four Dorr thickeners, 50- by 14-ft staves AP central shaft, 0.25 rpm Acid side: Four Dorr thickeners, 50- by 14-ft AP, u'f to Moore filter unit
			Purification			
Five bronze Shriver presses, 36 plates	Five bronze plate- and-frame Shriver presses	Dorr thickeners, Kelly filters, five 4 by 10 ft, nine 5 by 14 ft, 1,250 sq ft area, steel construction, canvas and cocoa matting			Shriver plate- and-frame filter presses	Shriver presses, canvas-scraped kraft paper

6-in. centers. A cake about 1½ in. thick is formed in 10 to 20 min. The cake is washed with 1.6 to 2.0 times its final water content, which takes from 40 to 50 min. After a partial drying under vacuum for 15 min, the cake is discharged into hoppers.

Each cake weighs approximately 11 tons on discharge and contains 6 tons dry residue, which includes 0.3 to 0.5 per cent water-soluble zinc

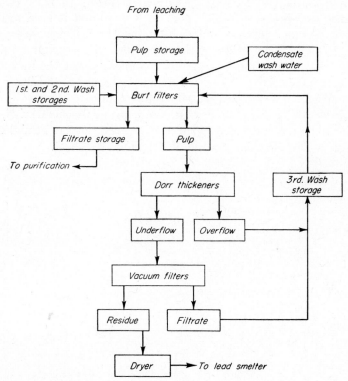

FIG. 12. Residue-washing circuit at electrolytic zinc plant, American Smelting & Refining Co., Corpus Christi, Tex.

and 0.2 to 0.3 per cent acid-soluble zinc. The output is approximately 106 tons per day.

A 25-ton electric crane is used to handle filter baskets. The filter cake is fed from the hoppers by screw feeders into three rotary dryers, heated directly by coal. The drums are 44 ft long and 4 ft 3 in., 5 ft 8 in., and 6 ft 6 in. in diameter respectively. The moisture content is reduced from 40–43 to 18–20 per cent with the evaporation of 50 tons water per day and a coal consumption of 11½ tons. The dried residue moves by conveyors to a bin and then by trucks for shipment to the lead smelter.

At the Sullivan Mining Co. plant residue pulp is delivered from the pulp storage tank through a 6-in. lead pipe to the Burt filters, of which there are 14, each 5 ft in diameter by 40 ft long. After the solution is filtered from the pulp, three successive washes of gradually decreasing zinc content are added, each wash being forced out as completely as possible before the next is added. The residue is then repulped with water and discharged by gravity through launders to Dorr thickener tanks, the overflow from which goes to storage and is used again for repulping residue. The underflow from the Dorr thickeners passes to 10 by 12 Oliver vacuum filters, the cake from which is conveyed by a belt conveyor to a Ruggles-Coles dryer, which reduces the moisture to about 15 to 20 per cent. The dried residue is shipped to the Bunker Hill lead smelter for recovery of lead, silver, and gold.

Residue washing at the A. S. & R. Co. plant at Corpus Christi, Tex., is similar to that at the Sullivan plant. The operation can be understood from Fig. 12, showing this portion of the plant flow sheet.

CHAPTER 5

SOLUTION PURIFICATION AND METAL RECOVERY

Various means have been developed to purify leach solutions prior to eventual recovery of the metals. The electrolytic and the various chemical methods of precipitation have been applied to several metals. Three categories require examination: (1) purification of solutions, (2) electrolysis of the leach solutions, (3) chemical methods of precipitation.

PURIFICATION OF SOLUTIONS—COPPER

Of the copper-leaching plants, Chuquicamata, Andes, and Katanga have found it necessary to purify their solutions before precipitation. Inspiration does not have to resort to purification.

At Chuquicamata, the essential steps in purification are to remove the chlorine present in the leach solutions, and to reduce as much as possible of the ferric iron in the solutions before they reach the tank house.

Strong solution from the leaching-plant sumps flows to the dechloridizing plant by gravity, and about 10 per cent is diverted to one or more Devereux agitators. An excess of cement copper is charged to the agitators and the resulting pulp is dropped back into the launder carrying the other 90 per cent of the strong solution. This mixture enters Parral agitators in which the ferric iron is reduced and the chlorine precipitates as cuprous chloride.

The agitators discharge the pulp into settling tanks, each one 32 by 28 by 9 ft. The solids settle out there and the dechloridized solution goes on to the electrolytic tank house.

After a water wash, the cuprous chloride is agitated once more with a hot solution containing about 180 gpl ferrous chloride. The cuprous chloride dissolves and the mixture of solution and residual cement goes through rotating bronze drums charged with scrap iron. The precipitated copper goes around back into the process again, as does the ferrous chloride solution (for details, see page 136).

Andes Copper uses, of necessity, a somewhat more complicated purification procedure. Flow sheets of the purification and the dechloridizing plants are shown[1] (Figs. 13 and 14).

[1] L. A. Callaway and F. N. Koeppel, Metallurgical Plant of Andes Copper Mining Co., *Trans. AIME*, Vol. 106, pp. 678–728.

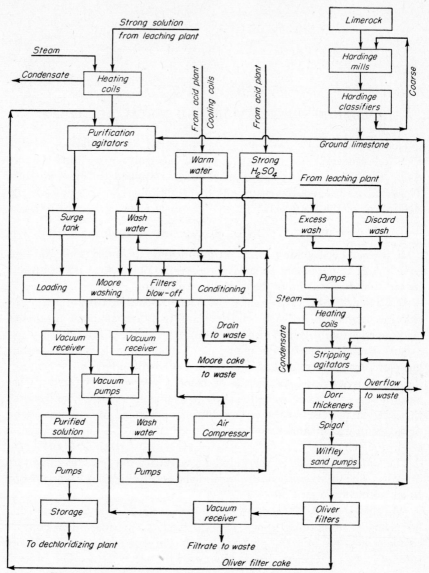

FIG. 13.   Leach-solution purification plant, Andes Copper Co.

The purification process at Andes consists of treating the strong solution from the vats with finely ground lime rock, together with the basic copper carbonate precipitate produced from the stripping of the wash water from the leaching plant.   The impurities come down for the most part with the calcium sulfate precipitate that forms.

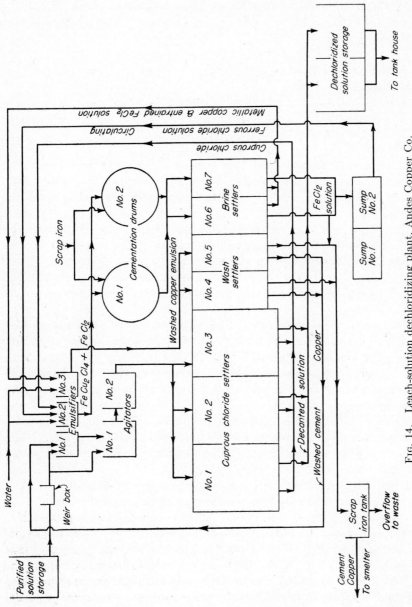

Fig. 14.   Leach-solution dechloridizing plant, Andes Copper Co.

After the completion of the precipitation from this heated strong solution, the latter goes through Moore filters and on to the dechloridizing plant. The washed precipitate is sent to waste. The process includes the following steps:

1. Lime-rock grinding.
2. Stripping.
3. Purification.
4. Filtration.
5. Dechloridizing.

1. Lime rock is ground dry to a fineness of not more than 20 per cent plus 200 mesh. If the lime is coarser, the reactions take place more slowly and there is a tendency for the larger particles to settle out of the precipitate.

2. The stripping operation recovers the copper from the discard and the excess wash solutions in a product from which the copper is extracted in the purification operation and made available for electrolytic deposition. The filtered cake from stripping is an efficient precipitant for the impurities in the strong solution and, in fact, is much more desirable than lime rock.

The solutions treated in the stripping operation consist of excess wash from the Moore filters and discard wash solution from the leaching plant. The solutions are heated to about 37°C. The stripping operation is continuous. The composite of the solutions from the two storage tanks is pumped to the heating tank at the rate of 60 to 80 tons per hr. An average analysis of the solution stripped is as follows: copper, 8.02 gpl; sulfuric acid, 0.39; iron, 0.46; aluminum, 0.74. From the heating tank, this solution is laundered to the first stripping agitator. The 11 agitators are connected in series. Compressed air at 25 lb pressure is used for agitation.

Ground lime rock is fed from the storate bins into agitators 1, 3, 6, 7, and 8 in amounts required for complete precipitation of the copper. An average of 48 grams of lime rock is added per liter of solution treated.

The pulp from the last agitator is laundered to two Dorr thickeners operating in parallel. The overflow is discarded and the spigot discharge is delivered by a 3-in. Wilfley sand pump to a distributing box above the Oliver filters. The filtered cake drops into a launder and is sluiced into the first purification agitator with strong solution. An average partial analysis of this cake is as follows: 10.28 per cent copper, 30.16 per cent calcium oxide, 1.10 per cent iron, and 24.84 per cent SO_4.

3. In the purification step, the strong solution from the leaching plant is treated in mechanical agitators with Oliver cake from step 2 and raw

lime rock. Most of the ferric iron and high percentages of other impurities deleterious to electrolysis are precipitated. The basic carbonate in the Oliver cake dissolves, releasing copper from electrolytic deposition.

The purification operation is continuous. The strong solution flows by gravity from the leaching-plant storage sumps to the heating tank at the head of the purification circuit, where it is heated to about 39°C. The normal rate of flow is 150 tons per hr. Most of the solution from the heating tank flows through a weir box into the first purification agitator.

The filter cake from the stripping operation is added and, if insufficient, raw ground lime rock is also placed in the solution. The reactions, which start immediately, result in the solution of the copper carbonate from the Oliver cake and the precipitation of most of the ferric iron, arsenic, phosphorus, molybdenum, and about 20 per cent of the aluminum. An excess of lime rock precipitates copper. This condition is corrected by adding fresh strong solution in sufficient amount to redissolve copper and consume excess lime rock. Raw lime rock is added at times to the lower end of the circuit. With a flow rate of 150 tons per hour the solution remains about 3 hr in the agitators. Purification data are shown in Table 25.

TABLE 25. PURIFICATION DATA, ANDES COPPER CO.

	Solution analyses, gpl		Impurity elimination, %
	Unpurified, strong solution	Filtered, purified solution	
Cu.................	41.55	42.09	
H$_2$SO$_4$..............	14.11	0.00	
Total Fe............	7.03	1.50	82.12
Ferric Fe...........	6.32	0.94	87.98
Al.................	4.99	4.13	21.85
As.................	1.40	0.11	92.32
P$_2$O$_5$..............	1.52	0.20	87.14
Cl.................	0.29	0.46	
Mo.................	0.033	0.003	91.12

4. The strong solution containing the precipitated impurities is passed through Moore filters. The filtrate is pumped to a storage tank at the dechloridizing plant, the excess wash solution transferred to the stripping division, and the filter cake goes to waste. Approximately 58 per cent of the cake is calcium sulfate, average analysis being as follows: 0.86 per cent total copper, 0.43 per cent water-soluble copper, 7.77 per cent iron, 1.3 per cent aluminum, 44.39 per cent SO$_4$, 23.44 per cent calcium oxide.

The average rate of filtration is 5.31 l of purified solution per sq ft of filter area per cycle.   Cake thickness is about $\frac{3}{8}$ in.

5. Purified strong solution contains about 0.46 g chlorine per liter.   In order to avoid deposition of cuprous chloride on the cathodes and the subsequent copper loss by volatilization during furnace refining, it is necessary to reduce the chlorine content of the solution to about 0.2 gpl.

Dechloridizing is similar to the procedure used at Chuquicamata, described on page 136.   The solution is agitated with cement copper which precipitates the chlorine as cuprous chloride.   After settling, the dechloridized solution flows by way of storage tanks to the electrolytic plant.   The settled residue, consisting of cuprous chloride and cement copper, is treated with ferrous chloride brine which dissolves the cuprous chloride.   The copper in this solution is precipitated by scrap iron and the resulting cement washed and reused for dechloridizing.

Copper from wash waters is precipitated by scrap iron and the cement sent to the smelter, the overflow being sent to waste.

Katanga purifies solutions to remove iron and alumina from the solutions.   The procedure used is somewhat similar to zinc leaching, resulting in separation of iron and alumina.   Precipitation in this way is not practicable for percolation leaching since the precipitate carries down copper and also interferes with percolation.

Tests indicated that, with ore in excess, an agitation time of 17 hr gives an effective elimination of iron and alumina.   With proper control of ore additions and with a finer point of classification on the purification classifier, the grade of purification tailing can be kept below 1 per cent copper, which, in view of the small quantity of tailing produced, is considered satisfactory.   Typical analyses to and from the purification agitators are as follows:

	To purification	From purification
Cu, gpl....................	35	56
Free H_2SO_4, gpl..............	15	0
Total Fe, gpl.	5	2
Al_2O_3, gpl..................	10	6

PURIFICATION OF SOLUTIONS—ZINC

Successful operation of zinc electrolysis depends on proper purity of the solutions to be electrolyzed.   The following statements as to the effect of impurities were made by Laist[1] et al.:

[1] F. Laist, R. B. Caples, and G. T. Wever, "The Electrolytic Zinc Process," in D. M. Liddell's *Handbook of Nonferrous Metallurgy*, McGraw-Hill Book Company, Inc., New York, 1945.

Antimony is undoubtedly the most injurious impurity yet encountered in electrolytic zinc operations. If present in any amount, its effect is noticeable at high temperatures and in a highly acid medium. Under normal cell conditions, 1 ppm is apparent. The zinc deposit becomes spongy and dark; sprouts, small at the zinc surface and large at the end, form in large numbers. Ampere efficiency is markedly lowered. As the period of deposition increases, the effects become more pronounced. Remedies include more thorough purification in the neutral leach, shortening of deposition period, and decreasing current density to lower cell temperature.

Arsenic alone is much less injurious than antimony. The presence of arsenic in solution, however, is a rather sure indication that some antimony is also present. The same purification methods used for the removal of antimony also remove arsenic, and with much less difficulty. Therefore, antimony may be present in small amounts without arsenic, but arsenic is rarely present without antimony, unless the material being treated is free of antimony. The early indicators of the presence of arsenic in the zinc cell are pronounced corrugation of the surface of the zinc deposit and absence of the usual luster. This is followed by sprouting and serious loss in ampere efficiency.

Copper may be present up to 10 mg per l without seriously affecting ampere efficiency and, with low acid strength, may go even higher. If zinc-dust purification is carried far enough to remove cadmium sufficiently to produce grade A zinc, there is little danger of trouble from copper. However, copper may also get into the solutions from corrosion of support bars and bus bars, from breaks in water or solution connections, or from roof leaks. Fresh solution is run into cells thus affected, the solution flow increased, and the cathodes removed and stripped as rapidly as possible.

Cadmium up to 0.5 gpl does not injure the character of the zinc deposit or lower the ampere efficiency, but of course must be removed if high-grade zinc is to be produced.

Cobalt, if present in amounts greater than 10 mg per l, causes re-solution of the zinc deposit unless special treatment is resorted to. At Risdon, Tasmania, larger amounts are reported to be present without serious loss in ampere efficiency, because large quantities of glue, which is of benefit in reducing the effects of some impurities, notably cobalt, are added.

Nickel seems to have less effect than cobalt but is classed as one of the highly undesirable impurities. It is not usually present in zinc-plant solutions.

Germanium is a highly injurious impurity.

Gallium and *indium* are not mentioned in the literature as to their effects in zinc electrolysis.

Iron in amounts up to 0.02 to 0.03 gpl has been present in solution without noticeably lowering ampere efficiency.   It is usually an indication of incomplete purification in the neutral leach, and arsenic, antimony, or both may also be present from this cause.   Iron is commonly encountered in amounts up to 0.03 gpl.

Manganese up to 3 to 4 gpl is not seriously injurious, but it may be in larger proportions.   The source of manganese is normally the dioxide used for oxidizing iron in the neutral leach.

Chlorine in amounts up to 100 mg per l does not materially affect ampere efficiency but corrodes the lead anodes.   If the concentrate treated carries silver, the chlorine content is usually insufficient to cause trouble.   At Risdon, Tasmania, excess chlorine is precipitated by a special silver-purification procedure.   Chlorine may be present in the electrolyte as perchloric acid, in addition to the chloride.   Perchloric acid is produced at the anode and is seriously corrosive to anodes when present in sufficient amounts.   At one time at Trail, 400 mg per l of chlorine was present, only 10 per cent of which was as chloride.   As a result of corrosion, the anode life was reduced to less than six months. At Risdon, pure solutions are reported to contain 139 mg per l total chlorine, of which 64 mg is chloride and 75 mg perchlorate.

Fluorine corrodes aluminum cathodes and causes serious trouble from sticking of the deposited zinc.   It may be partly removed by lime. Fluorine, if present in sufficient amounts, may also corrode lead anodes.

Arsenic, antimony, and germanium may be more or less completely removed in the neutral leach (see Chap. 1 for details).   The mechanism of removal is probably based on the fact that these elements form more or less indefinite complexes with precipitated basic iron salts and hydrates, which complexes are insoluble in water.   A considerable excess of iron may be required for the removal of arsenic and antimony and, if not present in sufficient amounts, it is usually added in the form of sulfate produced by dissolving scrap iron in sulfuric acid.   Manganese dioxide is a convenient reagent for oxidizing iron to the ferric state for hydrolysis and precipitation after neutralization.   Excess manganese dioxide is usually precipitated at the anodes in the electrolysis and this precipitate may be used in the neutral leach step, supplemented by amounts from outside sources.

In treatment by zinc dust, copper may be completely removed before much cadmium is precipitated.   Accordingly, the usual procedure is to purify by zinc dust in two stages, the first giving a copper product, usually sent to smelting, and the second a cadmium product which is oxidized, dissolved in acid, and electrolyzed to produce cadmium metal.

Cobalt is usually precipitated by nitroso-β-naphthol which at Trail is made from sodium nitrite and β-naphthol, dissolved in caustic soda. At Trail, a certain amount of cobalt may be valuable in reducing the lead content of the cathode zinc and in reducing corrosion of the lead anode.   Experience there demonstrates that a concentration of 3 to 4 mg per l gives lead control, with no loss of current efficiency.

At Risdon, the neutral solution carries 20 to 25 mg per l cobalt, the electrolyte only 10.   Accordingly from 55 to 60 per cent of the solution is purified down to 2 to 3 mg per l and blended with the remainder to give the required concentration.   The procedure is as follows: as the first portion of the impure solution is being charged, the requisite amount of a caustic soda solution of β-naphthol is added, the curd of zinc hydrate and β-naphtholate being broken up by violent agitation.   When the charging is complete, a slight excess of sodium nitrite crystals is added, followed by sufficient spent solution to bring the charge to 0.1 to 0.15 gpl acid.   Nitroso-β-naphthol is formed and unites with the cobalt to give a dark red precipitate.   The consumption of β-naphthol is about 9.5 parts per part of cobalt precipitated, and the sodium nitrite consumption is about one-half this amount.   Precipitation takes from 1 to $1\frac{1}{2}$ hr.   Excess reagent is detrimental to electrolysis and at the end of the period this is corrected.   The average amount of cobalt precipitated per day at Risdon is about 94 lb.

For the electrolytic production of manganese dioxide at the anode during zinc electrolysis, the presence of ferrous sulfate is objectionable, since the latter readily dissolves the manganese dioxide.   Any iron dissolved in the ferrous state is readily oxidized by the addition of manganese dioxide to the leach liquors.   Free acid can readily be neutralized by the addition of calcine but lime must be added to adjust the pH for precipitation of iron and any alumina present.   Adjustment to a pH of 6 is usually sufficient, and at this point there is only a small co-precipitation of manganese.   Other injurious elements may be present which do not precipitate at pH 6 and these may be kept within limits by raising a part of the solution to about pH 7.5, at which about 10 per cent of the manganese precipitates.   Above a pH of 7.5 to 8, the manganese loss is high.

PURIFICATION OF SOLUTIONS—MANGANESE

Electrolysis is in use for cathodic plating of manganese metal and for special anodic production of manganese dioxide for dry-cell use.   Solution purification is required for both of these procedures, the methods and the substances removed being quite different.

As with zinc, successful manganese electrolysis depends upon solution purity, and the specifications for purification are even more stringent than for zinc.

Operations of the Bureau of Mines electrolytic pilot plant at Boulder City, Nev., were described by Jacobs and others.[1]

At this plant, the reduced ore is leached with spent electrolyte containing 8 to 10 gpl manganese as sulfate, 135 to 140 gpl ammonium sulfate, and 43 to 50 gpl sulfuric acid, the finished leach being neutralized by ammonia.   The neutral pulp is settled in an acidproof thickener and the spigot discharge to be washed consists of barren tailing and ferric and aluminum hydroxides.

The thickener overflow contains small amounts of iron, arsenic, copper, zinc, lead, nickel, cobalt, and molybdenum, all of these requiring removal before electrolysis.   These are precipitated in a special apparatus by hydrogen sulfide.

The solution, freed of metallic impurities, still contains colloidal sulfur, colloidal metallic sulfides, and organic matter coming from the ammonium sulfate.   These materials are removed by adding ferrous sulfate and oxidizing it with air.   The precipitated iron absorbs the sulfur and colloids and also carries down any residual arsenic and molybdenum not precipitated by hydrogen sulfide.   Filtration is effected with Oliver precoat filters, using a mixture of diatomaceous earth and activated carbon as the filter precoat.   Activated carbon removes the aforementioned organic impurities.   Table 26 gives analyses of solutions.

TABLE 26.   PURIFICATION OF SOLUTION FOR ELECTROLYTIC MANGANESE

Constituent	Solution before purification, gpl	Solution after H_2S treatment, gpl	Solution after Fe treatment, gpl
Mn	35.8	35.1	34.4
$(NH_4)_2SO_4$	139.6	139.5	139.2
Cu	0.04	0.00008	0.00008
Fe	0.003	0.0015	0.0002
As	0.0014	0.0006	0.00015
Ni	<0.001	<0.001	<0.001
Co	<0.001	<0.001	<0.001
Mo	0.0005	0.0005	0.0003

At the Boulder City plant, cobalt and nickel are definitely the most harmful impurities that have been studied.   Although the results with trivalent arsenic were not consistent, it is deleterious.   Presence of 5 to 10 gpl zinc may even be beneficial since higher current efficiencies were frequently, but not always, obtained thereby.

[1] J. H. Jacobs *et al.*, *Trans. AIME*, Vol. 159, pp. 409–20, 1944.

Unlike electrolytic zinc, the appearance of manganese plated from solutions carrying impurities is not characteristic of the impurity. The first evidence of impurity is always a black border around the edge of the deposit. The width of this border increases with time and impurity concentration. When the solution is badly contaminated, black areas may appear in the center of the deposit.

Although calcium and magnesium in the solutions have no effect on the electrolysis, they are serious impurities because they crystallize out of the solution and plug up valves, solution lines, and pumps. Calcium sulfate continually precipitates wherever solutions are acid and magnesium precipitates continually as a triple salt (manganese, magnesium, ammonium sulfate) with a resultant loss of manganese and ammonium sulfates.

ELECTROLYSIS OF SOLUTIONS—GENERAL

Detailed discussion of electrochemical theory is beyond the purview of this book and may be found in a number of standard texts. However, certain practical aspects of electrolysis must be taken up in order to bring out the interrelationship between this process and leaching.

An electrolyte of any metal, such as a purified leach solution, begins to decompose when a voltage applied to it through suitable electrodes reaches a definite point, called the decomposition voltage. For each metal, there is a definite decomposition voltage, which varies according to the position in the emf series. If several metals are in solution, the one with the lowest decomposition voltage will plate out first. Hydrogen, always being present in aqueous electrolytes, remains in solution only as long as there are present ions of a metal lower than hydrogen in the emf series. For example, copper, being lower than hydrogen, plates out before hydrogen is discharged. The decomposition voltage of copper sulfate is 1.19 volts, that of zinc sulfate 2.35. Because zinc is well above hydrogen in the emf series, one would expect hydrogen to evolve instead of zinc. However, the hydrogen overvoltage with respect to zinc is high enough to let zinc plate out of zinc sulfate solutions, although some hydrogen is indeed given off in the process.

Power consumption, expressed in kilowatthours for an electrolytic operation, is simply the product of the amperes used per hour times the total voltage applied in the circuit. Power cost in electrolysis is usually a substantial fraction of the total plant-operating cost. Therefore, any possible reduction of voltage is of considerable importance. Current leakages and electrode short-circuiting are equally important as cost factors and must be kept to a minimum.

The total voltage required for an electrolytic cell is the algebraic sum of several factors.   These begin with delivery of alternating current to the electrolytic plant, go on through conversion of this power to direct current, the resistance of various contacts, the anode resistance, various anode reactions, and the resistance of the electrolyte itself.   Then follow the cathode reactions, the cathode resistance, and the resistances of the various contacts that complete the circuit.   An algebraic sum is mentioned because all these factors do not work in the same direction.   At either electrode, polarization may act to increase the cell voltage and depolarization may act to decrease it.   These factors are briefly discussed in the following paragraphs.

Power conversion from alternating to direct current cannot, of course, be accomplished without power losses.   Rotary converters have been used for many years to supply a pulsating direct current for electrolytic plants, dust-collecting plants, and other uses, but few new installations have been made in recent years.   Rotary converters at Trail have an efficiency of 92.3 per cent, which is in the range of efficiencies (92 to 94 per cent) typical for such devices.

Motor-generator sets, although widely used in smaller plants and for lower-voltage installations, are less efficient than rotary converters.   Trail's motor-generator sets give an efficiency of 85.2 per cent.   Recent installations of such sets include the conversion equipment for the new Kennecott electrolytic copper refinery at Salt Lake City, completed late in 1950.   The plant has a capacity of 12,000 tons of refined copper per month, with provision for expansion to 16,000 tons.   Six motor-generator sets are provided, each including a 2,900-hp synchronous motor and two 1,000-kw 125-volt d-c generators.

Most efficient of the three available conversion devices is the mercury-arc rectifier, the so-called ignitron.   Using no moving parts, these rectifiers yield an efficiency of around 95 per cent.   At Magdeburg, Germany, mercury-arc rectifiers were about 94.5 per cent efficient; rotary converters, 93 per cent.   At the new plant of American Zinc Co. of Illinois, conversion equipment includes four 12-anode 5,500-amp 700-volt water-cooled mercury-arc rectifiers, and two 5,000-amp 600-volt d-c generators driven by an 8,400-hp 13,800-volt synchronous motor.   The motor-generator set is supplied primarily to replace the rectifiers that are removed from service for repairs.   Operating efficiency of the rectifiers is about 95 per cent at 93 per cent power factor.

It is possible, of course, to generate direct current directly from steam. At the Corpus Christi, Tex., electrolytic zinc plant of A. S. & R. Co., power is generated by five d-c generators of 2,500-kw capacity geared to steam turbines.   Auxiliary power is supplied by two a-c turbogenerators of 2,000 kw each.

Resistance losses, both entering and leaving the cell, occur mainly in bus bar contacts. Reduction of such losses is a matter of proper design and of good housekeeping. In the Inspiration electrolytic copper plant, leakage has never exceeded 1 per cent, with voltage as high as 350 volts. A tank-house survey showed an electrical loss of 0.62 per cent through the copper busses, and a contact loss of 0.87 per cent.

Owing to its influence on conductivity, anode material may have a considerable effect on voltage. Thus, at Chuquicamata, lead-antimony anodes have greatly superior efficiency as compared with the "Chilex" anodes. As a result, the former do not heat the electrolyte as strongly as do the latter.

In zinc electrolysis, manganese dioxide is deposited on the anodes and thus cuts down their conductivity. Silver-lead anodes decrease the quantity of such deposits and thereby appreciably reduce the voltage needed.

Anode reactions may either increase or decrease voltage. In copper electrolysis, voltage can be reduced considerably if enough ferrous sulfate is present and if the electrolyte is agitated and the temperature held high. The voltage reduction is due to depolarization brought about by oxidation of ferrous to ferric sulfate.

Theoretically, sulfur dioxide is also a depolarizer but it is not used extensively for this purpose. At Chuquicamata, solutions going to electrolysis carry about 0.2 to 0.5 gpl, an amount so small as to have little depolarizing effect, probably not more than the equivalent of 0.01 volt.

Electrical depolarization, by current interruption or by superimposing an alternating current on the direct current, is possible in theory. For copper electrolysis, this has been done in the laboratory with current interruption, whose depolarizing effect may be due to partial suppression of an insulating layer of gas around the anode. In a small electrolytic copper test cell, using an insoluble anode, the voltmeter needle jumps to a certain point when the current is turned on and then gradually rises to a point where it remains constant. This indicates that when electrolysis begins the anode is entirely in contact with the solution. Then, during the next few minutes, a gas layer forms over the anode surface, causing the voltmeter needle to rise slowly from its first position. When the layer is complete, the voltage holds constant but at a relatively high level, owing to the insulating effect of the gas layer. If the current were interrupted at intervals more or less corresponding to the time required to build up the gas layer, it would be possible to operate a cell at a considerably lower voltage than that required for continuous operation without interruptions.

Such current interruptions would have no effect on the ampere efficiency, and metal can be recovered with a reduction in power cost. The same effect can be obtained in zinc electrolysis, but the effect on ampere efficiency is not known. Unfortunately a means of interrupting very large currents at frequent intervals has not yet been worked out, although it is certainly not impossible for some method to be developed.

Generally speaking, there are several chemical processes possible for anodic depolarization in copper electrolysis, but no chemical depolarization methods are feasible for zinc cells.

TABLE 27. CONDUCTIVITIES OF SOLUTIONS OF $CuSO_4 \cdot 5H_2O$ AND H_2SO_4*
(In reciprocal ohms per cubic centimeter)

Temperature	25°C					45°C				
Grams H_2SO_4 per 100 cc	0	5	10	15	20	0	5	10	15	20
Grams $CuSO_4 \cdot 5H_2O$ per 100 cc 0		0.208	0.410	0.565	0.683		0.246	0.492	0.683	0.839
5	0.053	0.204	0.388	0.531	0.646	0.0205	0.242	0.461	0.643	0.791
10	0.0221	0.195	0.350	0.500	0.600	0.0294	0.222	0.422	0.606	0.738
15	0.0343	0.189	0.338	0.458	0.558	0.0468	0.217	0.381	0.545	0.690
20	0.0423	0.182	0.319	0.433		0.0574	0.212	0.378	0.521	0.643

* Data from Richardson and Taylor, *Met. Chem. Eng.*, 1911, IX, 536. For other data see Table 28.

An important side effect of anodic depolarization in copper electrolysis is its influence on anode disintegration. This is especially marked if graphite anodes are used. Ordinarily, if graphite is used as an insoluble anode in copper electrolysis, it rapidly disintegrates, probably under the disrupting action of minute gas bubbles forming in the pores of the anode. Anodic depolarization inhibits formation of these bubbles.

As a result of pilot-plant work at Douglas, Ariz., in 1915, Van Arsdale and Addicks were able to show that carbon (graphite) anodes would stand up in copper sulfate solutions if properly depolarized. Copper recovery ran as high as 2.25 lb of copper per kwhr, under proper conditions. The high recovery was due to the voltage reduction obtained through anodic depolarization. Graphite anodes are much more expensive than lead anodes and have no scrap value. However, a recovery of 2.25 lb per kwhr is about twice the average yield at Andes, Chuquicamata, and Katanga, and it is nearly three times the yield at Inspiration.

This system of ferrous iron depolarization is usable only under two conditions: (1) if the plant needs excess acid for leaching and (2) if the plant needs ferric sulfate for direct leaching of copper sulfides. The excess acid can be made by reducing the ferric iron with sulfur dioxide. Both conditions satisfy the essential requirement that some means of

TABLE 28.   SPECIFIC CONDUCTIVITY OF SOLUTIONS OF H_2SO_4, $CuSO_4$, AND OF SOLUTIONS CONTAINING FREE H_2SO_4 AND $CuSO_4$*

(Conductivity in reciprocal ohms per cubic centimeter)

Solution temperature, 25°C					
Grams free H_2SO_4 per 100 cc..............	0	5	10	15	20
Grams $CuSO_4 \cdot 5H_2O$ per 100 cc $\quad$ 0	......	0.2165	0.4069	0.5559	0.6684
5	0.0148	0.1977	0.3714	0.5123	0.9195
10	0.0252	0.1868	0.3480	0.4815	0.5729
15	0.0333	0.1772	0.3214	0.4392	0.5256
20	0.0402	0.1750	0.3017	0.4087	0.4852

Solution temperature, 40°C					
Grams free H_2SO_4 per 100 cc..............	0	5	10	15	20
Grams $CuSO_4 \cdot 5H_2O$ per 100 cc $\quad$ 0	......	0.2490	0.4722	0.6498	0.7901
5	0.0191	0.2233	0.4272	0.6016	0.7433
10	0.0320	0.2096	0.3989	0.5619	0.6792
15	0.0425	0.1992	0.3688	0.5135	0.6263
20	0.0517	0.1956	0.3486	0.4807	0.5810

Solution temperature, 55°C					
Grams free H_2SO_4 per 100 cc..............	0	5	10	15	20
Grams $CuSO_4 \cdot 5H_2O$ per 100 cc $\quad$ 0	......	0.2751	0.5262	0.7312	0.8981
5	0.0229	0.2418	0.4740	0.6731	0.8339
10	0.0382	0.2250	0.4394	0.6313	0.7733
15	0.0510	0.2135	0.4055	0.5765	0.7144
20	0.0623	0.2059	0.3835	0.5403	0.6643

* Data from Kern and Chang, *Trans. Am. Electrochem. Soc.*, 1922, XLI, 181.

control and reduction be applied to the ferric iron content of the solutions going round through the leaching-electrolysis cycle.

Specific resistance per unit of volume of the electrolyte accounts for an important fraction of the total voltage. Electrolyte composition, addition agents, circulation or agitation, and electrolyte temperature are all important factors. They are to a large degree interdependent.

Higher temperatures are usually favorable to electrolyte conductivity and thus they help decrease voltage. At the anode, when insoluble products are plated out, higher temperatures enhance deposition efficiency. An example is anodic production of manganese dioxide. At the cathode, elevation of temperature is usually unfavorable to deposition efficiency but the loss may be compensated by increased current density.

TABLE 29.   EFFECT OF THE PRESENCE OF $FeSO_4$ ON AN ELECTROLYTE CARRYING
135 GPL FREE H_2SO_4 AND 35 GPL Cu
(Conductivity in reciprocal ohms per cubic centimeter)

Fe, gpl	25°C	40°C	55°C
0	0.4094	0.4766	0.5307
10	0.3726	0.4345	0.4834
20	0.3424	0.4003	0.4469

Cathode reactions, particularly in zinc electrolysis, are many and complicated and are not too well understood. To ensure good deposition efficiency, it is necessary to achieve practically complete removal of impurities before electrolysis.

For copper electrolysis, the most important cathode reaction is the solvent action of ferric iron on copper already deposited. Formation of trees or bending of cathodes can cause short circuits and act to lower cathode ampere efficiency.

Addition agents seem to cause an increase in voltage but their effect on efficiency is not clear. Theoretically, addition of a wetting agent, for example, should have appreciable effect at both anode and cathode in electrolysis. A complete investigation of the effect of wetting agents on both copper and zinc electrolysis would be valuable.

ELECTROLYSIS OF SOLUTIONS—COPPER

Electrolytic refining of copper became essential when the electrical industries and other consumers of copper demanded a higher purity of metal than could be obtained by the fire-refining process. Approximately 90 per cent of the copper used today is refined electrolytically.

Most electrolytic refining of copper starts with an impure copper anode, cast directly from a refining furnace. The impure anode and a pure copper cathode, or starting sheet, are suspended in an electrolyte of copper sulfate and sulfuric acid. Direct current is applied to the cell, the anode being the positive pole, and the cathode the negative. Under proper conditions, copper is dissolved from the anode and plated out on the cathode. There is no net change in copper content of the solutions, the only shift being an increase in the content of impurities in the electrolyte.

Electrolytic recovery of copper from leach solutions is effected with insoluble anodes. The direct current causes copper to plate out on the cathode, and the electrolyte is continuously depleted in copper. Impurities are removed before electrolysis; therefore there is no build-up in the cell. The spent electrolyte is simply used over again as the solvent in leaching.

For full details on copper electrolysis, the reader is referred to one of the standard works on copper metallurgy,[1] but it seems advisable here to include a broad outline of the process.

There are two systems now in use for connecting the electrodes for copper refining. In the series system, the electrodes are connected in series, the back of one cast-copper anode serving as the cathode for the next. Copper simply travels from one electrode to the next, and when the original anode portion is completely dissolved, the new pure electrode is pulled from the tank.

The multiple connection is used for electrolysis following leaching. The electrodes are connected in parallel within each tank, although there are a great many systems for making these connections in such manner as to save space, copper in bus bars, and electrical energy. Electrodes are usually about 3 ft square, set into the tanks on about a 2-in. spacing. The tanks are usually made of wood or reinforced concrete, lead-lined, about 11 ft long, $3\frac{1}{2}$ ft wide, and $3\frac{1}{2}$ ft deep. Such a tank holds about 30 anodes.

The most common current density is around 20 amp per sq ft of cathode area, which means that approximately 10,000 amp is supplied to each tank. Current density must be carefully chosen to balance several factors, but, in general, slow deposition at low current densities favors better condition of the final deposit and higher current efficiency. It is possible under certain conditions to deposit a copper powder by running current density very high.

Current efficiency is simply the ratio of the amount of metal deposited in a unit of time to the amount that should have been deposited, according to Faraday's law. One ampere-hour should yield 1.186 g of copper at 100 per cent efficiency. Under the multiple system of connection, current efficiency should run over 90 per cent. Losses of current can occur because of poor connections, leakage in various parts of the circuit, insufficient circulation of electrolyte (which may cause hydrogen to form

[1] For example, see D. M. Liddell, *Handbook of Nonferrous Metallurgy*, McGraw-Hill Book Company, Inc., New York, 1945; or J. Newton and C. L. Wilson, *Metallurgy of Copper*, John Wiley & Sons, Inc., New York, 1942.

at the cathode), or actual short-circuiting of electrodes through "tree" formation or bending of starting sheets.

Electrolyte composition is usually held to about 35 gpl of copper, and 150 to 200 gpl of sulfuric acid.   Temperature is held at about 130°F,

TABLE 30. TANK-ROOM DATA, COPPER ELECTROLYSIS

	Inspiration	Andes	Chuquicamata	Katanga
Capacity, tons Cu per day	75	100	715	92 (orig.) 220 (re-modeled)
No. of cells.........	120	576	1098	160
Cell dimensions......	33 ft long by 4 ft 3 in. deep by 4 in. wide	10 ft 3 in. long by 2 ft 10 in. wide by 3 ft 9 in. deep	19 ft 2 in. long by 3 ft 11 in. wide by 10 ft deep	62 ft 6 in. long by 3 ft 2½ wide by 4 ft 2½ in. deep
Cell construction.....	Concrete, lead-lined	Concrete, lining 6 lb lead, 6% Sb	Concrete, mastic-lined	Concrete, asphalt, mastic-lined
Cell capacity, cu ft...	67,320	61.185	393.830	135,728
Cell capacity, cu ft per ton Cu per day	897	611	550	1,475 (orig.), 617 (remodeled)
Cathodes............	42 by 42 in. sub-merged	28 by 37½ in.	3 by 4 ft sub-merged	2 ft 9¾ in. wide by 3 ft 5¼ in. long
Anodes.............	Cast lead 8% Sb ½ in.	39¼ in. by 26½ in. by 42 in. cast lead, 15% Sb, 1% As	Chilex and lead	2 ft 5⅞ in. by 3 ft 7 in. by ⅜ in. cast lead, 6% Sb
Cathodes per cell....	95	34	55–73	48
Anodes per cell......	96	35	56–74	50
Spacing, center to center, cathodes...	4 in.	3½ in.	3–4 in.	2⅜ in.
Amp per sq ft.......	11.8 to 14.2	10.69	7–18	15.8
Cathode efficiency...	67.9%	85.63%	85–92%	93.29%
Anode efficiency.....	54%			
Kwhr per lb Cu pre-cipitated..........	1.431 (a-c)	0.958	1.07	1.17
Cu, gpl, in..........	26.4	29.2	21–26	
Cu, gpl, out.........	21.6	10 71	14–16	
Total acid, in........	33.8	47.8		
Total acid, out.......	41.1	75.95		
Kwhr per lb Cu......	1.431	0.958	24–28 lb Cu per kw-day	1.17 (a-c)
Starting sheets.......	....	24 hr	24–48 hr	48 hr
Deposition time......	5 days	8 days	5–15 days	10–14 days
Anode corrosion per ton Cu...........	....	0.844 lb		
Ferric Fe, in........	4.0	....	0.65	
Ferric Fe, out........	8.6	1.08	2.0	
Total Fe............	20.0	1.73	2.5	

sometimes by heating with steam.   The high temperature decreases cell resistance and therefore increases efficiency.

Preparation of Electrodes.   At present there are four large-scale elec-trolytic copper plants in which the electrolyte is derived by leaching of ores.   Table 30 gives the essential data on these plants.   In this type of electrolytic copper plant, preparation of electrodes is of considerable importance and is discussed below.

For copper electrolysis, all plants use pure copper "starting sheets" that are plated out, stripped from blanks, trimmed, flattened, and provided with loops for hanging in the cells. These may be plated out from plant solutions, but they are usually better when plated from special solutions by special electrical circuits, using soluble anodes of cast copper.

With the exception of Chuquicamata, all plants have used lead anodes. Owing to changes in the ore, practice is also changing in this respect at Chuquicamata, where the original plant used anodes of fused magnetite "made in Germany." These were unsatisfactory because their brittleness is an adverse factor in commercial operation. Later "Chilex" anodes, developed by C. G. Fink and associates, were used; they consisted mainly of copper silicide.

Instead of the lead anodes used elsewhere, special anodes were required because of the chlorine, iron, and nitric acid impurities in the Chuquicamata electrolyte. Antimonial lead anodes at Chuquicamata produce approximately 12 per cent more copper per kilowatt day than the Chilex anodes, and are now usable because of lower iron, chlorine, and nitric acid content in the electrolyte. Cathodes from either anode are equal in purity.

At Katanga, the original anodes were chemical lead. Warping and peroxidation were very serious and the chemical lead anodes did not last very long. They were replaced by 6 per cent antimonial lead, cast $\frac{3}{8}$ in. thick, which was satisfactory.

At Inspiration, the original anodes were of 4 per cent antimonial lead, $\frac{1}{4}$ in. thick, each being punched for porcelain insulators. The $\frac{1}{4}$-in. anodes warped badly and were replaced by $\frac{1}{2}$-in.-thick 8 per cent antimonial lead, cast and fabricated at the plant, which proved satisfactory.

At Andes, with the anodes as originally cast, the supporting bar between the edge of the tank and the anode proper was exposed and corroded to such an extent that the bars failed and some anodes dropped. This was corrected by casting lead as far around the supporting bar as possible.

Starting-sheet production is similar to copper refining, *i.e.*, soluble anodes of cast copper are used. At Katanga, a separate pure solution is used for 48 hr. The cathodes bearing the starting sheets are stripped on racks at the end of the building, looped on standard Morrow clip machines, and flopped on tables.

At Andes, means are provided for discarding impure starting-sheet electrolyte to the commercial circuit. Make-up is from dechloridized purified solution, water, and acid. Anodes are cast with heavy supporting lugs and weigh from 550 to 600 lb each.   Analysis of anodes and starting sheets is:

	Anodes, %	Starting sheets, %
Cu........................	99.30	99.935
S.........................	0.49	0.0011
Fe........................	0.048	
As........................	0.041	0.0016
Sb........................	0.002	0.0006
Ag, oz per ton............	3.0	0.15
Au, oz per ton............	0.27	Trace
Cl........................	.....	0.0007

Blanks at Andes are $\frac{1}{8}$-in. rolled copper sheets to which the supporting bars of copper are riveted with the joints soldered.   Milled grooves are provided near the edge of the blank on each side and bottom.   A light engine oil, applied with felt rollers, is satisfactory for oiling the blanks. Stuck sheets are rare.   About 11 per cent of the sheets are cut into strips, annealed, looped, and clipped to the sheets with a Morrow clip machine. When the electrolyte in the commercial circuit carries 2 gpl or more of ferric iron, it is necessary to paint the lower part of the loops with an acid-resisting paint.

At Inspiration starting sheets are made in a special circuit using fire-refined copper anodes.   A refiner and casting plant was set up for this purpose at the International Smelter in 1931.   The anodes weigh from 900 to 1,100 lb.   About 24 per cent anode scrap is returned to the smelter.

New rolled copper blanks grooved at sides and bottom are thoroughly cleaned to remove any oxide, amalgamated with mercuric nitrate, and oiled with a cheap grade of oil applied with cloth swabs.   After stripping, the blank is touched with amalgam solution wherever scratched, it is oiled, and returned to the circuit.   About 15 per cent of the production is estimated for loops, blanks not stripped, and scrap.   Loops are 20 in. long by 4 in. wide before looping, and 2 in. is allowed on the ends of the starting sheets for looping, the entire loop and punching being above solution level.

At Chuquicamata, starting sheets are produced from freshly dechloridized and reduced strong solution, using lead-antimony anodes.   The blanks used are made from oversize starting sheets built up to thickness by electrodeposition.   They are trimmed, ground, riveted to the supporting bars, amalgamated, and oiled before use.   Edges of the blanks are grease-coated, the grooved edge not being used.   All sheets are trimmed on all four sides before looping. The sheets as trimmed measure 3 ft by 4 ft 1 in., of which 3 by 4 ft is immersed. The sheets are equipped with two loops fastened to the sheets by Long and Austatler machines. About 8 per cent of the total sheets is used for loops and about 2 per cent is scrap.

At Chuquicamata and Andes, the cathodes are fire-refined, cast into shapes, and shipped. Table 31 gives available analyses of cathodes and wire bars.

TABLE 31. ANALYSES OF ELECTROLYTIC COPPER PRODUCED BY COPPER-LEACHING PLANTS

	Inspiration		Andes		Chuquicamata		Katanga
	Cathodes	Wire bars	Cathodes	Wire bars	Cathodes	Wire bars	
Cu..............	99.87	..	99.927	99.961	99.90	99.96	99.5–99.7
Fe..............	0.021	..	....	0.0013	0.005	0.0016	
Ni and Co......	0.006	..	....	0.0001	None	None	
Zn.............	Trace	..	....	....	0.0003	Trace	
Sb.............	0.0005	..	0.0003	0.0002	0.0004	0.0004	
As.............	Trace	..	0.0006	0.0005	0.0002	0.0002	
S..............	0.045	..	....	0.0017	0.03	0.0016	
Se and Te.......	Trace	..	....	....	None	None	
Cl..............	Trace	..	0.0087	....	0.005		
Pb.............	....	..	....	....	0.0016	0.0008	
Sn.............	....	..	....	....	0.0011	0.0006	
Bi.............	....	..	....	....	None	None	
Mn.............	....	..	....	....	0.0001	None	
Insoluble........	....	..	....	....	0.06		
O...............	....	..	....	....	....	0.032	
Mo.............	....	..	0.0351	....	....	0.0001	
Ag, oz per ton...	....	..	0.019				

ELECTROLYSIS OF SOLUTIONS—ZINC

It has been known for about 80 years that zinc could be recovered from its solutions by electrolysis, but no commercial use was made of this fact until 1914, when the Anaconda Copper Mining Co. and the Consolidated Mining & Smelting Co. of Canada began independently to develop a large-scale electrolytic process for zinc. Both investigations were successful, and from Montana and Canada use of the process spread to Australia and eventually all over the world.

Leaching of zinc calcine and purification of the leach solution have been discussed in Chap. 1. Composition of solutions fed to electrolytic plants is by no means uniform. It is a universal requirement that electrolytic

124   *HYDROMETALLURGY OF BASE METALS*

plant feed be of an almost absolute purity, but the content of zinc varies widely from plant to plant.

Neutral solution from the purification step in most plants carries about 100 to 150 gpl of zinc as zinc sulfate. In the Sullivan plant in Idaho, which uses the Tainton high-density, high-acid process, the zinc content is over 200 gpl. The electrolysis step in all plants is so organized that only about 50 to 75 per cent of this zinc is removed in any one pass through the tank house.

Neutral solution is added to the electrolytic cells in controlled amounts, either continuously or in batches. The objective is to keep the zinc content and the acid content of the electrolyte about uniform. In the so-called low-acid plants, acid strength of the electrolyte is held at a level between 100 and 200 gpl of sulfuric acid. In the Sullivan high-acid plant, a kind of batch operation is maintained in which the acid strength of a cell is reduced to about 400 gpl by withdrawing spent electrolyte and replacing it with neutral strong solution. As the electrolysis proceeds and the acid strength has risen once more to about 550 gpl, a portion of the electrolyte is withdrawn to the leaching plant and neutral solution added again. Table 32 shows the solution strengths prevailing at various points in different plants.

Current density, measured in amperes per square foot of cathode area, varies among plants from 20 to over 100 amp. Most plants operate in the range of 20 to 40 amp per sq ft. In general, a higher current density means higher voltage per cell, higher acid strength needed, greater flow of cooling water per cell, faster deposition, less floor space and less solution to handle, better purification, closer electrode spacing, and need for heating leach solutions. Choice of current density depends on how these various factors balance up at each plant location.

Cell temperatures are held to about 35 to 45°C by circulating cooling water through lead coils placed in each cell. A good part of the energy supplied to the cell is dissipated as heat, and cooling coils are needed to keep this generation of heat within bounds. In general, a higher cell temperature decreases resistance and decreases voltage, with a consequent saving in power. However, higher temperatures also increase the bad effect of impurities on ampere efficiency; therefore, the benefits of operating at a high cell temperature can only be secured in those plants able to achieve an extremely high purity of solution.

Voltage required for electrolysis of zinc sulfate solution is theoretically 2.35 volts. Actually, 3.25 to 3.50 volts is required, owing to losses in the various ways mentioned in the general discussion of electrolysis. Under approximately the conditions mentioned for most electrolytic zinc plants, *i.e.,* 100 gpl zinc, 100 gpl acid, 30 amp per sq ft current density, and

35°C temperature, the voltage is about 3.4 volts per cell. In the high-density process, where current density runs up to 100 amp, the voltage is also very high, except that it is held down by the high acid strength (around 500 gpl) of the electrolyte.

TABLE 32. SOLUTION ANALYSES, ELECTROLYTIC ZINC PLANTS

	Corpus Christi	Sullivan	Trail	Risdon	Great Falls, Anaconda	Am. Zinc Co. of Illinois	Norske Zink-compani
Spent electrolyte:							
Zn, gpl..........	50–60	36	....	50–55	50	....	55–60
free H_2SO_4 gpl...	200	540–560	....	90	115	135	100
Neutral solution before purification:							
Zn, gpl..........	175	215	....	....	...	....	110–130
Cu, gpl..........	0.9	300 mg	....	....	...	....	0.1–0.2
Cd, gpl..........	1.3	600 mg	....	....	.....	....	0.2–0.5
Co, mg per l.....	12	15 to 30	....	....		....	6–12
Ni, mg per l.....	......	......	....	....		....	0.2–0.3
Fe, mg per l.....	5.0	......	....	0.27 gpl	...	....	5–10
SiO_2, gpl.......	......	......	....	0.8–1.5			
As, mg per l.....	0.5	} 3 to 3	....	0.020–0.04 gpl			
Sb, mg per l.....	0.3		....	0.001 gpl			
H_2SO_4, gpl.......	......	......	....	1.5			
Purified electrolysis feed:							
Zn, gpl..........	172	215	127	111.6	...	135	
Mn, gpl..........	4	......	0.56	7.9			
SiO_2, gpl........	......	......	133 mg	0.101			
Co, mg per l.....	1 or less	<1.0	3.7	9.9	...	0.5–1.8	5–7
Cu, mg per l.....	1 or less	......	0.11	0.08		1.4	<5.0
Cd, mg per l.....	1 or less	<1.0	4.5	6.1		1.5	<1.0
Cl, mg per l.....	......	......	113	60.9			
Sb, mg per l.....	1 or less	<1.0	} 0.08	0.08	...	....	<0.1
As, mg per l.....	1 or less			<0.1		Trace	<0.1
Fe, mg per l.....	15	......	0.0198 gpl	1.1	...	20	
Ni, mg per l.....	......	......	....	....	...	....	<0.1
Ge, mg per l....	......	......	....	....	...	0.4–1.8	<0.1
F_2, mg per l.....	......	......	23				
$CaSO_4$, gpl......	......	......	1.9				
$MgSO_4$, gpl......	......	......	7.0				

Ampere efficiency of electrolysis is simply the ratio of the actual recovery of metal to the quantity that should have been recovered by the amount of current used, according to Faraday's law. For zinc, 1 amp-hr should yield 1.219 g. Multiplying the ratio of the actual to the theoretical yield of metal by 100 gives the percentage efficiency of the electrolysis.

An efficiency of 95 per cent is extremely good for zinc electrolysis and it would be hard to maintain such a figure in most plants over a long period of time. A long-term average of 92 to 94 per cent is considered good.   Assuming that other cell conditions are in balance, the chief factor in lowering ampere efficiency is the presence of impurities.   These generally act to cause re-solution or improper deposition of zinc, and minute quantities can have a devastating effect.   For a detailed discussion of the effect of impurities, see the section of this chapter dealing with solution purification.

Other factors affecting ampere efficiency are temperature, addition agents, the period of deposition, and the ratio of zinc to acid in the electrolyte.   The first three are tied up with the effect of impurities, which is increased by raising the temperature or increasing the period of deposition.   Addition agents, like glue and various metal salts, are intended to inhibit the effect of impurities, but it is far better if possible to get rid of the impurity than to try to counteract it in the cell with some other chemical.   The ratio of zinc to acid is important in that the ampere efficiency drops sharply if the zinc content of the electrolyte drops below a certain point, usually around 25 to 30 gpl.   At low zinc concentrations, hydrogen begins to be evolved instead of zinc.

Operating period varies with the cell conditions that are set up.   In the Risdon, Tasmania, plant a 72 hr period is used.   In the Sullivan high-density plant, cathodes are pulled every 8 to 12 hr.   Most plants operate on a basis of pulling cathodes every 24 to 48 hr.   Longer operating periods go with purer solutions, yet the Risdon plant, which uses a 72-hr run, also has an extremely severe cobalt condition, which might be expected to cause the re-solution of zinc.   This is inhibited by adding a mixture of glue, β-naphthol, and antimony.   It would be preferable, however, to remove the cobalt, but Risdon has found this impossible.

Frequent cleaning of cells is also necessary owing to the slime that forms on the anodes and on the cell bottoms.   This is largely manganese dioxide, brought in with the electrolyte, where it was added to oxidize iron in the neutral leach.   It forms on the anode as a slime coating and although much of it falls off as a sludge into the bottom of the cell, the remainder has to be removed once it builds up beyond a certain point.

Electrodes for Zinc Electrolysis

Aluminum is used for cathodes in all plants, the thickness varying from $\frac{1}{8}$ to $\frac{3}{16}$ in.   Cast or rolled sheet lead is used for anodes in all plants (see Table 33 for zinc tank-room data).

For many years it was considered that anodes for zinc electrolysis should be of the purest lead available.   The use of a lead alloy carrying small amounts of silver was first investigated by C. G. Fink[1] and was

---

[1] C. G. Fink, *Transactions of American Electrochemical Society*, pp. 46, 349, 1924; *ibid*, pp. 49, 85, 1926.

later tested on a practical scale by Tainton[1] for the Sullivan Mining Co. The following is abstracted from the article by Tainton *et al.* on this subject.

Plain lead anodes gradually disintegrate during electrolysis, so that the life of an anode, say ½ in. thick, is frequently not more than two years. Part of the lead from the anode finds its way to the cathode, lowering the purity of the deposited zinc and decreasing the hydrogen overvoltage. A further part of the lead goes into the manganese dioxide precipitated at the anode, rendering this unsalable as a high-grade product. A further disadvantage of plain lead anodes is their tendency to buckle or bend during electrolysis, making it necessary to use a fairly wide electrode spacing to avoid short-circuiting, thus leading to a higher cell voltage. Power consumption is also affected by the high decomposition voltage at a lead peroxide surface.

Research at Kellogg showed that an anode with 1 per cent silver and 99 per cent lead reduced voltage and decreased the current efficiency but put less lead in the manganese dioxide and in the zinc. Reduced spacing gave a voltage of 3.32 but a cratered deposit of zinc. Addition of silicic acid corrected the deposit character but also required the addition of gum arabic. Agar and glue were not satisfactory. Ternary alloys with tin and arsenic both gave good results, the latter showing less current efficiency in the tests but yielding less lead in the manganese dioxide and in the deposited zinc. It was therefore adopted for the large plant in which the voltage averaged 3.35 per cell, occasionally being as low as 3.18. Current efficiency averaged around 87 per cent, occasionally reaching 94 per cent. Analysis of the average sample of zinc produced over a month gave

Metal	Assay, %
Cadmium	0.0005
Lead	0.0015
Copper	0.0008
Iron	0.0004
Zinc	99.9968

Metals other than cadmium, lead, copper, and zinc were not found.

As noted in Table 33, the majority of zinc plants, including some European plants not tabulated, use the silver-lead anode. At Trail, anodes of pure refined lead, cast ¼ in. thick, are used and their life there is stated to be considerably in excess of three years. Excessive chlorine in solution at one period reduced anode life to less than six months.

---

[1] U. C. Tainton, A. G. Taylor, and H. P. Ehrlinger, Lead Alloys for Anodes in the Electrolytic Production of Zinc of High Purity, *Trans. AIME*, 1929.

TABLE 33. TANK-ROOM DATA, ZINC ELECTROLYSIS

	A. S. & R. Co., Corpus Christi	Amer. Zinc Co. of Illinois	Risdon	Sullivan Mining Co.	Cons. M. & S. Co., Trail	Anaconda, Great Falls	Hudson Bay M. & S. Co., Flin Flon
Capacity, tons Zn per day...	100	112	225	105	450	440	150
No. of cells......	320	180	5 units, 144 each	2 circuits 150 each	144 per group	6 units, 144 each	3 circuits, 160 cells each
Cell dimensions.	7.5 by 2.5 by 4.5 ft	7 ft 10 in. by 3 ft by 5 ft 2 in. deep	12 ft 10.5 in. by 2 ft 9.5 in. by 4 ft 6.5 in.	....	....	10 ft 3 in. by 2 ft 10 in. by 5 ft	Outside, 3 ft 1 in. wide, 3 ft 11 in. deep, 7 ft 6 in. long
Cell capacity, cu ft........	25,200	44,878	113,724	....	....	....	42,750
Capacity, cu ft per ton Zn per day........	252	400	505	....	....	....	218
Cell construction	4-in. concrete 8-lb lead lining	Concrete, lead lining	Wood, lead-lined	Wood, lead-lined	Special concrete and lining	Wood, lead-lined	Concrete, asphalt, and sulfur, sand lining
Cathodes......	Rolled aluminum, $3/16$ by 21 by 36 in.	Rolled aluminum $1/4$ in. by 3 ft 6 in. by 24 in.	Rolled aluminum, $3/16$ in. by 3 ft 9 in. by 2 ft 1 in.	Aluminum plates, $1/8$ in.	Aluminum sheets, $3/32$ in., 12 sq ft area	Aluminum $3/16$ in. by 2 ft by 3 ft 6 in.	No. 8 B&S gage aluminum, ca. 9.5 sq ft area
Anodes........	Silver-lead alloy, $5/16$ by $19\frac{3}{8}$ by 31 in. rolled grids, $9/16$ in. holes	Silver-lead alloy, $1/4$ in. rolled grids, $3/8$ in. holes	Cast lead, $3/8$ in. by 23 in. by 3 ft $7\frac{1}{2}$ in.	Silver-lead alloy	Chemical lead, $1/4$ in., area, 10.9 sq ft	$3/8$ in. lead	Cast pure lead, $5/16$ by 22 by 38 in. submerged area, 9.7 sq ft

TABLE 33. TANK-ROOM DATA, ZINC ELECTROLYSIS.—(*Continued*)

	A. S. & R. Co., Corpus Christi	Amer. Zinc Co. of Illinois	Risdon	Sullivan Mining Co.	Cons. M. & S. Co., Trail	Anaconda, Great Falls	Hudson Bay M. & S. Co., Flin Flon
Cathodes per cell...........	24	27	33	12	23	27	18
Anodes per cell.	25	28	34	24	24	28	19
Spacing........	Anodes 3 in. center to center	3 in. center to center	3½ in, 3¾ in., 4 in.	⅝ in. between surfaces	3 in. center to center	4 in. center to center	
Voltage per cell.	....	....	3.6-3.56-3.54	3.35	....	3.8	
Amp per sq ft..	60.0	35	Anode 30 Cathode 37	100	....	30	Anode, 32.8 Cathode, 35.2
Ampere efficiency........	84.7	88.5	92.8	....	....	82–88	
Deposition time.	24 hr	24 hr	72 hr	8–12 hr	24 hr	48 hr	

TABLE 34.   ALLOY ANODES IN ZINC ELECTROLYSIS

Anode composition	Voltage	Addition agent	Current efficiency	Pb in MnO_2	Pb in Zn	Character of deposit
Rolled Pb, 99.99 % Pb.....	3.77	Glue 3 lb per	86.15	18.5	0.055	Normal, smooth
1 % Ag, 99 % Pb........	3.65	ton Zn	83.5	2.1	0.009	Rather dark, cratered
⅜-in. spacing:						
Rolled Pb, 99.99 % Pb...	3.7	Glue 3 lb per	85.0	26.0	0.057	Normal, smooth
1 % Ag, 99 % Pb........	3.32	ton Zn	81.8	1.72	0.002	Cratered
Silicic acid:						
1 % Ag, 99 % Pb........	3.71	Glue 3 lb per ton Zn	82.1	2.18	0.0005	Rough, cratered
1 % Ag, 99 % Pb........	3.66	H_2SiO_3 2 lb per ton Zn	89.2	1.79	0.0002	Smooth, bright
1 % Ag, 99 % Pb........	3.64	SiO_2 2 lb per ton Zn	85.7	0.6	0.0035	Smooth, bright
1 % Ag, 99 % Pb........	3.62	SiO_2 4 lb per ton Zn	84.8	1.1	0.0047	Smooth, bright
1 % Ag, 99 % Pb........	3.59	SiO_2 6 lb per ton Zn	85.2	1.4	0.0062	Exceptionally smooth
Various addition agents:						
1 % Ag, 99 % Pb........	3.57	SiO_2 2 lb, gum arabic 1 lb per ton Zn	80.5	1.5	0.0055	Gray, slightly cratered
1 % Ag, 99 % Pb........	3.54	SiO_2 2 lb, gum arabic 2 lb per ton Zn	83.0	1.4	0.0056	Gray, fairly smooth
1 % Ag, 99 % Pb........	3.52	SiO_2 2 lb, gum arabic 2 lb per ton Zn	81.0	1.5	0.0056	Gray, fairly smooth
1 % Ag, 99 % Pb........	3.61	SiO_2 2 lb, gum arabic 2 lb per ton Zn	86.0	n.d.	n.d.	Smooth, bright
1 % Ag, 99 % Pb........	3.62	SiO_2 2 lb, agar 0.5 lb per ton Zn	87.7	n.d.	n.d.	Dull, extremely tough
1 % Ag, 99 % Pb........ large cells	3.74	SiO_2 2 lb, glue 3 lb per ton Zn	78.0	n.d.	n.d.	Dark, cratered
1 % Ag, 99 % Pb........	3.37	SiO_2 2 lb, gum arabic 2 lb per ton Zn	91.5	n.d.	n.d.	
Ternary alloys:						
1 % Ag, 0.5 % Sn, 98.5 % Pb	3.57	SiO_2 2 lb, gum arabic 2 lb per ton Zn	87.6	0.18	0.0005	Exceptionally smooth, satin sheen
1 % Ag, 0.2 % As, 98.8 % Pb	3.60	SiO_2 2 lb, gum arabic 2 lb per ton Zn	85.8	0.08	0.0003	Dull, slightly cratered

Over 400 mg per l chlorine was present largely as perchloric acid, only 10 per cent of the chlorine being present as chloride.

Risdon supports the cathodes between the anodes by two copper bars, 1½ in. by ⅜ in. by 3 ft 10½ in., riveted to each side of the top of the sheet, one end resting on the cathode bus bar and the other on porcelain insulators at the back of the cell. Wood or rubber edge strips are not used at this plant, grooving of the cathode sheet to facilitate stripping having proved satisfactory. The anodes, 23 in. by 3 ft 7½ in., are cast onto a copper head bar 1¼ in. by 3 ft 7½ in.

Sullivan welds an aluminum header bar to the aluminum plates by means of the atomic hydrogen welding process. This header bar is copper plated and slips into a copper clip attached to the bus bar, thus giving copper-to-copper contacts. The electrodes are held in place in the cells by lead-covered wooden frames which are wedged in place in the cells. The guides for the cathodes are of wood, impregnated with paraffin. The cathodes slide in these wooden guides, which also serve as spacers for the anodes, which are held in position against the side of the guides. The wooden guides are replaced about every 60 days.

Trail's cathode life is in excess of two years. Correct spacing of cathodes is ensured by two spacing sticks of hard wood, which are slotted to fit over the lower ends of the anodes. There is also a cathode slot centrally spaced between two anodes.

Pumps in Zinc Electrolysis

Pumps in the Trail electrolytic zinc plant are made of various materials, according to the nature of the solution handled. Constant experiment is carried on with new materials to find better ways of handling the corrosive solutions.

For the tank room, acid carrying about 100 gpl of free sulfuric acid is pumped by hard lead pumps. Stainless steel, however, seems to do well in this service. Although Duriron works well, its brittleness makes extremely careful handling necessary. For low-acid pulps (10 gpl acid) with abrasive solids, ferric iron, copper, etc., hard lead pumps are used. Here again, stainless steel seems satisfactory.

Neutral pulps carrying abrasive materials are handled with bronze pumps. Acid pulps with no abrasive materials but with copper and iron in solution require lead pumps. Clear neutral solutions containing copper are handled in bronze pumps; neutral solutions free of copper, acid, or abrasive materials are pumped in iron or bronze pumps.

The hard lead used contains 13 per cent antimony. The stainless steel analyzes 20 per cent chromium, 7 per cent nickel, 0.25 per cent carbon, 4 per cent tungsten, 2 per cent copper.

CHEMICAL METHODS OF PRECIPITATION—COPPER

We can define chemical methods for copper precipitation negatively as those not using electrolysis. Obviously there are a considerable number of theoretically possible precipitants, but only three are in actual use. These three are

1. Precipitation by iron, usually called cementation.
2. Precipitation as cuprous chloride by metallic copper from solutions carrying chlorine.
3. Precipitation from ammonia solutions by decomposing and driving off the solvent.

In addition to the above there are several possible methods which may come into use in the future. Among these are

4. Precipitation by sulfur dioxide from sulfate solutions.
5. Precipitation by hydrogen sulfide.
6. Precipitation by reducing agents such as hydrogen or carbon monoxide from ammoniacal solutions. (Process of Chemical Construction Corp.)

1. Cementation. Precipitation on iron, which utilizes one of the earliest known chemical reactions, has been in use for many years. In Spain at Rio Tinto, pig iron was in use for precipitation of the liquors from the large heap-leaching operation there. Scrap iron has been widely used in this country and elsewhere, but although it is cheaper than others, it is not an efficient precipitant and its cost is usually high due to the labor required in handling. In several plants in the Southwest baled, detinned, and shredded tin cans have replaced scrap iron. These bales can be handled by magnets and labor costs are therefore considerably less than for scrap iron.

While the basic reaction for copper precipitation by iron is very simple, in actual operation other reactions may occur and several other factors take part, the more important of which are acidity of the solutions, the amount of ferrous and ferric iron and copper present, the rate of flow, etc. These affect the iron consumption and the grade of copper produced.

The amount of free acid in solution may have two effects. If the acidity is sufficiently high, iron consumption is increased. If acidity is too low, precipitation of copper slows down appreciably and the grade of the copper is lowered, owing to co-precipitation of basic salts and hydrates of iron. At the limiting condition of an almost neutral solution, with considerable iron in solution and quite small amounts of copper, metallic copper is not precipitated by metallic iron.

The rate of flow is of considerable importance.   If it is too slow, *e.g.*, at the Ohio Copper plant, experience has shown that recovery is poor and the grade of the precipitate low.   This can be understood from the fact that the cementation reaction takes place only at the iron surfaces in contact with the solution.   Accordingly, circulation must be rapid enough to bring fresh solution into contact with the iron surfaces in a reasonable time; otherwise partial or complete neutralization of the solution at the surface occurs.   This is analogous to circulation in electrodep-

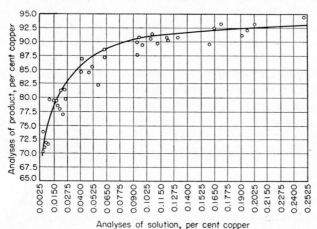

Fig. 15.   Relation of grade of copper precipitated to per cent copper in solution treated, Ohio Copper Co.

osition of metal, which is needed to bring fresh solution to the electrode surfaces.

The amounts of copper and of acid are factors both in regard to recovery and grade of copper produced.   This is shown by Table 35.[1]

TABLE 35.   PERCENTAGE RECOVERY OF COPPER IN VARIOUS SECTIONS OF LAUNDER

Average volume, pregnant solution, 1276 gpm
Average copper per 1,000 gal pregnant solution, 17.031 lb

Sections	1–2	3–4	5–6	7–8	9–10	All
Recovery, % of total	37.2	29.2	17.9	8.7	4.3	97.3

Average copper, pregnant solution, 0.204% (17.02 lb per 1,000 gal)
Average copper, barren solution, 0.0058% (0.48 lb per 1,000 gal)

The relation of the grade of precipitate to the percentage of copper in the solution treated by the Ohio Copper Co. is shown in Fig. 15.

[1] A. E. Anderson and F. K. Cameron, Recovery of Copper by Leaching, Ohio Copper Co., *Trans. AIME*, Vol. 73.

Copper cementation is usually carried out in launders, although other equipment has been in use occasionally, mainly with the idea of avoiding the high labor cost of handling scrap iron, separating and recovering cement, etc. Cementation from leach liquors from treating pyrite cinders is usually done continuously in revolving barrels. The following data are taken from operations in several plants using launder equipment.

The underground precipitation plant of the Ohio Copper Co. comprised a total of 3,200 ft of launders, 32 by 32 in. A false bottom of wood lattice with $\frac{1}{4}$-in. square openings was supported 17 in. above the floor of the launder. Detinned iron in bales was torn apart and placed on the lattices. Average monthly copper production was stated to be about 600,000 lb or 20,000 lb per day. According to the foregoing dimensions, launder capacity for solution was about 21,632 cu ft which is equivalent to about 1 cu ft of launder per lb copper per day.

The Andes Copper Co. cementation plant has three parallel concrete launders, lined with brick set in mastic and arranged for a series flow of solution. Each launder is divided into six scrap-iron compartments, dimensions of which are 64 by 10 by 6 ft, giving a launder capacity of 69,120 cu ft.

Solution feed (July–December, 1931) was 641,184 tons, equivalent to about 3,562 tons per day. Solution assays in and out were 2.48 and .069 gpl copper, making a net recovery of 2.41 gpl or 0.24 per cent of the total weight of solution. Therefore, the amount of copper precipitated daily during this period was $3,562 \times 0.0024 \times 2000 = 17,097$ lb.

The Andes launder capacity is thus approximately 4.0 cu ft per lb of copper precipitated per day. Recovery of the copper in the solution fed is 97.2 per cent.

Cementation data are shown in Table 36.

TABLE 36.   CEMENTATION DATA, ANDES COPPER CO., JULY–DEC., 1931

Solution inflow:

Volume, tons	641,184
Cu, gpl	2.48
H_2SO_4, gpl	2.74
Fe, gpl	8.93
Temperature, °C	13.1

Outflow:

Cu, gpl	0.069
H_2SO_4, gpl	1.62
Fe, gpl	11.52
Temperature, °C	14.3
Cu precipitated, %	97.2
Scrap iron per lb Cu produced	1.375

At the Inspiration slime plant there are seven double launders, 40 by

20 ft by 5 ft deep, giving an approximate capacity of 28,000 cu ft.   Based on the treatment of 500 tons of slimes per day, with copper in feed and tailing 1.243 per cent and 0.218 per cent respectively, about 10,250 lb of copper is precipitated per day.   This is equivalent to a capacity of 2.6 cu ft of launder per lb copper precipitated by cementation per day. Average recovery of dissolved copper during 1930 and 1931 was 97.43 per cent.

The cementation launders at the main leaching plant are similar to those at the slime plant, but comprise nine double-section launders, as compared with seven at the slime plant.   Consumption of iron per lb copper at the main plant is high, caused by high amounts of acid and ferric sulfate in the solution going to the launders.   The average for 1927–1931 was slightly over 2 lb.

A different application of precipitation on iron has been worked out through the pilot-plant stage (1951) for treating the oxidized copper ores to be mined in Anaconda Copper Mining Co. Greater Butte project. Briefly the process includes crushing the ore to minus 1 in., scouring it in tumbling mills with sulfuric acid at a pH of about 2, desliming in drag classifiers, lime-xanthate flotation of sands, precipitation of dissolved copper in slimes with sponge iron, and flotation of precipitated copper along with sulfide copper in an acid circuit.[1]

As outlined by F. F. Frick, metallurgical engineer for Anaconda, the sponge iron used contains about 50 per cent metallic iron and is supplied at about 35 mesh size.   Precipitation takes place in agitators much like conventional flotation cells.   Both pulp and iron are fed at a calculated rate that precipitates all the soluble copper and leaves quite a large excess of sponge iron.

After precipitation, the pulp, at a pH of about 3.4, is conditioned with Minerec, this being an essential step.   Flotation of precipitated copper then follows.

The excess of sponge iron serves to reprecipitate any copper that may be redissolved in the process owing to the low pH of the pulp.   Excess sponge iron is recovered by settling the iron and some sand in a hydro-separator, then cleaning the iron concentrate in a Crockett-type magnetic separator.

Anaconda's sponge iron is produced from the iron oxide remaining from use of a pyrite concentrate in the company's acid plant.   Natural gas and slack coal are available at a fair price.   The elements of the process are as follows: Iron calcine from the acid plant is roasted once more, then dropped into a Bruckner-type furnace along with slack coal.   The

[1] F. F. Frick, "Plans for Treating Greater Butte Project Ores," American Mining Congress, Salt Lake City, Utah, September, 1950.

Bruckner furnace, widely used in the 1890's for sulfide roasting, is a cylindrical revolving furnace, with length about twice diameter. The intake and discharge diameters are about 40 to 50 per cent of the inside diameter. This causes build-up of a bed of material inside the furnace about 30 in. deep.

Carbon monoxide forms from the coal under the furnace temperature (1850°F) and reduces the iron oxide. Coke does not work as well as a reducer, owing apparently to the difficulty of producing enough carbon monoxide at this relatively low temperature.

A boring bar has to be provided because, at 1850°F, sintering of the charge begins and a deposit builds up on the furnace shell at a rate of about 1 in. per hr. It scrapes off readily if not heated too long. The bar is a water-cooled section of 8-in. pipe, provided with a scraping knife and mounted on a movable bridge.

The reduced product is cooled under natural gas, then crushed and screened to 35 mesh. Fine coal is separated with a magnetic separator and returned to the furnace.

2. Precipitation as Cuprous Chloride. Precipitation of chlorine is an important part of operations at Chuquicamata and at Andes. The functions of the dechloridizing plant at Chuquicamata are as follows:

1. Precipitation of chlorine as cuprous chloride from strong solution.
2. Reduction of ferric iron in strong solution.
3. Stripping of copper from electrolyte to be wasted.
4. Recovery of cement copper from cuprous chloride by solution in ferrous chloride brine and cementation on scrap iron.
5. Preparation of a high-grade cement copper suitable for melting in a reverberatory furnace for the production of a high-grade fire-refined copper.

Description of the dechloridizing plant operations at Chuquicamata follows:[1]

Strong solution from the leaching plant sumps enters the plant by gravity through three 15-in. wood-stave pipe lines. Of this solution, 10 per cent enters one or more Devereux mechanical agitators, into which is also charged cement copper elevated by crane bucket and fed through hoppers.

The resulting pulp leaves the agitators and is dropped through pipe lines into the remaining 90 per cent of the strong solution, which is passing in an adjacent launder. The mixture then enters one or more Parral agitators where the ferric iron is reduced and the chlorine is precipitated

[1] T. C. Campbell, Reduction Plant of Chile Exploration Co., *Trans. AIME*, Vol. 106, pp. 583–589.

as cuprous chloride. The Parral agitators discharge into launders that convey the solution and suspended cement and cuprous chloride to nine settling tanks, each 32 by 28 ft by 9 ft deep. The solids settle out here and the dechloridized strong solution passes through launders to a pump house, where it is elevated to the head tanks of the electrolytic tank house.

These cuprous chloride settlers are cut out of service in rotation and drained by pumps. After the cuprous chloride is washed by water, it is dug and elevated by clamshell bucket to small mechanical agitators where it is treated with hot ferrous chloride brine carrying 100 gpl of chlorine (100 gpl Cl = 178.7 gpl $FeCl_2$). The cuprous chloride dissolves and the mixture of solution and residual cement is run into seven sets of rotating bronze drums charged with scrap iron. The iron, cut up by arc torches, is charged through a removable door from a charging floor above the drums.

The copper in solution is cemented in these drums and the pulp passes to settling tanks. The brine solution runs out of the settlers to a sump tank and from there to pumps by which it is elevated to the cuprous chloride dissolving agitators. A small volume is by-passed to the stripping agitators.

The coarsest of the cement is excavated, pulped with water, and passed through a ball mill and a Dorr classifier. The fines are returned to process and the coarse passes to filter bottom tanks from which, after further washing and draining, it is dug and shipped to the smelter, dried, melted, refined, and cast into shapes.

The remainder of the drum cement is dug and fed by crane bucket to a Devereux agitator, into which is run a small amount of ferrous chloride brine, plus the electrolyte that is to be stripped and wasted. Copper is precipitated from the electrolyte as cuprous chloride. The pulp passes to settlers and the barren solution overflowing the settlers is piped to waste. In this operation, a small excess of ferrous chloride and, as in the dechloridizing reaction, a large excess of cement copper are required to bring the reaction to completion in the limited time available.

The solids in the settlers carry about 7 per cent chlorine. This product is dug and washed in two Devereux agitators in two stages. In the first stage waste electrolyte does the washing before it enters the stripping agitator. In the second stage the leaching-plant discard solution does the washing. The pulp passes to settlers after each wash and the runoff is returned to the stripping agitator.

The final washed cement is then ready for use in dechloridizing. It is dug by crane and elevated to a Devereux agitator, where it is pulped with strong solution, passing then to the dechloridizing Parrals.

Four traveling cranes handle the cement through the various operations. At full production they move 2,500 wet tons per day. Settlers and mechanical agitators are of reinforced concrete construction, mastic-lined, and the Parrals are of cast reinforced mastic. Clamshell buckets, brine pumps, agitator shafts, and paddles are of bronze.

Iron consumed amounts to 50 kg gross per 100 kg of copper precipitated from cuprous chloride. Brine solution, formerly handled by air lift, is now pumped in order to cut down oxidation of ferrous chloride.

The amount of chlorine precipitated from the strong solutions gradually diminished as the surface ores were depleted, until it became insufficient to operate the plant. Sodium chloride, obtained locally, is used to balance the operation. At Chuquicamata precipitation as cuprous chloride has been most efficient and satisfactory as a means of stripping solutions for discarding and also as a means of reducing ferric iron in solutions to be electrolyzed, whereby electrodeposition efficiency is increased. Table 37 gives data for this plant section.

TABLE 37. DECHLORIDIZING PLANT DATA, CHUQUICAMATA

Capacity, cubic meters strong solution per 24 hr.	25,000
Capacity, tonnage to cementation, short tons per 24 hr.	140
Normal Cl in entering strong solution, gpl.	0.50
Normal Cl in leaving strong solution, gpl.	0.05
Scrap Fe consumption per unit of cuprous Cu.	0.50
Solution grade to stripping, gpl Cu.	8–40
Solution grade from stripping, gpl Cu.	0.4

The diagrammatic flow sheet, Fig. 16, shows the operation of the Chuquicamata dechloridizing plant.

3. Precipitation from Ammonium Solutions. Ammonia leaching is misnamed, although the solvent used contains ammonia and ammonium carbonate. The actual solvent is cupric ammonium carbonate, which is reduced to the cuprous compound by the copper being dissolved. It is therefore necessary to have a sufficient amount of the cupric compound present in order to obtain leaching efficiency. Air oxidation of the cuprous compound provides the needed cupric ammonium carbonate.

Precipitation, in its simplest terms, as described by Benedict,[1] consists in driving off ammonia and carbon dioxide gas by steam, condensing and recombining them for reuse, and collecting the precipitated copper. The final product is a mixture of cuprous and cupric oxides. There are several possible intermediate compounds, including cuprous and cupric carbonates and hydrates, and these, when precipitated, tend to form a hard scale.

[1] C. H. Benedict and H. C. Kenny, Ammonia Leaching of Calumet and Hecla Tailings, *Trans. AIME*, Vol. 70, pp. 595–610.

Precipitation as carbonate tends to deplete the solutions of carbon dioxide and reduces the product grade in addition to forming a hard scale.   Precipitation from the cupric compound gives more carbonate than from the cuprous and therefore the first portion of the effluent solution carrying copper is largely distilled in the cuprous state.

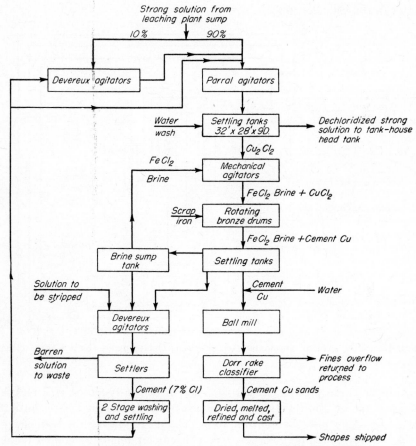

Fig. 16.   Flow sheet of dechloridizing plant, Chile Copper Co.

In the distillation process, a special type of ammonia still, termed a roughing still, is used.   This consists of a cylindrical, cast-iron vessel carrying a series of horizontal, slightly concave shelves, each shelf provided with a scraping arm carried on a central shaft.   Each shelf has an outlet and these outlets are staggered so that solution passing down through the still flows across each shelf in turn.   Steam is admitted at the bottom of the still and flows upward countercurrently through the same shelf openings.

The solution temperature is raised to the boiling point and the current of steam carries off the ammonia and carbon dioxide volatilized by the boiling through the outlet opening in the top of the still. The ammonia and carbon dioxide are then cooled and absorbed in water, to be used later in the leaching process.

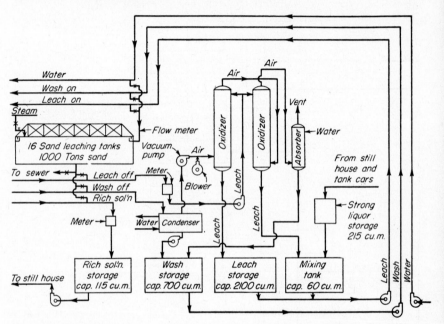

Fig. 17. Flow sheet of ammonia-leaching plant, Calumet and Hecla Consolidated Copper Co.

Copper oxide precipitates on the shelves of the roughing still and is scraped off by the revolving arms, passing down through the solution openings along with the solution, to be caught in a trap at the base of the still. These roughing stills are very efficient for removing copper oxide but the waste solution from them is not barren. It is run to a second unit, called a finishing still, in which the removal of copper, ammonia, and carbon dioxide is completed. Figures 17 and 18 show diagrammatic flow sheets of the leaching and the precipitating sections of the Calumet and Hecla plant.

4. Sulfur Dioxide Precipitation. Copper may be precipitated from sulfate solutions by sulfur dioxide, either as sulfite or as metallic copper. Strong sulfur dioxide bubbled through a solution carrying about 10 per cent bluestone precipitates a small part of the copper as sulfite. If the copper sulfate solution is saturated with sulfur dioxide and then heated under pressure, a part of the copper is precipitated as metallic copper, probably according to the equation:

$$CuSO_4 + SO_2 + 2H_2O = Cu + 2H_2SO_4$$

An early patent on this process (U.S. Patent 723,949) was taken out by Van Arsdale and a later patent by Jumau covered precipitation at specific temperatures and pressures.

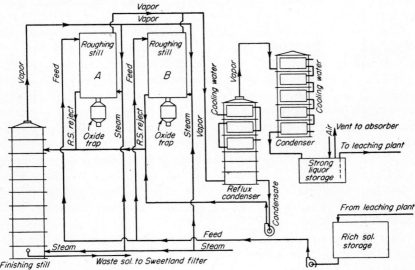

Fig. 18. Precipitation still for ammonia-leaching plant, Calumet and Hecla Consolidated Copper Co.

Using a 10 per cent solution of bluestone and heating to about 100°C at a pressure of about 50 lb per sq in., about half of the copper is precipitated as metal, accompanied by the production of free sulfuric acid, according to the foregoing equation. Complete precipitation of the copper is probably inhibited by the presence of the free acid.

This proposal was tested on a pilot-plant scale during preliminary research for establishing leaching methods for Inspiration and Andes Copper Co. At Inspiration, the scheme was not adopted because a method was sought which would be capable of dissolving both the oxide and sulfide forms of copper. Even if the solutions carried iron, precipitation by sulfur dioxide would put the iron into the ferrous form and render it useless as a solvent for copper sulfides. Ferrous sulfate is not readily oxidized by air in acid solutions and for this reason treatment of the solutions after precipitation, to oxidize the iron, was believed impracticable for Inspiration.

At Andes, leaching of sulfides was not a part of the problem and the foregoing method was therefore considered. However, in the test work the precipitated copper adhered strongly to the lead lining of the precipitation vessels and became difficult to remove, which was one reason why the method was not considered further for Andes.

In the laboratory, the precipitated copper does not adhere to glass and it is therefore possible that autoclave linings other than lead may solve the adherence difficulty. No accounts of work on such a method have been published.

The method has attractive features, especially where sulfur dioxide is available. It might, for example, be considered for the treatment of copper sulfide concentrate. Recent work has shown that such concentrates may be sulfatized so as to give a calcine in which copper is water-soluble to any extent desired, up to nearly 100 per cent. Obviously, sulfur dioxide for saturation and waste heat for precipitation would be available from such roasting. As compared with electrolytic precipitation which requires cheap power and involves fairly large and expensive installation, the sulfur dioxide method would be applicable to small-scale operations. Installation costs would be comparatively low. With waste heat available from roasting, cost of precipitation and the purity of the precipitated copper would probably compare favorably with electrolysis.

Any silver present in the solution would be precipitated with the copper, either by the well-known reaction

$$AgSO_4 + Cu = Ag + CuSO_4$$

or possibly by direct precipitation according to

$$AgSO_4 + SO_2 + 2H_2O = Ag + 2H_2SO_4$$

Experimental work on the latter has not been carried out, but the reaction seems probable.

The behavior of several metals other than copper and silver in this process is not definitely known. As these are sulfate solutions, lead in appreciable amounts is not present. If zinc is present, it is not precipitated, by reason of the ready solubility of zinc in sulfuric acid. Iron is not precipitated but is of course completely reduced to the ferrous form. The behavior of nickel and cobalt is not known. Arsenic and antimony may be present and, if so, they may contaminate the precipitated copper. These last impurities, however, are readily removable by standard solution-purification methods, and standard methods are also known to prevent build-up of impurities. The precipitated copper may carry a small amount of sulfur as undecomposed sulfite.

It is theoretically possible to design a treatment method for copper concentrate consisting of the following steps:

1. Sulfating roast.
2. Leaching.
3. Absorption of sulfur dioxide.
4. Precipitation by sulfur dioxide and return of solution to leaching.

Note that if the sulfatization is 100 per cent, a large excess of acid is normally produced. Obviously, in order to compensate for this, the amount of copper sulfatized in the roast should be reduced correspondingly, *i.e.*, if the oxide copper in the calcine requires the theoretical amount of acid for its solution, a 50 per cent sulfatization is sufficient. Alternatively, the excess acid may be neutralized.

5. Hydrogen Sulfide Precipitation. Theoretically, hydrogen sulfide is a possible precipitant for copper and has the advantage of regenerating appreciable amounts of free acid at the same time:

$$CuSO_4 + H_2S = CuS + H_2SO_4$$

A serious disadvantage is that hydrogen sulfide is extremely poisonous; in concentrated form, it is probably as toxic as hydrocyanic acid. It is also stated to be a cumulative poison. Use of hydrogen sulfide in connection with copper leaching has been proposed many times, but plant design must minimize the hazard of poisoning.

A theoretical advantage of such a process is the possibility of its use for precipitation of copper from solutions too dilute for electrolysis. On the other hand, the cost of raw materials and of producing the reagent is high. A number of proposals for producing the hydrogen sulfide have been made, none of which is especially attractive from the cost standpoint. Hydrogen sulfide might be produced by direct reduction of copper sulfides to metal by means of hydrogen or reducing hydrocarbon gases. Copper sulfide, CuS or Cu_2S, which is the stable form above certain temperatures, may be reduced to metal by heating under proper conditions as follows:

$$Cu_2S + 2H = 2Cu + H_2S$$
$$2Cu_2S + CH_4 = 4Cu + 2H_2S + C$$

This reduction goes to completion in the presence of sufficient excess gas. Hampe published the first account of this reaction years ago. The reduction temperature is considerably below the fusion point of copper, and the FluoSolids reactor (see Chap. 2) suggests itself as a suitable apparatus for carrying out the reduction reaction.

Obviously, a cyclic method using this reaction would consist of the following steps:

1. Leaching with acid return liquor from precipitation.
2. Precipitation of copper by hydrogen sulfide.
3. Settling, washing, and drying sulfide precipitate.
4. Reducing precipitate in FluoSolids reactor by hydrogen or methane, furnishing hydrogen sulfide for step 2, and copper metal as product.

Since copper sulfide is quite insoluble, this proposal is theoretically applicable to very dilute solutions, such as mine waters or heap-leaching solutions.

For the above cycle, the only reagent required is hydrogen or methane. Natural gas is now obtainable at several mine localities in the Southwest at very reasonable cost. Theoretically, the amount required per unit of copper is very small. From the above equations, 1 lb of hydrogen accounts for the precipitation and production of 63 lb of copper, and 1 lb of methane for about 15 lb of copper.

CHAPTER 6

OPERATING DATA FROM PRACTICE—COPPER

At present there are only four large operating copper-leaching and electrolytic plants, approximate rated capacities of which are as follows:

Approximate Yearly Capacity,
Short Tons Copper

Chile Exploration Co. (Chuquicamata)......	340,000
Union Minere du Haut Katanga............	75,000
Andes Copper Co.........................	37,000
Inspiration Cons. Copper Co.:	
Electrolytic............................	23,490
Cement...............................	2,764
Total..................................	478,254

These are described here in detail (see also Table 38). In addition, the copper-leaching plant of Cyprus Mines Corp. is described briefly as a modernized version of acid leaching of a pyritic copper ore. A discussion of the Henderson process for leaching pyrite cinders and some notes on the new N'Changa leaching plant are also presented.

UNION MINIERE DU HAUT KATANGA

Owing to recent changes in operation and installation, the Katanga plant, which was designed for an output of 30,000 tons copper metal per year, has raised its output to approximately 75,000 tons per year, thus taking second place in this type of copper production.

TABLE 38. An Analysis of Solutions to and from Leaching at Four Copper-
leaching Plants
(In grams per liter)

	Katanga	Andes	Chile Copper	Inspiration
Cu to leaching.................	16.26	10.71	14.9	22.3
Cu from leaching...............	30.51	41.55	37.0	28.8
Acid to leaching................	34.35	75.95	70.0	44.7
Acid from leaching.............	5.50	14.11	27.5	31.6
Ferric Fe to leaching...........	3.97	1.08	1.30	9.4
Ferric Fe from leaching.........	5.43	6.32	1.35	4.56
Cu removed per cycle...........	14.25	30.84	22.1	6.5

The following notes on leaching and electrolytic operations for copper recovery from the ores of the Union Miniere du Haut Katanga are abstracted from a recent account by E. Roger,[1] consulting engineer of the company, and published by the Belgian Royal Colonial Institute.

The ores at Katanga, their grade and character, and the treatment methods used differ radically from copper ores and leaching practice elsewhere. Wheeler and Eagle[2] described development, installation, and operations in 1932, and changes since then are described in the article by Roger.

Agitation leaching instead of percolation was decided upon, not from preference, but because the character of the ore and the minerals compelled this decision.

At Katanga, mineral particles in the ore occur in various sizes, ranging from powder to ½-cu m blocks. The quantity of powder and of primary slimes of more or less colloidal character is large. The copper minerals may occur disseminated as multiple veinlets, in small isolated grains, and occasionally impregnating an entire mass uniformly. Tests soon proved the impracticability of leaching the entire ore by percolation, nor was there any advantage in percolation of sands and agitation of fines. A further factor against percolation was the large proportion of copper present as carbonate. It released carbon dioxide on leaching and interfered seriously with either upward or downward percolation.

Complete agitation was decided upon. It seemed best to crush and grind the ore to pass 20 mesh and to keep production of minus-200-mesh fines at a minimum.

The plant was planned to treat 1,500 tons per day of crude ore carrying 6 to 9 per cent copper. Annual output was to be 30,000 metric tons of electrolytic copper. The steps were

1. Coarse crushing and uniform mixing of ore lots.
2. Drying the crushed ore.
3. Grinding the dried ore.
4. Leaching.
5. Solution purification.
6. Tailing separation and washing.
7. Clarification of solutions.
8. Electrolysis.
9. Melting cathodes and casting.

The flow sheets of the primary and secondary crushing section and of

[1] E. Roger, *Min. Inst. Roy. Col. Belge,* Tome 4, 1948.
[2] A. E. Wheeler and H. Y. Eagle, Development of Leaching Operations of the Union Minere du Haut Katanga, *Trans. AIME,* Vol. 106, p. 609, 1932.

the drying and grinding section are shown in Chap. 2, page 46. The
leaching and washing sections are shown in Fig. 19.

It is interesting to note that this plant has some similarity to standard
zinc-leaching practice in that the leaching flow sheet is divided into acid

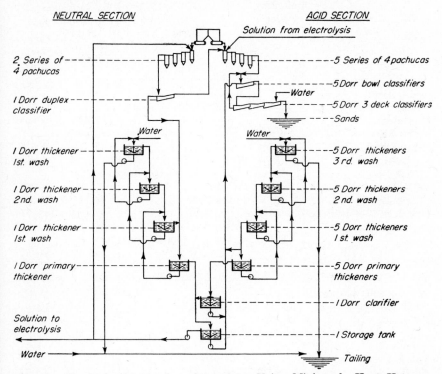

Fig. 19. Copper-leaching and washing plant, Union Miniere du Haut Katanga,
Belgian Congo, Africa.

and neutral sections, and in the latter iron is precipitated as in zinc
operation.

Tables 39, 40, and 41 are from the description by Roger, who describes
certain changes in equipment and operation that resulted in more than
doubling the original plant output.

The figures given in the first column of Tables 39, 40, and 41 are those
for the monthly average for the period from August to November, 1930,
about a year after the starting of the plant. It can be seen that the
production per year (31,596 tons) was more than the planned capacity
of 30,000 tons. The leaching extraction (96.4 per cent) was good; the
copper recovery (85.81 per cent) somewhat low, on account of difficulties
in decantation in the neutral section. The acid consumption (45.31

TABLE 39. ANALYSIS OF FEED, KATANGA LEACHING PLANT

Treatment of ore		Treatment of concentrate		
			Monthly average	
Feed	Monthly average, Aug.– Nov., 1930	Feed	Apr.– June, 1939	Dec., 1939– Mar., 1940
Acid section:		Acid section:		
Dry ore, tons.........	32,649	Flotation concentrate, dry tons...........	11,445	15,668
Neutral section:		Fines concentrate, dry		
Dry ore, tons.........	4,952	tons...............	2,212	2,513
Total tons............	37,601	Neutral section:		
Cu, %...............	8.04	Fines concentrate, dry		
Tons Cu fed..........	3,023.12	tons...............	2,520	3,060
Ore dried section, tons		Total tons............	16,177	21,241
per hour............	20.37	Cu, %...............	28.69	28.77
Coal, as % of dry ore..	2.46	Tons Cu fed..........	4,641.18	6,111.04
		% Cu in flotation con-		
		centrate...........	67.30	70.53
		% in fines concentrate.	32.70	29.47
Leaching and washing:				
Extraction by leaching,				
%.................	96.40	....	98.32	98.46
Cu recovered, %......	85.81	....	93.60	93.45
Undissolved Cu loss, %	3.59	....	1.68	1.54
Cu loss, entrained solu-				
tion, %............	10.59	....	4.72	5.01
Total acid consumed,				
tons..............	1,704	....	1,064	1,417
Kg acid consumption				
per ton ore.........	45,310	....	65,580	66,710
Kg acid consumption				
per kg Cu recovered.	0.33	....	0.93	0.68
Average tailing, % Cu.	0.658	....	0.244	0.248

kg per ton ore, or 0.658 kg per kg copper recovered equals 0.65 lb per lb copper) was of the order expected at the time.

The ampere efficiency (78.97 per cent) and the energy efficiency (47.34 per cent) were both low, owing either to insufficient iron removal or to the condition of the anodes after a year of service. On the whole, results were satisfactory, considering the short time since this large and complex operation had been started.

Serious difficulty arose in that cathode quality was only fair, due to the amount of solids suspended in the electrolyte. Wet cathodes were difficult to melt and to work in the furnace. Too many wire bars were not perfect and required recasting.

While this problem was being studied, the decantation flow sheet was modified by rearranging the 26 Dorr thickeners, easily done by shifting launders.

TABLE 40. OPERATING DATA, KATANGA LEACHING PLANT

	Ore	Concentrate	
	Monthly average, Aug.–Nov., 1930	Monthly average, Apr.–June, 1939	Monthly average, Dec., 1939– Mar., 1940
Tailing:			
Tailing, tons.............	32,315	8,229	10,766
Sand, % feed.............	40.92	10.52	9.47
Acid slime, % feed.......	38.72	37.13	38.81
Neutral slime, % feed....	5.87	3.14	3.01
Copper content:			
Sand, %.................	0.34	1.47	1.62
Acid slime, %...........	0.22	0.68	0.57
Neutral slime, %........	1.07	2.24	2.57
Solution in tailing:			
Sand, cu m..............	5,820	463	596
Cu gpl..................	8.24	9.30	13.03
Acid slime, cu m.........	14,480	6,673	11,287
Cu, gpl.................	10.02	19.95	21.55
Neutral slime, cu m......	2,215	558	709
Cu, gpl.................	15.36	19.74	23.26
Total volume, entrained solution, cu m........	22,215	7,694	12,593

For several reasons it was then decided to feed concentrate as well as ore as a part of the charge to the leaching plant. Because of the depression these concentrates, previously smelted, were being stockpiled. It was also desirable to use all the hydroelectric power available.

This mixed feed of ore and concentrate obviously gave operating advantages. Because the concentrate carried 26 to 32 per cent copper, a very much smaller quantity of feed gave the same weight of cathodes. Solubility of the copper in the concentrate was equal to or better than that of the ore because certain refractory minerals were rejected in the concentration. Owing to the diminished amount of slime, washing recovery was better. Because the concentrate carried less soluble iron in proportion to copper, iron removal was more nearly complete. A smaller quantity of solution than formerly had to be treated and less iron precipitate, which is hard to wash properly, was formed.

In addition to these technical advantages, tank-house current density could be increased, a move said to be impracticable under former conditions. This step increased tank-house production, and at the same time set a lower unit power cost by increasing the total power used. All these factors gradually brought about a shift to treatment of concentrate alone.

TABLE 41. ELECTROLYTIC PLANT DATA, KATANGA LEACHING PLANT

	Ore	Concentrate	
	Monthly average, Aug.–Nov., 1939	Monthly average, Apr.–June, 1939	Monthly average, Dec., 1939–Mar., 1940
Cu deposited, tons.........	2,633.517	4,330.962	5,729.080
Starting sheets, tons.......	193.932	225.300	341.154
Weight of cathodes, tons...	2,827.449	4,556.261	6,070.234
Total plant power, kwhr....	6,885,910	10,819,866	14,795,880
D-c power to cells, kwhr....	5,741,000	9,262,305	12,495,700
A-c power to electrolysis, kwhr..................	6,254,694	10,451,430	14,260,180
Use of power, kwhr per ton Cu deposited...........	2,614	2,498	2,582
Ampere efficiency, %.......	78.97	93.67	93.20
Energy efficiency, %.......	47.34	48.67	47.96
Current density, amp per sq m..................	100.2	148.3	171
Current density, amp per sq ft..................	9.3	13.7	15.8

The tables give monthly averages for the all-concentrate flow sheet for the period April to June, 1939. Improvements were as follows:

Consumption of acid was reduced from 638 to 244 kg per ton of copper. Recovery of copper was raised from 85.81 to 93.6 per cent. Leaching extraction was 98.4 as against 96.4 per cent and loss in entrained solution reduced to 4.72 as compared with 10.59 per cent.

Electrolytic results were also good. Ampere efficiency was raised from 78.97 to 93.67 per cent, largely due to less ferric iron in solution (1.66 gpl as against 6.36 gpl). In spite of the increased current density the energy efficiency was raised from 47.34 to 48.67 per cent. Pregnant and spent solutions assayed 63.98 and 33.06 gpl of copper, respectively, as compared with previous averages of 37.54 and 22 gpl. The acidity of the spent electrolyte was 54.5 as compared with 34.96 gpl.

Consumption of alternating current at the substation was reduced from 2,652 to 2,498 kw per ton of copper. Cathode production reached 4,330.9 tons per month as compared with 2,672 formerly. Total power increased from 6,885,910 to 10,819,866 kwhr, permitting a reduced power cost in view of the larger quantity used. Increase in current density was possible because of oversize bus bars originally installed to avoid current losses. Increased output caused no difficulty in the cells. The mastic cell linings withstood well the temperature increase (to 51–52°C).

A further increase in production from concentrate was considered but before doing so, better removal of suspended solids was necessary. This was accomplished by changes in the washing arrangement plus installation of gravity filters.

The third column in the tables gives monthly averages for the period from December, 1939, to March, 1940, during which current density was raised to 171 amp per sq m (15.8 amp per sq ft). Cathodes obtained were of better quality and the production was raised to 5,729 tons per month. The total a-c consumption rose slightly from 2,498 to 2,582 kwhr per ton of copper.

Katanga's increased production ranks it as the world's second largest copper-leaching and electrolytic plant. Chuquicamata is the largest.

CHILE EXPLORATION CO. (CHUQUICAMATA)

Copper is extracted from the Chuquicamata oxide ore by a hydrometallurgical process.[1] The ore is crushed to ⅜ in. and leached with a sulfuric acid electrolyte. Chlorine is precipitated (see Chap. 5) and the ferric iron reduced in the enriched electrolyte, after which the copper is recovered by electrolysis with insoluble Chilex and lead-antimony anodes, the spent electrolyte being returned to leaching.

Cathodes are melted and refined in market furnaces and cast into commercial wire-bar and cake shapes. Sulfuric acid for the process is supplied by the brochantite ($CuSO_4$) in the ore. Water for washing the ore is advanced through the solution system and, after depletion by electrolysis to from 6.0 to 16.0 gpl, is completely stripped by the cuprous chloride method and run to waste.

The cuprous chloride so obtained, plus that resulting from precipitation of chlorine from strong solution, is dissolved in ferrous chloride brine and the copper cemented on scrap iron. The cement is in part used to reduce ferric iron in electrolyte and, because it is of exceptional purity, it is also furnace-refined and cast into an exceptional quality of fire-refined copper.

The reduction plant is composed of seven divisions as follows: (1)

---

[1] T. C. Campbell, Reduction Plant of the Chile Exploration Co. at Chuquicamata, Chile, S.A., *Trans. AIME*, Vol. 106, pp. 559–608.

crushing, (2) leaching, (3) tailings disposal, (4) dechloridizing (see Chap. 5), (5) sulfur dioxide treatment, (6) electrolytic tank house, (7) smelting and melting. A brief description of these divisions will be given, omitting (1) and (7) because of space limitations.

Leaching Plant—Equipment. The ore is leached in 13 leaching vats, each of approximately 11,500 short tons net capacity. These vats are arranged in two units, each served by one loading and two excavating bridges of the gantry type, the latter spanning the former. Two main loading conveyors run the length of the north side of the two vat units and four tailings trains operate on the south side, taking the discharge from the four excavating bridges. Each vat is 150 ft long by 110 ft wide by 16½ to 18½ ft deep to the top of the filter bottom. Vats are made of reinforced concrete in blocks of three or four and are set on piers to facilitate inspection of the vat bottoms. A mastic-sand mixture is used to line the vats. This mastic is reinforced with expanded metal tied to the side walls and bottoms. The linings are 4 in. thick and are cast in place on the walls, using collapsible metal forms. The vats are equipped with special filter bottoms.

Twenty-five solution sumps placed to the north of, and parallel to, the ore vats and four auxiliary storage sumps located beyond the dechloridizing plant serve the leaching vats. The total capacity of these sumps is 75,000 cu m. They are placed on ground higher than the vats and solutions are run from them by gravity. Their construction is similar but somewhat lighter than that of the leaching vats. The sumps are used for transient storage of treatment advance and wash solutions, and as buffer tanks for spent and strong electrolyte.

Solutions are carried throughout the plant in wood-stave pipe lines. These lines are of the discontinuous type and are made up in 17-ft lengths. Sections are coupled with wood-stave couplers and many sections terminate in cast-iron bell flanges to which the cast-iron fittings are bolted. Pipe is milled and made in Chuqui's shops from selected Oregon pine and Douglas fir. The staves are assembled with mastic joints and steel hoop bolts with malleable-iron shoes. Pipe fittings have been made of cast iron, mastic-lined, utilizing collapsible forms, although the company gradually shifted to hard lead linings, similarly placed in the cast-iron shell.

Four sizes of pipe are in use: 8 in., 12 in., 15 in., and 24 in., depending upon the service. The leaching plant and tank-house pipe-line system has 68,865 ft of pipe with 885 valves and 2,090 elbows and tees. Wood-stave pipe is the best material for pressure lines required to resist the attack, when air is not present, of a sulfuric acid electrolyte containing ferric iron, chloride, and 1.0 per cent nitric acid. The success of wood-stave pipe in acid service is based on the prevention of leaks which subsequently concentrate in the sun and char the wood from the outside. The installed pipe is in excess of actual requirements in order to obtain flexibility and to facilitate repairs. The average life of wood-stave pipe in acid service in pressure lines is $5\frac{1}{2}$ years.

Solutions are handled by nineteen 15-in. and four 9-in. vertical centrifugal pumps with hard-lead-covered runners, casings, and boots. The intake of these pumps is connected to mastic-lined reinforced concrete sumps equipped with cast-lead screens. These sumps act as traps for tailing that may be carried through the filter bottom and down the pipe lines if the filter is broken by the excavating bucket.

Automatic sampling devices are attached to the pump sumps and every solution produced from the vats is sampled by these devices. A relatively large sample is taken, cut down, and deposited in a cool, covered wooden tank. The samples are extremely accurate because the pumping rate is uniform.

Leaching Plant—Operation. The method of leaching may be termed batch percolation in distinction to countercurrent percolation in use elsewhere. Extraction is superior with the countercurrent system, but the batch system is the more flexible of the two.

The ore is loaded either into solution or into a dry vat, depending upon the relation of the time of ore loading to the time of production of the treatment solution coming from another vat. No difference in extraction is found between loading into solution or into a dry vat. The ore is not bedded but is loaded in one operation from the bottom to the top before the bridge is advanced.

After loading, the ore is leveled by hand and the fines on the surface of the ore are turned in. Slime pockets are avoided by this simple operation. After leveling is finished, the remainder of the treatment or covering is run on through the bottom and the ore is submerged to the marker level. Approximately 3,500 cu m of solution is required to submerge 10,000 metric tons of average ore containing 1.5 per cent of moisture. Of this volume 750 cu m is absorbed and 2,750 cu m is drainable.

After submergence, the ore is allowed to soak in the treatment solution from 8 to 24 hr, then the production of first strong solution is started with a solution called "first advance" going on the top. This solution is produced to a cutoff limit and its volume varies from 3,000 to 6,000 cu m, depending upon the ore grade.

Following the production of the first strong solution, a second soaking period ensues, which varies from 24 to 72 hr, after which the production of second strong solution is started with a solution called "second advance" going on top. This second strong solution is likewise produced to a cutoff limit and its volume varies within practically the same limits as that of the first strong solution.

A third soak of variable duration then follows, after which first advance solution is produced with the volume advance and spent electrolyte going on top. The first advance is produced to a volume somewhat less than the volume of the first strong previously produced. A fourth soak follows, when the second advance is produced, with spent electrolyte going on top. The fifth and final soak then follows, after which the washing process starts. Six washes of decreasing copper grade from 9 to 1 gpl, followed by fresh water, are put on top of the vat successively and treatment or covering solution, volume advance, the six washes, and volume discard are produced in that order. The vat is then drained for at least 4 hr, after which it is ready for excavation.

The first strong solution from one vat and the second strong solution from another vat are produced simultaneously. The strongs in this way are thoroughly blended, resulting in a uniform grade for the tank house. Leaching operations are scheduled on a time chart days in advance. Ninety-six hours is the minimum cycle for good operation. The cycle increases, of course, with lower ore tonnage. The plant is capable of handling a maximum of 1,400,000 short tons of ore per month and is thus quite well synchronized with crushing capacity.

Of the total copper content of the ore mined in 1933, approximately 90 per cent was oxide copper and 10 per cent sulfide copper. Of the former, 98 per cent, and of the latter, 40 per cent was extracted in the leaching process. Ore containing 60 per cent of its copper content as oxide and 40 per cent as sulfide, called borderline mixed ore, was also leached in moderate tonnages. This ore was treated with large volumes of solution containing ferric iron. Chemically equivalent tonnages of scrap iron were saved in the dechloridizing operation by the ferric iron reduced by sulfides in the ore. The sulfides in the ore are largely chalcopyrite and pyrite but very little of the latter is decomposed. As high as 70 per cent of the sulfide copper is extracted from mixed ore.

The spent electrolyte as it goes on the ore carries 2.0 gpl ferric iron and its temperature is 30°C. The strong solution produced carries 0.8 gpl ferric iron and its temperature is 20°C. The electrolyte is therefore heated approximately 10°C, owing to its resistance in electrodeposition. These low temperatures are not conducive to the best results in the leaching of sulfides, but no heating of electrolyte other than that caused by its resistance in electrolysis is resorted to. At a high production rate the leaching period is shortened by the electrolyte which is 10° to 15°C hotter and leaching results are about equal both for oxides and sulfides.

Table 43 shows the composition of spent electrolyte in 1928 and 1933.

The lower impurity content in 1933 was due to higher acid gain from the ore, plus decreased impurity content of the ore, coupled with lower extraction of impurities because of lower free acid. Furthermore, the ore of 1933 was harder than that of previous years and the gangue was not decomposed to the same extent as formerly.

TABLE 42.   ANALYSIS OF ORE GOING TO LEACHING PLANT, CHILE EXPLORATION CO., CHUQUICAMATA, CHILE, 1933

	%	Ore, kg per metric ton	Extraction, kg per metric ton	Extraction, %
Cu	2.100	21.0	19.5	93.0
Fe	0.95	9.5	0.15	15.8
Cl	0.012	0.12	0.04	33.3
As	0.002	0.02	0.01	50.0
Sb	0.001	0.01	0.004	40.0
Mo	0.010	0.10	0.01	10.0
H_2NO_3	0.015	0.15	0.08	53.5
Na	1.10			
K	5.20			
Silica	68.0			
Al_2O_3	16.0			

In 1933 the ore contained approximately 90 per cent of its copper as oxide and 10 per cent as sulfide. Of the first, 98 per cent, and of the second, 40 per cent is extracted in the leaching process. Mixed ores carrying 60 per cent oxide and 40 per cent sulfide are also leached, and at least 70 per cent of the sulfide is extracted from the mixed ores by the action of ferric iron in the leach liquors.

Copper extraction has not altered with the drop in free acid content. The lower spent electrolyte temperature is practically offset by a longer leaching cycle. While the electrolyte was more active in 1928 owing to oxidizing effect of higher nitric acid, this was offset by higher ferric iron in the spent electrolyte of 1933 because of the oxidation of ferrous iron by lead-antimony anodes, which is greater than that by Chilex anodes. Increased sulfides in the ore and a stable electrolyte put more ferric iron in the spent electrolyte and prevent an increase of load on the dechloridizing plant (for operation of the dechloridizing plant, see Chap. 5, page 136).

Leaching Plant—Tailings Disposal. Each bank of vats is served by two gantry tailings-discharging bridges. These bridges are of three types, the most modern embodying dynamic braking and Ward Leonard control. Buckets are of the clamshell type and vary in capacity from 8 to 12 tons. Two bridges operate together on a single vat, discharging an average of 11,000 short tons of tailings in 7 to $7\frac{1}{2}$ hr.

Bucket lips are tipped with manganese steel, and since ore washing is thorough there is little corrosion. The vats are not dug clean, there being approximately 800 tons of tailings left on the bottom. This practice protects the bottom and the bucket and increases the digging rate. It also weighs down the bottom, preventing it from floating if a covering solution is run on before the ore is loaded.

The buckets discharge into hoppers built in the pier leg from which the tailings are run into 12-yd dump cars in trains of 26, each handled by a

TABLE 43.   COMPOSITION OF SPENT ELECTROLYTE AT CHUQUICAMATA
(In grams per liter)

	1928	May, 1933
Cu	14.9	15.6
H_2SO_4	70.0	60.0
HNO_3	3.51	1.50
Total Fe	4.50	2.40
Ferric Fe	1.30	1.90
Ferrous Fe	3.20	0.50
Mb	0.19	0.30–1.00
As	0.31	0.22
Sb	0.02	0.01
Se	Trace	Trace
Te	None	None
Ca	0.50	0.40
Na	7.82	6.20
K	2.31	1.75
Al	3.51	2.10
Mg	1.33	0.75
Cl	0.18	0.12
Total solids	207	155
Temperature, °C	40.0	31.0

70-ton electric locomotive to the fan-shaped tailings dump which is 4.5 km in circumference and ranges from 25 to 75 m in height.

Sulfur Dioxide Treatment. With proper stabilization of the electrolyte, Chuqui can make all starting sheets from commercial solution and the sheets are of a quality superior to those made from soluble anodes and electrolyte derived from bluestone.

Approximately 3,000 tons of fine copper cement is carried as working stock in the dechloridizing plant. Up to 25,000 cu m of solution can be reduced and dechloridized per day (see Chap. 5, page 136).

In 1930 a sulfur-burning and sulfur dioxide absorption plant was constructed to stabilize electrolyte. This was found necessary in order to prevent decomposition of nitric acid catalyzed by molybdenum salts and to dissipate nitric acid from solutions.

Operation at the sulfur dioxide plant consists of crushing and burning local volcanic sulfur ore, absorption of the gas in electrolyte, and distribution of the gassed electrolyte to necessary points in the solution system.

TABLE 44. LEACHING-PLANT DATA, CHUQUICAMATA

Leaching-plant capacity, short tons per month	1,400,000
Short tons per leaching charge	11,500
Cycle time, days	4–16
Extraction percentage	88–94
Acid gained, kg per metric ton ore	6–12
Cu recovered, kg per metric ton ore	14–20
Fe dissolved, kg per metric ton ore	0.15
Mo dissolved, kg per metric ton ore	0.01–0.05
Cl dissolved, kg per metric ton ore	0.04
Moisture in tailings, %	9.0
Water per metric ton ore, liters	235
Total available acid in electrolyte, gpl	80–90
Temperature of leaching solutions, °C	14–30
Cu in spent electrolyte, gpl	14–16
Cu in strong solution, gpl	32–45
Cu in first wash, gpl	9.0
Cu in sixth wash, gpl	1.0
Water-soluble content of tailings, %	0.01–0.02

The gas of 8 to 14 per cent grade, depending on the sulfur ore grade, passes to a cyclone, then to a lead-curtained, brick-walled and packed scrubber tower, 5 ft 6 in. square inside dimension by 32 ft 8 in. high. Two lead-cased fans, one of which is a spare, with lead-covered steel

TABLE 45. LEACHING-SOLUTION DATA, CHUQUICAMATA
(Grams per liter)

	First strong solution	Second strong solution	Spent electrolyte
Cu	42.0	32.0	15.0
H_2SO_4	25.0	32.0	58.0
Total Fe	2.5	2.5	2.5
Ferric Fe	1.7	1.0	2.0
Ferrous Fe	1.8	1.5	0.5
HNO_3	1.5	1.5	1.5

rotor, are between the scrubber tower and the absorption tower. The latter, which is a lead-curtained tower with lead pan, measures 10 by 20 ft by 44 ft high, and is packed with 2-by-4 pine lumber. The two towers are served by 3- by 4-in. horizontal lead centrifugal pumps, one of which is a spare, at the tower level in closed circuit with a 15-in. vertical centrifugal pump at pump house No. 1, east of the tank house, which picks up the outflow from the starting-sheet sections.

Eight spray nozzles of the type used in acid towers distribute 300 to 400 cu m per hr in this tower, while four similar but smaller sprays supply the scrubber tower with 40 to 60 cu m.   The runoffs from the two towers join and mix and are piped in gravity lines to a six-weir box unit in which the gassed solution is measured off for delivery to the electrolytic tank house and other vital points.

Over-all plant sulfur recovery is approximately 99 per cent.   The plant capacity is 25 tons of fine sulfur per day, producing close to 50 tons of sulfur dioxide gas of 14 per cent grade.   The gassed electrolyte carries 0.7 to 2.0 gpl of sulfur dioxide.

Sulfur dioxide is not added to reduce ferric iron, and very little such reduction takes place in the operation as followed today, owing to time limitations.   Approximately 90 per cent of the absorbed sulfur dioxide is converted by anodic oxygen to sulfuric acid, and there is practically no odor of SO_2 in the electrolytic tank house, with electrolyte containing 0.2 to 0.5 gpl sulfur dioxide, the escape of which in electrolysis is prevented by the oil blanket used to cover the electrolyte in the cells.

Electrolytic Tank House.   The tank-house building measures 1,187 ft long by 160 ft wide and is divided into three bays.   The floors and foundations are of reinforced concrete and the building itself is of structural steel, covered on the windward sides with corrugated iron or corrugated asbestos board, and roofed with Guayaquil cane and corrugated iron.   This type of construction is possible because of the warm dry climate and, as in many other similarly constructed buildings in the plant, results in excellent ventilation.   The concrete floors and column foundations are protected with mastic, and the structural steel by a mastic paint.   Solution feed lines and runoff canals are in the basement. This space is of ample height and its floor is pitched to drain spills and wash water to a central sump.

There are 1,098 electrolytic tanks in the building, each tank measuring 19 ft 2 in. by 3 ft 11 in. by 4 ft 10 in. deep, inside dimensions.   These tanks are constructed of reinforced concrete and are lined with mastic. Sixteen or seventeen tanks arranged in cascade comprise a section, and four to eight sections in series electrically make a circuit, of which there are 10 in the house.   Each circuit is powered from one or more rotary converters or motor-generator sets.   This converting equipment is tied together by a system of busses so that most machines can be cut in on any of the nine commercial circuits.   One circuit and a variable number of tanks in one other circuit are used for the deposition of starting sheets, while one or more sections are always in use in the service of plating down solution to be discarded. The remainder of the house is engaged in commercial cathode deposition.

The deposition tanks rest on piers with ground footings and are constructed independently of the building proper. Tanks of the newer type are cast in unit blocks of 17 with but 1-in. pitch from inflow to outflow end, the direction of flow being across the short dimension of the tank. Tanks of the older type are cast singly and arranged in cascade, being connected by ports at alternate ends of the tanks, the direction of solution being with the long dimension of the tanks. The newer type of tank is much superior, as circulation is better, solution flow can be controlled more easily and with less danger of submerging anode lugs, and in the case of power failure the solution run off to be disposed of is very small. The tank tops are 2 to 3 ft above the floor level. Four 10-ton cranes in each bay, or 12 in total, handle cathodes, anodes, and starting sheets.

The tank house is equipped with 60,000 anodes, part of which are Chilex and part lead-antimony. Starting sheets are made from lead-antimony anodes and dechloridized strong solution. They may also be made from soluble anodes and electrolyte made from bluestone, for which separate head tanks, dissolving tanks, and pumps are provided.

Chilex anodes measure 2 ft 9 in. by 5 ft 11 in. by 1 in. thick, and are spaced on $3\frac{1}{2}$- or 4-in. centers, depending upon operating conditions. Lead-antimony anodes of the same width and length but 0.5 to 0.6 in. in thickness are spaced on 3- or $3\frac{1}{2}$-in. centers. Each cell therefore carries 56 to 74 anodes and 55 to 73 cathodes, depending upon the spacing. The lead-antimony anode produces approximately 12 per cent more deposition per kw-day than the Chilex anode and is gradually replacing the latter. The brittleness of the Chilex anode is a decidedly adverse factor in commercial operation, with electrodes the size of those employed at Chuquicamata, and the low iron and nitric acid content of present-day electrolyte is a favorable factor in the substitution of lead-antimony anodes. The cathodes from both anodes are of equally high purity. Warping of cast antimony-lead anodes under current is unknown here.

Commercial Starting Sheets. Starting sheets are deposited to 12 lb weight in 24 to 48 hr on copper blanks from freshly dechloridized and reduced strong solution, using lead-antimony anodes. Each tank in this service carries 72 anodes and 71 blanks and the cathode current density ranges from 7 to 15 amp per sq ft. The edges of the blanks are coated with a nonconducting grease and the entire sheet is stripped from the blank, the grooved edge not being used. Both wooden and steel tools are used in stripping the sheets from the blanks. All sheets are trimmed on all four edges prior to looping in order to facilitate straightening before and during deposition. The flow through each tank is independent and amounts to approximately 100 l per min.

The sheet as trimmed measures 3 ft by 4 ft 1 in., of which 3 by 4 ft are immersed in electrolyte. The sheets are equipped with two loops cut from starting sheets, which are fastened to the sheet on Long and Alstattler machines. Approximately 8 per cent of the total sheets made are used for loops and about 2 per cent is trimming scrap. Blanks are amalgamated at intervals and are, of course, oil-coated before each deposition. The blanks used are made from oversize starting sheets built up to thickness by electrodeposition. They are trimmed and ground and riveted to the suspension bars, after which they are amalgamated and ready for use.

Chlorine in electrolyte over 0.2 gpl ruins commercial starting sheets, embrittling them so that they can be broken readily in the hand into small pieces. Looping such sheets is impossible. Ferric iron also prevents deposition of good sheets. All starting-sheet anodes are equipped with spacers of insulating material to prevent short circuits. Anodes do not warp but the copper blanks have to be straightened occasionally and rolled lead cathode blanks, which are sometimes used, warp seriously.

Commercial Deposition. The outflow solution from the starting-sheet tanks is pumped to the sulfur dioxide plant and is returned then to the commercial deposition section. A small portion joins the strong solution, before and after dechloridizing, for the purpose of stabilization. The current density for commercial deposition ranges from 7 to 18 amp per sq ft of cathode surface, depending upon conditions. The inflow solution to the tank house is a mixture of this solution in the proportion of approximately 1:2, with the effluent of Chilex anode cells, which is high in ferrous iron and is not yet cut to spent grade. The mixture runs to the cells by gravity from the head tank through two main headers of 24-in. pipe.

Seven 12-in.-diameter lateral loop lines in the basement with 4-in. risers and 4-in. valves bring the solution to each individual section. The outflow from the Chilex cells is a first-stage spent electrolyte and is returned to the head tank for mixing, as described above. The outflow from the lead-antimony cells is highly oxidized, is of spent grade for leaching, and is returned to the leaching plant. A portion of the latter solution, approximately 12 per cent, is by-passed to plating-down sections where it is further cut to suitable grade prior to complete stripping by the cuprous chloride reaction.

The electrolyte is therefore cut in three stages from strong solution to spent electrolyte, and in four stages to a grade lower than spent for stripping prior to discarding. Each volume of strong solution passes through the tank house four times for the two stages of commercial deposition, once for the cut in the starting-sheet cells and once for the plating-down cut.

The flow is very fast in order to ensure formation of hard cathodes and to decrease polarization. Each section takes a flow of approximately 750 l per min, although the maximum flow may be as high as 1,200 l per min. The flow varies inversely with the grade of electrolyte and the current density. The limit is 8 gpl for one pass through 16 cells, or in other words 0.5 gpl per cell, whereas the minimum is as low as 2.0 gpl per 16 cells. The current efficiency drops off down the cascade as the electrolyte warms up and the ferric iron increases. The inflow solution carries 0.2 to 0.5 gpl sulfur dioxide and the outflow from Chilex cells carries 0.05, while that from the antimony-lead cells has none. The depolarizing effect of the sulfur dioxide used is very slight, being equal to not over 0.01 volt.

The spent electrolyte temperature varies with the ampere load and atmospheric conditions, ranging from 30 to 45°C. From 36 to 39°C is considered the most efficient temperature for Chilex anodes and 34°C for lead-antimony anodes. The latter, of course, have greatly superior anode efficiency and as a result do not heat the electrolyte as much as the Chilex anodes.

The electrolytic tanks are covered with a petroleum oil known as smoothing oil, which is frothed mildly by the gassing of the electrolyte and forms a blanket over the solution, preventing the escape of spray and dissolved sulfur dioxide. There is considerable traffic on the tops of the tanks and this oil covering is a necessary feature to establish good working conditions and to protect equipment. The oil is held in the tanks by baffles. Because of the heavy traffic on the tanks a small attachment is used for the heads of the anode bars, which prevents the cathode bar from sliding off the anode bar when men walk on it. This prevents the edges of the Whitehead contacts from being rounded by arcing and results in a lower voltage drop over the contact as well as reduction of current losses and inconvenience due to shorts between bars.

The cathodes are deposited to 150 lb in 5 to 15 days, depending upon the current density. At this weight they are pulled, loaded on to steel cathode cars equipped with acid and waterproof bearings, and sent to the washing plant. They are then weighed, sampled, and are ready for the market furnaces.

Cathode analysis is as follows: copper, 99.900 per cent; chlorine, 0.005 per cent; arsenic, 0.0002 per cent; antimony, 0.0004 per cent; lead, 0.0016 per cent; tin, 0.0011 per cent; selenium, none; tellurium, none; bismuth, none; iron, 0.0050 per cent; sulfur, 0.03 per cent; manganese,

0.0001 per cent; zinc, 0.0003 per cent; nickel, none; moisture, 0.02 per cent; insoluble (silica), 0.06 per cent.

TABLE 46. ELECTROLYTIC TANK-HOUSE DATA, CHUQUICAMATA

Number electrolytic tanks in house....................	1,098
Number insoluble grid anodes to equip tanks...........	62,000
Current density, amp per sq ft cathode area...........	7–18
Entering solution, Cu, gpl...........................	21–26
Entering solution, ferrous Fe, gpl......................	1.6–2.1
Entering solution, total Fe, gpl......................	2.5
Entering solution, °C...............................	26–34
Leaving solution, Cu gpl............................	14–16
Leaving solution, ferrous Fe, gpl.....................	0.5
Leaving solution, total Fe, gpl.......................	2.5
Current efficiency, %...............................	85–92
Lb Cu per kw day	24–28
Capacity, kw load..................................	55,000

Cathodes are melted, fire-refined, and cast into market shapes.

Wire-bar analysis is as follows: copper, 99.96 per cent; oxygen, 0.032 per cent; sulfur, 0.0016 per cent; arsenic, 0.0002 per cent; antimony, 0.0004 per cent; lead, 0.0008 per cent; tin, 0.0006 per cent; selenium, none; tellurium, none; bismuth, none; iron, 0.0016 per cent; manganese, none; zinc, trace; molybdenum, 0.0001 per cent; nickel, none.

ANDES COPPER MINING CO.

In the ore bodies of the Andes Copper Co., the copper occurs in both sulfide and oxide form. However, the cutoff between oxide and sulfide ore is sharp and there is little or no mixed ore. Because of the necessity for treating these two classes of ore, two separate metallurgical plants were constructed.[1] They are interdependent only to the extent that the sulfuric acid for leaching the oxide ore must be produced through the roasting of sulfide concentrates, there being no other available source of cheap sulfur. Figure 20 shows the general arrangement of the various plant units.

Oxide Metallurgical Plant. The oxide ores as delivered from the mine are crushed in the coarse-crushing plant used for both sulfide and oxide ores. The oxide fine-crushing plant crushes broken ore from the coarse crushers to minus $\frac{1}{2}$ in. maximum size. Pilot-plant work on the Andes oxide ore demonstrated that the fines in the crushed ore were detrimental to leaching. Soon after work at the leaching plant was started, it became evident that merely moistening the ore before charging would not give satisfactory leaching results. An increased percentage of fines in run-of-

[1] L. A. Callaway and F. N. Koeppel, The Metallurgical Plant of the Andes Copper Mining Co. at Potrerillos, Chile, *Trans. AIME*, Vol. 106.

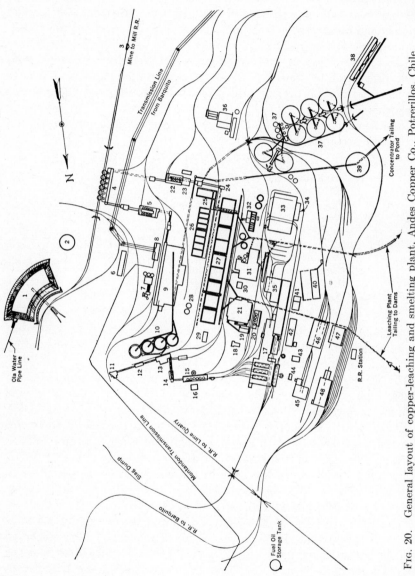

FIG. 20. General layout of copper-leaching and smelting plant, Andes Copper Co., Potrerillos, Chile.

mine ore, as well as variations in quantity, caused insurmountable difficulties in attempts to bed a uniform and permeable charge. Several
different methods of wetting and charging were tried, as well as both
upward and downward percolation. None of these improved the extraction appreciably.

Tests proved that the ore would leach satisfactorily provided a sufficient proportion of fines had been removed, and in order to remove
the most harmful portion, *i.e.*, the primary slimes, the washing plant was
constructed.

Representative fine-crushing and washing-plant data for a 7,500-ton
vat charge are given in Table 47.

TABLE 47.   DATA FOR 7,500-TON VAT CHARGE, ANDES COPPER CO.

Ore through fine-crushing plant, tons	7,908
Ore washed, tons	1,802
Fines to slimes-leaching plant, tons	408
Washed sand to vat, tons	1,394
Unwashed ore to vat, tons	6,106
All ore to vat, tons	7,500
Ore washed, % of total	22.79
Ore to slimes-leaching, % of total	5.16
Washed sands, % of vat charge	18.59
Washed sands, % moisture	11.52
Total charge to vat, % moisture	6.25

Leaching Plant. The leaching plant was designed to treat 7,500 tons
of ore per day by a 6-day countercurrent sulfuric acid leach, followed by
the usual countercurrent washing (see Fig. 21).

The leaching vats are of reinforced concrete and are supported on
concrete piers, 6 ft 3 in. high. They are built in four sets of two vats
each and a single vat. The inside dimensions of each vat are length, 105
ft, width, 115 ft, and depth 19 ft 6 in. The floors are lined with 1½ in.
of mastic and the walls with 8½ in. of acidproof brick, laid up in mastic
mortar. The filter bottoms are of the Inspiration type.

Six 12-in. outlet connections are in the bottom of each vat, three at
each end. Each outlet is connected to a 10-in. air lift. The center
outlet on the east end is also used for draining solution from the vat.
Four of the air lifts are used for circulation and two for advancing solution from the bottom of one vat to the top of the next. They discharge
over the vat walls and have a capacity of 250 tons of solution per hour per
lift. Air for these lifts is supplied by compressors in the purification
plant. The air pressure varies from 20 to 25 lb.

Solutions from the vats at Andes Copper flow by gravity to a central
pump house, whence they are elevated to the vat solution sumps by
horizontal centrifugal lead pumps. Lead pipe lines are used throughout,

the thickness of the lead being varied to conform with the different solution heads. The pipes are lagged on the outside with 1-in.-square wooden strips, bound with strap-iron hoops, and the whole line resting in wooden saddles. Ajo-type rubber-diaphragm lead valves are used.

The construction of the concrete solution sumps is similar to that of the leaching vats. There are two blocks of four tanks each. Each sump

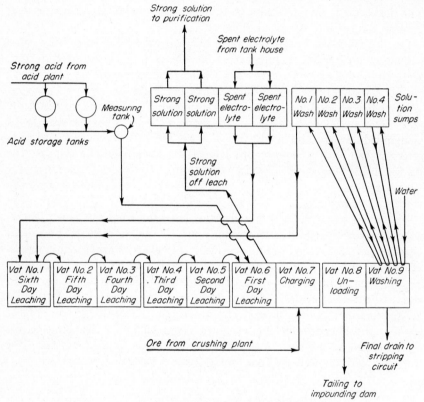

FIG. 21. Flow sheet of sand-leaching plant, Andes Copper Co.

in the first block is 52 by 89 ft by 18 ft. deep, and has a capacity of 2,500 volumetric tons of solution. The other two are lined with 10-lb sheet lead and are utilized for storing spent electrolyte. The second block of sumps is used for the storage of wash waters and these sumps are lead-lined. Two are 38 by 89 ft by 18 ft deep, and the other two are 42 by 89 ft by 18 ft deep. Each sump has a single outlet in the bottom.

There is a set of lead pipe lines above and below both the leaching vats and the solution sumps, connected in such a way that solutions can be transferred from the bottoms of the solution sumps to the tops of the vats, and from the bottoms of the vats to the pump house, from which they can be elevated to the solution sumps. Interconnections make it possible to transfer solutions in almost any manner desired.

The oxide ore treated in the leaching plant is found mostly in mineralized and altered diorite porphyry, although some ore extends into the limy and shaly sediments into which the porphyry has been intruded. The important oxidized copper minerals are malachite, azurite, and cuprite, named in order of abundance.

One leaching vat is charged, one charge is covered with solution, and one vat excavated for each day of 24 hr. Nine days are required to complete the leaching cycle, divided as follows: charging ore to vat, 1 day; leaching, 6 days; washing, 1 day; excavating, 1 day.

Normally about 15 hr is required for charging 7,500 tons of ore into the vat. The ore is not bedded. In charging a vat, it is the practice to fill along a side wall to the height to which the vat is to be charged. Thereafter, at the end of each round trip of the loading-bridge tripper, the loading bridge is moved forward 12 to 15 in. In this way the filled portion of the vat is carried at the final level. The ore column is approximately 17 ft high.

The ore is leached for 6 days by the countercurrent system. Downward percolation is used except when a new charge of ore is being covered. Upward percolation is used in covering. Six charges are leaching simultaneously with the solution on each charge circulating at approximately 2.5 tons per 24 hr per ton of ore, and also advancing from vat to vat at about 0.70 tons per ton of ore per 24 hr.

Appreciable amounts of iron and aluminum, and smaller amounts of arsenic, phosphorus, chlorine, etc., are dissolved in the leaching operation. About 82 per cent of the iron dissolved is in the ferric state. For the year 1931 the average iron and aluminum solubilities were

	Pounds
Iron dissolved per pound copper extracted	0.202
Ferric iron dissolved per pound copper extracted	0.165
Aluminum dissolved per pound copper extracted	0.066

The impurity content of the solutions is controlled by purifying all strong solution from the leaching plant. In the purification plant, ground lime rock is used for precipitating iron, aluminum, phosphorus, and arsenic. The chlorine is removed from the purified strong solution by cement copper.

The acid consumption varies with the nature and grade of the ore. Average acid figures for the year 1931 were: new 60°Bé acid used per ton

ore, 64.48 lb; 100 per cent sulfuric acid neutralized per ton ore, 62.30 lb.
Leaching-plant data for the year 1931 are given in Table 48.

TABLE 48. LEACHING-PLANT DATA FOR 1931, ANDES COPPER CO.

	To leaching		From leaching		Extrac-tion
	Ore	Spent elec-trolyte	Tailing	Strong solu-tion	
Moisture, %......................	6.27	.....	12.49		
Screen analysis:					
% on 4 mesh....................	51.60				
% on −20 mesh.................	19.92				
% on −200 mesh...............	6.01				
Total Cu, %.....................	1.370	.....	0.145	......	89.696
Acid-soluble Cu, %..............		.....	0.102		
Water-soluble Cu, %.............		.....	0.015		
Oxide Cu, %.....................	1.308	.....	......	......	91.309
Sulfide Cu, %....................	0.062	.....	0.028		
Cu dissolved per ton ore, lb.........		.....	......	......	24.573
Grams per liter:					
Cu..........................		10.71	......	41.55	
H₂SO₄........................		75.95	......	14 11	
Total Fe.....................		1.73	......	7.03	
Ferric Fe....................		1.08	......	6.32	
Al...........................		4.10	......	4.99	
Cl..........................		0.14	......	0.29	
HNO₃.........................		0.07	......	0.085	
As..........................		0.26	......	1.40	
P₂O₅.........................		0.21	......	1.52	

Slimes-leaching and Cementation Division. The slimes-leaching
division (Fig. 22) treats the slimes produced in washing the oxide ore
undersize in the oxide sand-washing plant. The slimes-leaching plant
was constructed after experience had demonstrated the necessity of
removing fines from the regular leaching circuit. Equipment installed
for leaching and washing slimes is as follows: two Dorr traction thickeners,
150 ft in diameter; three slurry mixers, 36 ft in diameter and 20 ft deep;
and three leaching agitators, 24 ft in diameter and 16 ft deep. These,
together with the necessary pumping and auxiliary equipment, deliver
the leached slime to two rows (three each) of countercurrent wash
thickeners, 150 ft in diameter, the two rows operating in parallel. The
wash thickeners are on a gentle slope, making possible a partial gravity
flow from the upper to the lower tanks.

Equipment ahead of the leaching agitators is not acidproof. The neutral thickeners and slurry tanks are of concrete construction. The moving truss of the thickeners, the agitator mechanism of the slurry tanks, the Wilfley sand pumps, and the pipe lines are all of iron and steel.

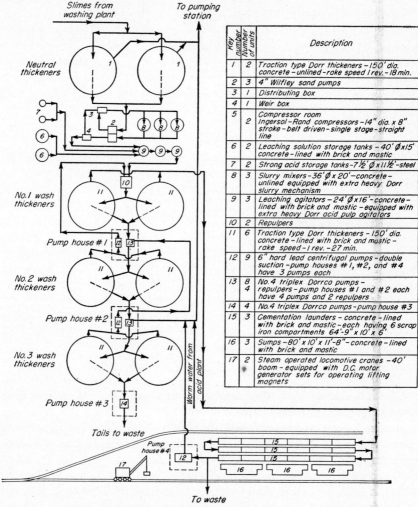

Key number	Number of units	Description
1	2	Traction type Dorr thickeners – 150' dia. concrete – unlined – rake speed 1 rev. – 18 min.
2	3	4" Wilfley sand pumps
3	1	Distributing box
4	1	Weir box
5	2	Compressor room Ingersol-Rand compressors – 14" dia. x 8" stroke – belt driven – single stage – straight line
6	2	Leaching solution storage tanks – 40' Ø x 15' concrete – lined with brick and mastic
7	2	Strong acid storage tanks – 7½' Ø x 11½' – steel
8	3	Slurry mixers – 36' Ø x 20' – concrete – unlined equipped with extra heavy Dorr slurry mechanism
9	3	Leaching agitators – 24' Ø x 16' – concrete – lined with brick and mastic – equipped with extra heavy Dorr acid pulp agitators
10	2	Repulpers
11	6	Traction type Dorr thickeners – 150' dia. concrete – lined with brick and mastic – rake speed – 1 rev. – 27 min.
12	9	6" hard lead centrifugal pumps – double suction – pump houses #1, #2, and #4 have 3 pumps each
13	8 4	No. 4 triplex Dorrco pumps – repulpers – pump houses #1 and #2 each have 4 pumps and 2 repulpers
14	4	No. 4 triplex Dorrco pumps – pump house #3
15	3	Cementation launders – concrete – lined with brick and mastic – each having 6 scrap iron compartments 64'-9" x 10' x 6'
16	3	Sumps – 80' x 10' x 11'-8" – concrete – lined with brick and mastic
17	2	Steam operated locomotive cranes – 40' boom – equipped with D.C. motor generator sets for operating lifting magnets

FIG. 22.   Flow sheet of slimes-leaching plant, Andes Copper Co.

Starting at the leaching agitators, all equipment is acidproof. The agitator tanks are concrete, lined with brick laid in mastic mortar, and are equipped with wooden stirring mechanisms and rubber-covered cast-iron rakes. The six 150-ft thickeners in the washing circuit are of concrete construction, lined with brick and mastic. The portions of the moving trusses that extend into the solution are made of wood. Rubber-covered steel rakes are used. All pumps, pipe lines, and valves are of lead. Launders for pulp are made of wood and lined with brick bound with mastic mortar.

Originally the cement copper was mixed with concentrate and smelted in the reverberatory furnace. This practice was abandoned because it resulted in slags of a high copper content. The cement copper is now shipped to the sulfide roaster plant and calcined. The calcined product is leached in agitating tanks with spent electrolyte from the tank house. The enriched solution is added to the purified strong solution as it enters the dechloridizing plant.

Metallurgical data pertaining to the leaching, washing, and cementation operations are given in Table 49.

Purification Plant. The purification plant function is the preparation of enriched solution from the leaching process for electrolytic deposition of copper through the removal of ferric iron and other harmful impurities dissolved from the ore.

Purification consists of the treatment of the so-called strong solution from the vats with finely ground lime rock, together with the basic copper carbonate precipitate produced from the ground lime rock stripping of wash waters from the leaching plant and the purification plant, an operation carried on in conjunction with purification. After the precipitation of impurities from heated strong solution, the solution is filtered through Moore filters and delivered to the dechloridizing plant and the washed precipitate is discharged to waste. The process includes the following operations: (1) lime-rock grinding, (2) stripping, (3) purification, (4) filtration.

The equipment of this plant, except the heating tanks and Dorr thickeners, is contained in a structural steel building. It consists of a system of heating tanks, agitator tanks, Moore filter equipment, Dorr settling tanks, Oliver filters, ball mills for grinding lime rock, compressors, vacuum pumps, and equipment for handling and distribution of materials and products.

Experience had demonstrated that the lime rock used in the purification process should not contain over 20 per cent plus-200-mesh material. If it is coarser, the chemical reactions involved take place more slowly and there is a tendency for the larger particles to settle out of the precipitate.

Stripping. The stripping operation recovers the copper from discard and excess wash solutions in a product from which the copper is extracted in the purification operation and made available for electrolytic deposition. The filtered cake from stripping is an efficient precipitant for the

TABLE 49.   SLIMES-TREATMENT METALLURGICAL DATA, ANDES COPPER CO.

	July–Dec., 1930	Jan.–June, 1931	July–Dec., 1931
Leaching			
Feed to agitators:			
Dry, tons..........................	55,602	47,386	48,709
−200 mesh, %....................	75.06	72.92	70.47
Pulp, % solids.....................	40.91	41.86	42.61
Total Cu, %.......................	2.38	2.395	2.338
Sulfide Cu, %.....................	0.13	0.12	0.126
Pulp temperature, °C..............	14.1	14.0	11.8
Solution to agitators:			
Volume, tons.....................	50,765	57,341	59,250
Cu, gpl..........................	9.68	11.26	6.14
H_2SO_4, gpl......................	42.58	56.54	56.91
Temperature, °C..................	18.9	23.0	23.1
New 60°Bé acid to agitators, tons....	2,092.5	502.3	549.3
Pulp from agitators, temperature, °C..	17.7	19.4	18.3
Washing			
No. 1 thickeners:			
Feed, % solids....................	7.77	5.99	6.79
Feed, temperature, °C.............	16.5	15.1	13.8
Overflow, gpl Cu..................	3.75	2.87	2.61
Overflow, gpl H_2SO_4...............	2.76	2.45	2.97
Spigot, % solids..................	32.42	40.77	42.58
No. 2 thickeners:			
Feed, % solids....................	7.77	5.99	6.79
Feed, temperature, °C.............	16.2	14.8	13.1
Overflow, gpl Cu..................	1.62	0.53	0.52
Overflow, gpl H_2SO_4...............	1.60	1.31	1.62
Spigot, % solids..................	28.07	38.39	36.85
No. 3 thickeners:			
Feed, % solids....................	7.77	5.99	6.79
Feed, temperature, °C.............	17.7	15.8	14.0
Overflow, gpl Cu..................	0.65	0.15	0.14
Overflow, gpl H_2SO_4...............	0.94	1.31	1.55
Spigot (tailing), % solids.........	25.25	34.21	33.99
Tailing:			
Total Cu, %.......................	0.367	0.189	0.225
Acid-soluble Cu, %...............	0.155	0.094	0.114
Water-soluble Cu, %..............	0.150	0.046	0.047
Sulfide Cu, %....................	0.062	0.049	0.064

TABLE 49. SLIMES-TREATMENT METALLURGICAL DATA, ANDES COPPER CO.—
(*Continued*)

	July–Dec., 1930	Jan.–June, 1931	July–Dec., 1931
Recovery			
Feed and tailing:			
Total Cu, %...................	86.27	92.36	90.59
Leach Cu, %...................	87.97	94.05	92.86
Over-all, based on total Cu in slimes and solutions to plant minus Cu in tailing, %.................	90.32	95.68	93.63
Acid Consumption			
Acid per ton slime, lb 60°Bé.........	174.9	199.4	204.7
Cementation Data			
Solution inflow:			
Volume, tons....................	507,230	673,948	641,184
Cu, gpl.........................	3.81	2.82	2.48
H_2SO_4, gpl.....................	4.22	2.45	2.74
Fe, gpl.........................	3.85	7.81	8.93
Temperature, °C.................	15.4	14.5	13.1
Outflow:			
Cu, gpl.........................	0.05	0.065	0.069
H_2SO_4, gpl.....................	2.26	1.45	1.62
Fe, gpl.........................	8.49	11.16	11.52
Temperature, °C.................	16.9	15.7	14.3
Cement, % Cu...................	....	72.74	71.52
Cu precipitated, %..............	98.69	97.71	97.20
Scrap-iron consumption, lb per lb Cu produced.....................	1.353	1.408	1.375

impurities in the strong solution; in fact, it is much more desirable than raw lime rock.

The solutions treated in the stripping operation consist of excess wash from the Moore filters and discard wash solution from the leaching plant. The solutions are heated to about 37°C and treated in a series of agitators with an excess of ground lime rock. The pulp from the agitators flows to Dorr thickeners. The overflow from the thickeners runs to waste. The spigot product is filtered and used as the precipitant in the purification operation.

Purification. In the purification operation the strong solution from the leaching plant is treated in mechanical agitators with Oliver cake and raw lime rock.   Most of the ferric iron and high percentages of the other impurities that are deleterious to the electrolytic deposition of copper are precipitated.   The basic copper carbonate in the Oliver cake is dissolved and thus this copper becomes available for electrolytic deposition.   The pulp containing the precipitated impurities goes to the Moore filter plant.

TABLE 50.   PURIFICATION DATA, ANDES COPPER CO.

| | Solution analysis, gpl | | Impurity eliminations, % |
	Unpurified strong solution	Filtered purified solution	
Cu............	41.55	42.09	
H₂SO₄.........	14.11	0.00	
Total Fe.......	7.03	1.50	82.12
Ferric Fe......	6.32	0.94	87.98
Al............	4.99	4.13	21.85
As............	1.40	0.11	92.32
P₂O₅..........	1.52	0.20	87.14
Cl............	0.29	0.46	
Mo...........	0.033	0.003	91.12

Filtration.   The solution that contains the precipitated impurities is filtered on Moore filters.   The filtered strong solution is pumped to a storage tank at the dechloridizing plant; the excess wash solution is transferred to the stripping division and the filter cake runs to waste.

Dechloridizing Plant.   The purified strong solution from the purification plant contains approximately 0.46 gpl of chlorine.   In order to avoid the deposition of cuprous chloride on the cathodes in the tank house and the subsequent volatilization loss during furnace refining, it is necessary to reduce the chlorine content of the solution to about 0.20 gpl prior to electrolysis.   This is done in the dechloridizing plant, where the chlorine is precipitated as cuprous chloride.   The solution is agitated with an excess of cement copper and the resulting pulp allowed to settle.   The clarified solution flows by way of storage tanks to the electrolytic plant. The settled residue, consisting of cuprous chloride and cement copper, is treated with a ferrous chloride solution, which dissolves the cuprous chloride.   The copper in this solution is precipitated on scrap iron, washed, and reused for dechloridizing.

Electrolytic Plant.   The electrolytic plant was designed for a daily deposition of 100 tons of copper from leaching-plant solution, and approximately 7 tons of starting sheets from blister-copper anodes.

The bus bars that enter the tank-house basement from the substation are suspended from insulated hangers. The center point of each electrical circuit is grounded through a low resistance in order to protect the workmen. Each of the three electrical circuits corresponds to a solution circuit from the commercial deposition of copper. The starting-sheet division, with a closed solution circuit, operates electrically in series with one of the commercial circuits.

Commercial Division. There are 576 electrolytic tanks in the commercial, or insoluble, anode division. These tanks are of reinforced concrete lined with 8-lb, 6 per cent antimonial lead. They rest on lead-capped concrete piers and have a porcelain insulating block under each corner. Inside dimensions are length, 10 ft 3 in.; width, 2 ft 10 in.; depth, 3 ft 9 in. Side walls are 5 in. thick and the ends and bottoms 4 in. thick. Each tank contains 34 lead anodes, spaced at $3\frac{1}{2}$-in. centers, and 33 cathodes. The insoluble lead anodes were cast from International antimonial pig lead and have the following average composition:

	Original anodes	Anodes recast
Pb, %.............	82.12	82.5
Sb, %.............	15.50	15.0
As, %.............	1.68	1.3
Cu, %.............	0.44	0.15

The anodes are $39\frac{1}{2}$ in. long by $26\frac{1}{2}$ in. wide by $\frac{1}{2}$ in. thick and weigh approximately 200 lb each.

The starting sheets are 28 by $37\frac{1}{2}$ in. They are suspended by two loops from $\frac{7}{16}$-by-$1\frac{1}{16}$-in. rolled copper bars, which are flattened at one end to make good contact. The sheets extend to within $5\frac{1}{2}$ in. of the tank bottom.

The three commercial circuits are equipped and operated in the same manner. Each circuit contains 192 electrolytic tanks. The tanks are first grouped into sections of 12 tanks each and then into divisions composed of four or six parallel sections. The tanks in each section are arranged in cascades of six tanks, two cascades to a section. Parallel tanks in a section are spaced $2\frac{1}{2}$ in. apart. There is a drop of 4 in. between tanks, or 20 in. in a cascade of six. Sections within the division are separated by 28-in. walkways, which are approximately 24 in. below the tops of the tanks. Each commercial circuit consists of three divisions, the first two in a circuit containing six sections, and the last one only four sections. The electrolyte flows through the three divisions of the circuit in series and through the cascades of each division in parallel.

The tanks of each commercial circuit are electrically connected in series, and the electrodes in each tank are in multiple.   The heavy, cast-copper bus bars, which rest on insulating boards on top of the outer walls of the tanks, are connected to the main bus bars in the basement by copper risers.   A rolled copper plate resting on an insulating board supported by the two inner tank walls forms the common contact between tanks.   Flat contacts are used.

The dechloridized purified solution, which forms the feed to the tank house, is mixed with acid and a portion of the spent electrolyte to form the feed solution to the electrolytic tanks.   This permits operating at a higher solution temperature and acidity and results in a lower voltage. It also increases the circulation rate of the electrolyte and aids in the production of a smoother deposit of copper.   The flow rate of the electrolyte is about 25 gpm per tank in the first two divisions of a circuit and 37 gpm in the last division.   The amount of acid added to the electrolyte at the tank house is governed by requirements of the leaching plant.

The dechloridized purified solution, which averages approximately 42 gpl copper and 15 gpl sulfuric acid, flows from the storage tanks at the dechloridizing plant through an 8-in. lead pipe to weir measuring boxes in the tank house.   Three weir boxes are provided, one for each of the head divisions of the three commercial circuits.   Sulfuric acid is added to the purified solution at each weir box and the solution then flows into the receiving tank below, where it is mixed with approximately 65 per cent of its volume of spent electrolyte carrying about 11 gpl copper and 75 gpl sulfuric acid.   The resulting mixture, which contains 28 to 30 gpl copper and 45 to 55 gpl sulfuric acid, forms the feed to the first division of the circuit.

The chemical analysis of tank-house solutions as well as power data is given in Table 51.

Starting-sheet Division.   The starting-sheet division consists of $4\frac{1}{2}$ sections, or 54 electrolytic tanks, situated at the south end of the center crane bay.   Except for small variations these tanks are constructed and arranged in the same way as the commercial tanks.   Each tank holds 25 soluble anodes, spaced at 4.8-in. centers, and 24 starting-sheet blanks. The anodes are unrefined blister copper from the smelter.   The blanks are $\frac{1}{8}$-in. rolled copper sheets with over-all dimensions of $28\frac{3}{4}$ by $43\frac{5}{8}$ in., to which the supporting bars of copper are riveted with joints soldered. Milled grooves near the edge of the blank, on each side and bottom, produce a 28- by $37\frac{1}{2}$-in. starting sheet.

Under normal conditions a current density of about 18.0 amp per sq ft is maintained.   This allows the stripping of 24-hr sheets weighing approximately 8 lb each.   Of this weight about 3 per cent is trimmings, which are shipped to the casting plant.   At this density the voltage drop per tank is about 0.33 volt. Ampere efficiency varies from 85 to 90 per cent and power yield from 160 to 170 lb per kw-day, direct current at the generator.

An average analysis of the starting sheets shows: copper, 99.935 per cent; iron, 0.0011 per cent; chlorine, 0.0007 per cent; arsenic, 0.0016 per cent; antimony, 0.0006 per cent; silver, 0.15 oz per ton; gold, trace.

TABLE 51. TANK-HOUSE DATA, ANDES COPPER CO.

Solutions

	Dechloridized purified solution	Feed to electrolyte tanks	Spent electrolyte
Cu, gpl...................	42.59	29.2	10.71
H₂SO₄, gpl................	14.38	47.8	75.95
Total Fe, gpl.............	1.73	....	1.73
Ferric Fe, gpl............	Trace	....	1.08
Cl, gpl...................	0.20		
Temperature, °C..........	27.9	32.5	38.6

Power

Current density, amp per sq ft............................	10.69
Average tank voltage.....................................	1.89
Ampere efficiency, %.....................................	85.63
Cu deposited per kw-day d-c at tanks, lb...................	27.90
Cu deposited per kw-day d-c at generator, lb..............	27.77
Cu deposited per kw-day a-c at substation A, lb...........	25.03
Kwhr a-c per lb Cu deposited.............................	0.958
A-c to d-c conversion efficiency, including line loss...........	90.12
H₂SO₄ regenerated per lb Cu deposited, lb.................	1.53

The anodes are cast with heavy supporting lugs and weigh from 550 to 600 lb each. They are the same width as the blanks and extend to the same depth in the tanks.

The average composition of the electrolyte in gpl is as follows: copper, 40.90; sulfuric acid, 150.70; iron, 1.19; nitric acid, 0.06; arsenic, 4.09; antimony, 0.14.

All the electrolytic copper produced is cast into wire bars. Each bar is rigidly inspected for defects. The portion of good bars averages approximately 93 per cent. The average chemical analysis of wire bars for a 3-year period shows: copper, 99.96 per cent; sulfur, 0.0017 per cent; arsenic, 0.0005 per cent; antimony, 0.0002 per cent; iron, 0.0013 per cent; nickel, 0.0001 per cent; oxygen, 0.0351 per cent; silver, 0.019 oz per ton; gold, trace. Conductivity has been: hard-drawn, 98.44; annealed, 101.25.

INSPIRATION CONSOLIDATED COPPER CO.

The operation of the Inspiration leaching plant differs radically from the others described, in that oxide and sulfide copper are leached together by the use of ferric iron.[1] This reagent is reduced during leaching and regenerated during electrolysis. The solutions are not purified and, as a matter of fact, the iron dissolved from the ore is insufficient for the requirements of the process. The deficiency is made up by iron added from cementation of wash waters.

The experimental and test-plant development of the process was described by Van Arsdale.[2] Figure 23 is a general flow sheet of the plant.

Leaching Division. The 13 concrete, lead-lined leaching tanks are each 175 ft long, 67.5 ft wide, and 19.5 ft deep, with an approximate capacity of 10,000 dry tons of ore per tank. They are lined with 7-lb chemical lead. On the side walls the lead is protected by a covering of 2-in. planks held in place by vertical posts. The filter boards are of 2-in. material, having fifteen $\frac{3}{8}$-in. holes per square foot of surface, each countersunk with a $\frac{3}{4}$-in. hole from beneath. The tank bottom slopes slightly toward the center as well as toward the end, where the drain pipe is located. There is but one opening in the bottom of each tank, a 14-in. lead pipe burned to the lead lining, entering at the opposite end from the overflow, just above the tank bottom and below the filter bottom. All solution enters the tank through this pipe and all drainage is taken out through it.

Lead work in the leaching tanks has a tendency to buckle or creep and leaks occur at such spots. This is not serious, however, as the lining is protected from the sun by the wood covering. The lead in open lead-lined launders consistently buckles, but such damage can easily be repaired because of the launder's accessibility.

After bedding, the ore is covered with a solution strong enough in acid to avoid neutrality at any point within the charge. Otherwise a decided loss in iron content would occur through the precipitation of iron salts, and a high copper content of the tailing usually accompanies such precipitated iron. Between 175,000 and 200,000 gal of solution is required to cover the ore. Percolation of solutions is upward. The solution overflows through a launder and goes to the suction of the pump serving the next tank, which permits the tanks under acid treatment to be in series. The circulation on each tank is approximately 2,400 gpm.

[1] H. W. Aldrich and W. G. Scott, The Inspiration Leaching Plant, *Trans. AIME*, Vol. 106, p. 675.

[2] G. O. Van Arsdale, Leaching Mixed Copper Ores with Ferric Sulphate, *Trans. AIME*, Vol. 73, p. 58.

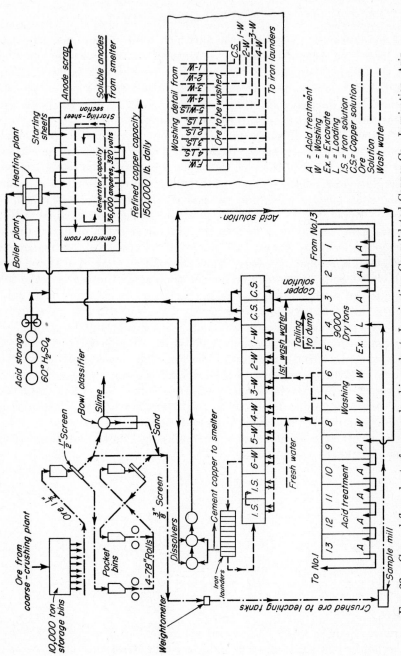

Fig. 23. General flow sheet of copper-leaching plant, Inspiration Consolidated Copper Co., Inspiration, Ariz.

The cycle is 13 days, eight tanks being under acid treatment, three being washed, one being filled, and one being excavated. The strong acid solution from the tank house, in which sulfuric acid and ferric sulfate have been regenerated and to which the required amount of new acid has been added, is delivered to the oldest ore under acid contact. This solution travels from tank to tank, constantly being reduced in solvent strength and increased in copper content, until it emerges from the newest ore and flows thence to the tank house.

Manipulation of solution and of solution strengths to preserve an economic balance between the ferric sulfate necessary for sulfide extraction, and avoidance of the penalty incurred by ferric iron in electrolytic precipitation efficiency, present delicate points in operation. As the ore is changing constantly in grade, particularly the relation of sulfide copper to oxide copper, the economic limit of solvent strengths must also change. General practice has been to hold the average strength of ferric sulfate during the leaching of any one charge at 7.5 gpl, with the maximum strength at approximately 10.0 gpl and the minimum strength at approximately 5.0 gpl. If the sulfide copper content of the ore is high, the reduction of ferric sulfate in leaching equations is naturally more pronounced and a larger quantity of ferric sulfate is consumed. The necessary strengths, however, are maintained by increasing the volume of solution to the leaching division. Should the sulfide content be low, or the acid contact time be increased because of decreased production, the volume of solution pumped to the leaching division is reduced, with a consequent reduction in strength of ferric sulfate to the tank house. The consumption of ferric sulfate is approximately the theoretical amount required for dissolving the sulfide copper.

The acid consumption, from 1927 through 1931, and from 1946 through 1949, was as follows:

Year	Pounds 60°Bé Acid per Ton of Charge
1927	31.4
1928	26.5
1929	33.3
1930	23.4
1931	23.3
1946	27.96
1947	29.26
1948	30.38
1949	28.89

There is a limit, however, to low acid concentrations, governed by operating conditions in the tank house, which will be referred to later.

From the standpoint of acid consumption, the ratio of production of electrolytic copper to production of cement copper plays an important part. To maintain an iron balance in leaching solutions, a definite amount of cement copper must be made or iron must be added in some other manner. Acid is regenerated in the tank house with the precipitation of electrolytic copper, while acid is consumed in the precipitation of copper as cement copper. Generally, only low-grade wash waters are sent to the cementation division.

Washing. Until recently, three days were used for washing, and 10 washes in all were used. The first five were called regular washes and were systematically advanced, the first wash going to the main solution system, the second wash becoming the first wash on the next tank to be washed, and so on, in the sequence noted. The fifth wash was taken from the cementation stock-solution tank and became the fourth wash on the next tank to be washed. The foregoing has now been replaced by nine washes, consisting of two solution washes, six iron washes, and a fresh-water wash. A normal wash is 175,000 to 200,000 gal.

Four cementation-solution washes follow and these likewise come from the cementation stock-solution tank. The used water is drained to a surge tank that supplies the cementation launders. Practically all the copper is precipitated, the total iron content of the solution is increased, and acid and ferric sulfate are consumed. The cementation tailing solution goes to the cementation stock-solution tank for further use. Fresh water is used for the last, or tenth, wash.

Normally, a batch wash is used; *i.e.*, the entire wash water is pumped on to the ore, circulated, and drained. At times, when a leaching tank has a short tonnage, the amount of wash water to fill the tank to its overflow would be so great that unbalanced wash-water volume would exist. Therefore, a piston or displacement wash is substituted. All conditions considered, batch washing is thought to be more positive if there is any doubt as to the rate of percolation through the ore.

The soluble iron in the ore amounts to less than $\frac{1}{2}$ lb per ton. The test-plant results over a long period showed that an average of only $\frac{1}{3}$ lb of iron per ton of ore was actually dissolved. As it is desired to carry about 20 gpl of total iron in the leaching solutions, the solution from the cementation system serves as an excellent means of controlling the total iron content. The amount of cement copper made has a direct bearing upon the iron put into solution by this method.

The only plant discard is the moisture in the tailing; therefore the wash-water volumes and wash-water advances are carefully watched. Every effort is made to add the fresh water as a final wash, as it is most valuable at this point. The volume balance for 1931 is shown in Table 52.

When operating 7 days per week, a normal wash-water volume would be between 125,000 and 150,000 gal. When operating at a reduced capacity, this volume can be increased, because the daily evaporation remains fairly constant.

TABLE 52. SOLUTION VOLUME, BALANCE, INSPIRATION

	Gallons per ton of ore		Gallons per ton of ore
Entering moisture (in ore)....	16.49	Moisture in tailing...........	24.73
Fresh water added as wash....	15.87	Evaporation per ton per day..	7.63
Total incoming water.......	32.36	Total outgoing water......	32.36

Solution Heating. From October to May, it is necessary to heat the solution overflowing from the tank house on its way to the leaching system; otherwise, a satisfactory extraction of the sulfide copper cannot be obtained. This heating is accomplished by steam at 5 lb pressure flowing through 1-in. chemical lead pipes having a $\frac{3}{16}$-in. wall, which are immersed in lead-lined tanks through which the solution flows (see Tables 53 and 53A).

TABLE 53. HEATING-PLANT DATA, INSPIRATION, 1931

	To tank house, °C	To heating plant, °C	To leaching tanks, °C	Atmosphere, °C
January.............	31.2	39.0	46.3	9.7
February............	34.4	40.7	47.1	12.3
March..............	33.4	39.4	45.8	15.1
April...............	33.4	39.1	44.5	18.9
May................	33.5	39.6	44.3	23.1
June................	33.2	40.8	40.8	27.4
July................	36.5	43.8	43.8	30.0
August.............	36.6	43.0	43.0	27.2
September...........	35.0	41.1	41.1	25.9
October.............	33.9	40.5	42.0	20.1
November...........	33.2	40.0	43.9	12.4
December...........	34.6	40.9	45.5	9.4

In all, 24,738 ft of pipe is used for this purpose. Two 500-hp boilers, fired with natural gas, furnish the steam. One-half of the heating surface is used on the inflow to the tank house and one-half of the surface is used on the outflow.

The raising of solution temperature may either precede or follow electrolytic precipitation. This gives a means of controlling the ferric sulfate balance, as will be mentioned under the description of the tank house. Operation of the experimental plant demonstrated the fact that a cold solution, approximately 20 to 22°C, would give a sulfide copper extraction, with a normal ore and under normal conditions, of between 40 and 50 per cent. By raising the maximum temperature on the oldest ore to 42°C, the minimum temperature rises to 28°, giving an average temperature on any individual charge of approximately 35°C. This condition,

TABLE 53A. HEATING-PLANT DATA, INSPIRATION, 1949

	To tank house, °C	From tank house, °C	From heating plant, °C	Atmosphere, °C
January.............	30.8	34.9	50.7	4.1
February............	34.9	39.0	53.9	8.1
March..............	36.3	41.8	53.5	12.7
April...............	37.9	43.6	55.0	18.2
May................	37.7	43.0	53.8	21.7
June...............	37.2	42.5	....	26.1
July...............	39.5	44.0	....	27.0
August.............	36.7	40.8	....	27.2
September..........	36.4	40.1	....	26.3
October............	33.6	36.7	49.0	16.8
November...........	36.0	39.4	52.1	14.8
December...........	33.3	37.2	52.2	7.1

other things being equal, produces a 75 per cent average sulfide copper extraction.

During the four summer months, when the heating plant is closed, the average solution temperature is about 38°C. The question of heating to a higher temperature in winter is one of economic balance. Radiation losses above 40° in winter are large, and as a result the cost of raising the temperature 1° increases rapidly. Solution leaving the heating plant at 50°C and pumped through an insulated 12-in. lead pipe line, 1,500 ft long, gives an average temperature to the coldest ore of 42°C.

Tailing Disposal. After a tank of ore has been leached, washed, and drained, it is ready for excavation. A Wellman-Seaver-Morgan bridge-type excavator spans the leaching tanks, with the bucket carriage traveling across the long dimension of the tank and the bridge moving the entire length of the 13 leaching tanks. Two 8-hr shifts are required to excavate a tank.

The filter bottoms are protected by 4- by 6-in. timbers laid on the 6-in.

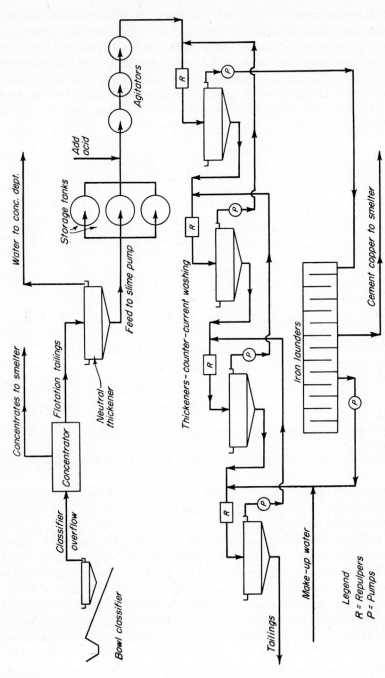

Fig. 24.   Slimes-leaching plant, Inspiration Consolidated Copper Co.

side, running parallel to the long dimension of tank on 4-ft. centers. This means leaving a 4-in. layer of tailing in the bottom of the tank at all times. The timbers must be renewed at intervals of five to six months.

Slime-treatment Division. The flow sheet of the slime-treatment plant is shown in Fig. 24. The classifier overflow pulp, with the addition of standard flotation reagents, directly enters an Inspiration-type flotation cell, as no grinding is necessary. The resultant concentrate is

TABLE 54. METALLURGICAL RESULTS AT THE SLIME PLANT, INSPIRATION

	1930	1931	1949
Feed:			
Dry tons..........................	104,037	145,001	234,982
Operating days....................	220	290	342
Tons per day......................	472.9	500.0	687
Solids, %.........................	38.1	38.5	42.9
Minus-200-mesh material, %.......	86.9	86.0	80.4
Oxide Cu, %.......................	1.175	1.068	1.018
Sulfide Cu, %.....................	0.161	0.175	0.175
Total Cu, %.......................	1.336	1.243	1.193
Tailing:			
Oxide Cu, acid-soluble, %.........	0.040	0.061	0.051
Oxide Cu, water-soluble, %........	0.022	0.035	0.042
Sulfide Cu, %.....................	0.101	0.122	0.139
Total Cu, %.......................	0.163	0.218	0.232
Extractions:			
Oxide Cu, %.......................	94.72	91.01	90.97
Sulfide Cu, %.....................	37.27	30.29	21.56
Total Cu, %.......................	87.80	82.46	80.76
Copper per ton, lb................	23.46	20.50	19.27
Lb 60°Bé acid per ton ore.........	108.3	100.3	77.1

settled in Dorr thickeners before filtration, while the tailing goes to Dorr thickeners, formerly used by the concentrator, which precede the slime-leaching plant. Table 54 gives slime-plant results, and Table 55 gives combined results from the main leaching and the slime plant.

Tank House. The tank-house personnel consists of 50 men, which includes all help for the starting-sheet section as well as for the commercial section. The tank house is capable of producing 200,000 lb of copper per day.

The generating equipment has a capacity of 36,000 amp at 320 volts. It consists of three units, each having two generators, centrally driven by a 5,450-hp 500-rpm synchronous motor.

As the tanks are arranged in two parallel lines, great precaution is taken to avoid tank short circuits, which result in a direct loss of power. An

11-ft length of 4-in. rubber hose is inserted in the solution feed line to each tank, and a 16-ft length of 12-in. rubber hose in each pump suction avoids short-circuiting at this point. Each tank overflow drops through a 6-in. rubber hose to a central distributing launder.

TABLE 55. COMBINED RESULTS FROM LEACHING AND SLIME PLANT, INSPIRATION

	1930	1931	1949
Original feed to leaching plant			
Oxide Cu, %....................................	0.704	0.655	0.599
Sulfide Cu, %....................................	0.536	0.665	0.412
Total Cu, %....................................	1.240	1.320	1.011
Combined tailing from leaching plant and slime plant			
Oxide Cu, %....................................	0.022	0.025	0.015
Sulfide Cu, %....................................	0.093	0.140	0.114
Total Cu, %....................................	0.115	0.165	0.129
Combined extraction			
Oxide Cu, %....................................	96.875	96.183	97.496
Sulfide Cu, %....................................	82.649	78.947	72.330
Total Cu, %....................................	90.726	87.500	87.240
Cu recovered per ton, lb...........................	22.50	23.10	17.64

TABLE 56. TYPICAL SOLUTION ANALYSES, INSPIRATION
(Grams per liter)

	To tank house from leaching	From tank house to leaching
Cu........................	28.8	22.3
H_2SO_4........................	31.6	44.7
Total Fe.....................	17.6	17.6
Ferric Fe.....................	4.56	9.4
Ferrous Fe...................	13.04	8.2
Ferric Fe solution from leaching..	2.7	

The tank house consists of 120 commercial tanks and 20 starting-sheet tanks. The original tank house was lost by fire in October, 1944. It was replaced by one using reinforced concrete tanks and center launder.

Starting-sheet Division. Considerable experimental work has been carried on in an endeavor to make a satisfactory starting sheet in the commercial division. To date, the conclusion has been reached that it is possible to make starting sheets from commercial solution but the operation would be very uncertain and it is not recommended. As the tank-house metallurgy must be regulated to suit leaching conditions, there are times when the circulating solution is not suited for the making of a good starting sheet.

This division is, in reality, a small refinery of 20 tanks; each tank has a capacity of 95 blanks (cathodes) and 96 anodes, making a total of 1,900 blanks, capable of making 3,800 starting sheets per day. The loops must be deducted from this production, so 15 per cent is usually allowed for loops, blanks not stripped, and scrap. This gives a capacity of 3,230 finished starting sheets per day. Production, however, is regulated to meet the requirements of the commercial department, which in turn is dependent upon the desired production of copper. The blanks are of refinery type, of rolled copper, with a groove on each side and on the bottom to produce a clean-cut sheet.

Electrodes are now spaced 6 in. from center of cathode to center of cathode, and blanks are stripped every 24 hr. A current density ranging from 14 to 16 amp per sq ft is used, and the average starting sheets weigh from 11 to 12 lb each before looping. The solution circulation rate is 15 gpm per tank and the solution carries from 38 to 40 gpl of copper and 150 to 160 gpl of acid. Accumulation of impurities is prevented by bleeding refinery electrolyte to the commercial division Two hot wells maintain a temperature of approximately 55°C. Glue is used at a rate of about 1 lb per 1,000 lb of copper produced.

A fire-refined anode is used, averaging 1,180 lb in weight. The anode scrap averaged 17 per cent during 1949.

Refinery mud, carrying gold, silver, and copper, is washed to settling tanks, dried in open pans, and shipped.

The finished starting sheet is 44 in. long by 42 in. wide. The loops, which are cut with power shears, are 20 in. long by 4 in. wide before looping. On the ends of the starting sheets, 2 in. are allowed for punching. This gives a finished sheet that allows 42 in. for submergence, with the entire loop and punching above the solution level.

A new, rolled-copper blank is thoroughly cleaned before use to remove any oxide, and amalgamated with mercuric nitrate. It is then oiled more heavily than normal and placed in operation. The first sheets to be stripped are usually not very good, but after a few days in operation there is no more trouble. If a blank is to be removed and stored, it is not stripped. In this way the surface of the blank is protected from oxidation.

Blanks are removed in groups of 14. The hoops on the lifting basket are spaced to lift alternate blanks, which permits more working room for stripping. At first, a steel tool made of small-size, hexagonal steel, properly sharpened and curved, was used for starting and stripping the starting sheets from the blanks. After 18 months of operation, a wooden tool was substituted; this was made from an ordinary pick handle, with a steel end suitably attached. This tool did not scratch the blank. A smooth blank naturally allows easier stripping and yields a higher percentage of satisfactory starting sheets, with less scrap.

After stripping, the blank is touched with amalgam solution wherever the steel starting tool may have scratched it. A cheap grade of oil is applied with cloth swabs, and the blank is then returned to the refining tanks.

The commercial division consists of 120 electrolytic tanks, 33 ft long, 4 ft 3 in. deep, and 4 ft wide. These are divided into eight banks of 15 tanks each, the electrolyte flowing in series through the banks. Each bank has a solution circulation of approximately 1,800 gpm.

Each tank has 96 cathodes and 97 anodes, spaced 4 in. from center of cathode to center of cathode and placed perpendicular to the direction of solution flow. This makes a total of 11,400 commercial cathodes and 11,520 lead anodes.

Originally, a 4½-in. spacing of electrodes was used. It was found that a current density of 11 to 12.5 amp per sq ft produced better results than higher current densities, and with less attention. A 4-in. spacing, which is now being used, permits greater cathode area and gives greater unit production at a lower current density. When operating with the current density mentioned, this spacing is the more economical. It was felt that the greater area would give a larger precipitating capacity, but inspection difficulties have greatly increased with this closer spacing and it is doubtful whether this advantage exists.

The original anodes were made of ¼-in., 4 per cent antimony lead, 38 by 40 in. submerged, and supported by copper bars. At present, all commercial tanks are equipped with ½-in. lead anodes containing 8 per cent antimony. These were cast and fabricated at this plant and are in excellent condition after more than two years of use. An oil-acid mixture is now successfully used as a sprout eliminator.

Since the tank-house fire, the labor setup in the tank house has completely changed. All tank work is on a team basis; accounting of work is shown on a large board and a competitive spirit has been instilled in the men. Considerable inspection is done on all electrodes but only the bad shorts and contacts are manipulated. This gives more operating time on all electrodes and more copper.

The starting sheets are threaded (insertion of copper supporting bar), painted, and straightened by contract labor. The painting is done just at the solution line with a single stroke of brush, using a cheap, semi-acid-resisting paint. A sheet not painted in this manner cuts off at the solution line in about five days. The sheets are then grouped on racks, moved by the crane opposite the tank where they are to be used, and are placed in the tank by hand.

Each cathode is straightened at the end of 24 hr.   Additional straightening or removal of sprouts is dependent upon operating conditions.

Best results are obtained by pulling a finished cathode weighing between 90 and 100 lb total weight.   The cathode life therefore varies with the current flow.   A 5-day cathode is pulled for a maximum production.

Results of operation in the tank house are given in Table 57.

TABLE 57.   TANK-HOUSE RESULTS, INSPIRATION

	1927	1928	1929	1930	1931	1949
Current density..........	14.2	11.8	14.6	13.3	11.9	10.5
Kwhr a-c per lb Cu precipitated.................	1.641	1.540	1.695	1.615	1.431	1.362
Cathode efficiency, %.....	61.4	64.7	61.8	64.1	67.9	71.82
Anode efficiency, %......	41.1	43.3	60.7	52.0	54.0	67.40
Cu, gpl, in..............	28.2	23.4	28.2	33.1	26.4	31.8
Cu, gpl, out.............	22.3	18.2	23.1	26.6	21.6	28.0
Total acidity, gpl, in......	41.1	30.6	25.5	26.9	33.8	18.6
Total acidity, gpl, out....	56.6	45.0	42.4	38.4	41.1	26.6
Ferric Fe, gpl, in.........	5.9	5.3	4.5	3.1	4.0	5.6
Ferric Fe, gpl, out........	10.2	9.3	10.0	9.1	8.6	10.1
Total Fe, gpl.............	17.3	16.0	18.6	16.4	20.0	16.5

Sampling of the cathode copper is done once a month, which serves as a control and a check on refinery results.   A typical analysis of electrolytic copper of March, 1931, is as follows: 99.87 per cent copper, 0.021 per cent iron, 0.0006 per cent nickel-cobalt, trace of zinc, 0.0005 per cent antimony, trace of arsenic, 0.045 per cent sulfur, traces of selenium, telerium, and chlorine.

Cementation Launders.   Nine double-section cementation launders, 60 ft long and 20 ft wide, with an average solution depth of 5 ft, are used in this service.   Shredded, loose tin cans are employed as a precipitant. Only copper from wash water is precipitated as cement copper, and inasmuch as the surge tanks above and below the plant are of sufficient size, the operation is continuous.   The solution flow in the tanks is in series and the distance of travel is regulated so as to remove practically all of the copper and, at the same time, lose as little of the acid as possible.

As at the slime plant, a traveling gantry crane spans the entire plant and, in general, the entire operation is the same.

The total amount of cement copper produced is practically the same as the amount of blister copper used for starting sheets and therefore approximately amounts to an exchange of copper with the smelter.

There being no discard at this plant, the purpose of iron precipitation is to assist in maintaining the desired iron strength in leaching solutions, and allowing a cleaner wash of leached tailing with a minimum addition of fresh water. Table 58 gives some general results. The consumption of iron seems very high but this is caused by high percentages of acid and ferric sulfate in the solution going to the launders. This division has produced as high as 1,000,000 lb of cement copper per month with one craneman and three laborers per shift, working two shifts per day.

TABLE 58. COPPER-PRECIPITATION DATA, INSPIRATION

	Pounds Cu precipitated per ton ore leached	Pounds Fe consumed per lb Cu
1927	3.16	1.924
1928	2.79	2.054
1929	4.34	2.048
1930	2.77	1.868
1931	2.33	2.209
1949	4.426	1.702

CYPRUS MINES CORP.

In July, 1949, Cyprus Mines Corp. decided to investigate the possibility of acid-leaching their pyritic Mavrovouni ore. The objective was to recover basic copper sulfates that are not soluble in water and are not recoverable in the existing flotation plant.

J. L. Bruce and Leo Abell of Cyprus Mines conceived a plan to remove the acid-soluble copper before rather than after flotation. The Dorr Company was engaged to do consulting work in designing the process and the necessary plant.

Laboratory investigation and preliminary design were completed by April, 1950. The decision was then made to go ahead with the plant. Construction on the island of Cyprus began June 1, 1950. The plant was scheduled for completion around May 31, 1951.

The process consists of leaching 2,000 long tons per day of minus-$\frac{1}{2}$-in. raw Mavrovouni ore, using 4 per cent sulfuric acid containing 2 gpl of ferric iron. Leached material is separated into a sand and a slime fraction. Sand is washed in four countercurrent classifiers; slime is washed in four countercurrent thickeners. The combined washed sand and slime goes to the existing grinding and flotation circuits. The pregnant solution from leaching goes to an iron cementation plant for recovery of dissolved copper.   The company expects to increase total copper recovery about 10 per cent with this new leaching plant.

Acid Supply.   The sulfuric acid for leaching is to be provided by a new company-owned acid plant.   Because strong acid is not required, the Keyes' Autoxidation process was decided upon.   For design purposes a pilot plant using this process was operated in Phoenix, Ariz., for some time.   It produced 1 ton per day of sulfuric acid (100 per cent basis) at strengths of 5, 7.5, and 10 per cent.

The acid plant in Cyprus consists of a 12-hearth Pacific Foundry roasting furnace, 21 ft 6 in. in diameter, for producing 7.5 per cent sulfur dioxide gas from Cyprus pyrite ore.   The gas is cleaned in British Buell International cyclones and the temperature is adjusted in automatically damper-controlled gooseneck standpipes.   The gas is further cooled and washed in spray towers before it is compressed with Sutorbilt stainless steel, cycloidal blowers and sent to the Keyes acid-cell distributing pipes. Air for the acid cells is supplied by Nash rotary compressors through Aerox porous silica tubes.   Ferrous iron is used as a catalyst in the ratio of 1 gpl of iron to 20 gpl acid produced.

A feature of the plant is the use of safety absorption towers packed with Berl saddles to prevent atmospheric pollution by escaping sulfur dioxide. The entire acid-making system is under slight vacuum and all exhaust gas must pass through the absorption towers.

Leaching Plant.   The leaching apparatus consists of two Mine & Smelter Supply Co. rubber-lined leaching drums, 7 ft 6 in. in diameter by 16 ft long.   These are further lined with fused cast-basalt blocks to take the wear from the coarse pyrite ore.   The leaching cycle is 10 min maximum.

The sand-slime separation is made in a Dorr HX classifier, 7 ft wide, all underwater parts of which, including the tank, are made of No. 316 stainless steel.   Bolted construction is used throughout on the stainless steel.   A separation at 100 mesh is made in this first classifier and the sand then goes on to three more identical classifiers, arranged counter-currently for washing the sand.

The first classifier overflow goes to a series of four Dorr Centerpier torque thickeners arranged for countercurrent washing of the slime and recovery of the copper-bearing solution.   These thickener mechanisms are made entirely of bolted No. 316 stainless steel for all underwater parts. . The thickener tanks themselves are heavily reinforced concrete, lined with layers of laminated asphalt and Fiberglas.   The 6-in. type W Dorrco diaphragm pumps for the thickeners are also built of cast and bolted No. 316 stainless steel.

The cementation plant has been patterned closely after the new

Inspiration Consolidated plant in Arizona. It consists of eight double troughs, each 20 by 60 ft, which are charged with shredded iron and operated according to the Inspiration cycle.

A 70-ft British Irving gantry crane spans the cementation launders for charging the shredded iron and removing cement copper. It is equipped with a 65-in. lifting magnet and a $1\frac{1}{2}$-cu yd clamshell bucket. Cement copper is cleaned by passing it through an Inspiration-type trommel screen fabricated by J. F. Poole, Ltd., in England. It is 4 ft in diameter by 12 ft long with $\frac{3}{16}$-in. plate perforations.

Construction Details. A novel method was used to pour the four 120-ft diameter concrete thickener tanks. These were poured in monolithic form, entirely without construction joints. A rotating bridge distributed the concrete about the periphery of the thickener area. The first tank was completely poured in 60 hr; the second went in, after a 25-day preparation interval, in 67 hr. The third was poured in 55 hr after an 18-day interval; the fourth, in 48 hr after a 19-day preparation interval.

All concrete tanks are lined with Wailes-Dove Bituplastic and Fiberglas in laminated coatings. All solutions and pulps are transferred in 4-in. rubber hose. Pipe fittings are of lead, and valves are the lead-lined Saunders type. Sumps are of wood; launders and pump boxes have lead connections. Except for the thickener underflow diaphragm pumps, all pumps are the rubber-lined Vacseal centrifugal pumps of the British International Combustion Co. All sulfur dioxide gas piping is in lead, or lead-lined steel, ducts. The only stainless steel used in the entire acid-making plant is in the Sutorbilt blowers, which are made of solid cast and machined alloy 20 stainless steel.

Operating control in the acid plant is aided by elaborate instrumentation. British "Integra" Leeds & Northrup instruments are used for temperature, temperature control, sulfur dioxide content, and sulfuric acid strength measurements. British Lea V-notch recorders are used on all acid and solution flows. Draft gages, pressure gages, and orifice meters are all British George Kent instruments.

Transite pipe is used only where acid strengths are under 0.2 per cent, as for the transfer of pregnant copper solution from the leaching plant to the cementation plant, 2,500 ft away, and for some large flow lines in the cementation plant.

HENDERSON PYRITE LEACHING PROCESS

Used mainly to treat roasted pyrite, the Henderson process has been applied successfully in both the United States and England. The elements of the processes used in these two countries will be described in the following pages.

For many years prior to 1940, between 200,000 and 300,000 long tons of Rio Tinto cupriferous pyrite was imported into the United States annually, roasted to produce acid, then leached to recover the copper. In recent years, however, Rio Tinto pyrite has given way in acid plants to native sulfur and to pyrite from sources in the United States and Canada.

The original Henderson process recovered only copper, silver, and some gold from the pyrite cinders, leaving salable iron ore as the residue. However, these cinders usually contain lead, zinc, cobalt, or other rare metal as well, and modern practice aims at recovering these elements. Sodium sulfate, or glauber salt, is now also recovered in salable form.

PROCESS IN ENGLAND

The following description of pyrite cinder leaching in England is abstracted from an article by N. H. Dennis.[1] Figure 25 gives a flow sheet of the method described and Table 59 gives leaching-plant data.

Pyrite (FeS_2) is of fundamental importance, especially to the economy of Europe. The supply of sulfuric acid, the basis of the chemical and many other industries, is largely dependent on the supply of pyrite. The residue remaining after the sulfur has been driven off forms an important source of pig iron. In addition, small quantities of nonferrous metals, notably copper, are invariably present and form a much-needed addition to European metal resources. Usually pyrite cinder containing nonferrous metals is not acceptable to iron and steel makers and must be leached. The chief European sources of pyrite are Spain, Norway, Cyprus, Greece, Italy, and Germany. The total production before the Second World War amounted to about 2,000,000 tons.

In general, the pyrite is sold to sulfuric acid manufacturers who roast it and then convey the cinders to leaching works to recovery the nonferrous metals. As transport charges loom very largely in the economics of the process, the leaching works are usually located at or near the cinder-consuming iron centers.

Outline of Process. Pyrite is roasted in mechanical hearth furnaces, the sulfur dioxide produced passing to the acid plant for the production of sulfuric acid. The residue, known as cinders, containing copper, zinc, cobalt, iron, and precious metals, is ground, mixed with salt, and reroasted. This chloridizing roast renders the nonferrous metals soluble. The salt,

---

[1] N. H. Dennis, Recovery of Non-ferrous Metals from Pyrite. *Mine & Quarry Engineering*, December, 1947.

after yielding up its chlorine, combines with sulfur to form sodium sulfate (glauber salts).   Copper chloride is leached out, leaving iron oxide behind.   The iron residue is sintered to render it fit for blast-furnace practice, mixed with coke and limestone, and run down to pig iron. The liquor remaining after the precipitation of copper contains the other

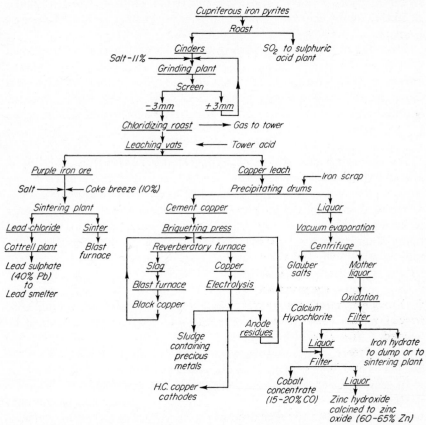

FIG. 25.   Flow sheet of the Henderson process for leaching pyrite cinders for copper.

nonferrous metals.   They are recovered by successive precipitation and filtration.

Roasting.   Commercial iron pyrite contains 38–44 per cent sulfur, 35–46 per cent iron, 7–16 per cent silica, 0.5–2 per cent copper, together with small amounts of lead, zinc, cobalt, etc.   The calcine is of purple color and is commonly known as "purple ore."

Roasted pyrite or cinder, consisting mainly of iron oxide, is not further treated at the acid works, for its chief use is in the production of pig iron,

TABLE 59.   LEACHING-PLANT DATA, HENDERSON PROCESS IN ENGLAND
(Solids in %; solutions in gpl)

	Throughput per month	Cu	Au	Ag	Pb	Zn	Co	Ni	As	Fe	SiO_2	S	Cl	Acid
Cinders	8,500 tons	2.0	0.2 g per ton	37 g per ton	0.70	2.0	0.06	0.02	0.06	46	8	3.5	7.5	
Cu leach	8,000 cu m	20				20	0.6	0.2		0.7			90	6
Cu leach (weak)		15			0.07	3	0.1			1.5		12	35	20
Purple ore		0.07				0.07				60	10	0.2		
Cement Cu	190 tons	90	5.5 g per ton	920 g per ton	0.7			0.2	0.1				0.1	
Anode Cu (cement + scrap)	800 tons	99.0	1.8 g per ton	500 g per ton	0.2			0.1	0.15	0.03				
Electrolyte		30–50						8–22	8–22	4			0.06	190
Cathode	640 tons							3						
Anode slime	2 tons		650 g per ton	200,000 g per ton	20			0.8	0.1	11				
Anode slag	70 tons	40			2			1	0.3	1				
Black Cu	35 tons	91		160 g per ton										
Black Cu slag	25 tons	1				4				30	26		120	
Pb leach	4,500 cu m				6									
Cement Pb	30 tons	4		125 g per ton	8.5					2				
Au Solution			0.7 g per cu m											
Au slime			3	5 g per ton										
Purple ore	6,700 tons	0.07	0.2 g per ton		0.1	0.07	0.01		0.1			0.2	0.2	
Glauber salt	650 tons													

the extraction of any nonferrous metal being incidental to the process. If the proportion of nonferrous metals is negligible, the cinders are sintered directly. If, however, economic quantities of copper, zinc, or cobalt are present, the copper is first extracted, and the residual ferric oxide is sintered and sent to the blast furnaces.

Copper in the cinders amounts to 1 to 3 per cent, and there must be sufficient sulfur to fulfill the ratio 3 mol S:2 mol Cu, the excess sulfur being necessary to maintain heat of reaction in the chloridizing roast. If insufficient sulfur is present, green or pyritic ore must be added.

The type of roaster is the same as used for pyrite roasting, except that in Europe the Ramen roaster is more commonly employed. The Ramen is of Swedish origin, and is a smaller edition of the Wedge, having only four to five hearths. Throughput is 40 to 50 tons per day, against 120 to 150 tons in the Wedge. The heating system is also somewhat different, in that many units have no firebox, heat being supplied only to the top hearth.

Salt amounting to 8 to 10 per cent is added to the cinders, the mixture is crushed to pass a 3-mm screen, and fed to the furnace. The reaction is exothermic, heat in the form of producer gas being necessary only to initiate the chloridizing action. The ore passes from hearth to hearth, sufficient heat being generated to complete the reactions:

$$2Cu_2S + 8NaCl + 4FeSO_4 + 5O_2$$
$$= 4CuCl_2 + 4Na_2SO_4 + 2Fe_2O_3 + 2SO_2 \quad (1)$$
$$4NaCl + 2CuO + 2S + 3O_2 = 2Na_2SO_4 + 2CuCl_2 \quad (2)$$
$$2NaCl + CuS + 2O_2 = Na_2SO_4 + CuCl_2 \quad (3)$$

Comparatively little iron chloride is found in the finished product, although it is presumed that ferric chloride is formed during the course of the reaction. It becomes a chloridizing agent, losing its chlorine to the other metals and being converted to iron oxide. Cinders containing appreciable amounts of zinc (over 3 per cent) are difficult to treat efficiently, as zinc oxide has a tendency to combine with iron oxide and form zinc ferrite, which is insoluble. This leads to loss of zinc and other nonferrous metals tied up in the ferrite.

The gases from the chloridizing roasters pass through scrubbing towers, down which water is trickling. The sulfur dioxide and hydrochloric acid are absorbed to form an acid solution. This tower acid forms the lixiviant to dissolve copper from the chloridized ore.

Leaching tanks are of acidproof brick set in cement and holding 100 to 200 tons each. The hot ore is unloaded into the tanks by grab cranes and solution introduced, the temperature being maintained at 35 to 40°C, the period of leach varying from 24 to 36 hr. Frequent difficulty is experienced in leaching, due to the formation of hard balls of material that resist solution. In Sweden, Ramen designed what is termed a preleaching machine in which a thin layer of the hot ore is sprayed with hot solution which breaks down the lumpy material, enabling the subsequent treatment to proceed more smoothly.

The first leach solution taken off contains 20 to 25 gpl of copper and up to 300 gpl of glauber salt. It is replaced with a wash, which is allowed to soak and is then removed. It forms, together with tower acid, the first leach for a succeeding batch of ore. The leached cinder, after being allowed to drain, is emptied out and conveyed to the iron-sintering plant, where it is mixed with powdered coke and treated in the usual manner on Dwight-Lloyd sintering machines. Sinter is mixed with flux and run down in blast furnaces.

Copper is recovered from the solution by precipitation on scrap iron. This is usually done in "tumblers" consisting of drum-shaped steel vessels lined with acid brick. The vessel is set at an angle and rotated. Copper is precipitated as cement copper, according to the reaction $CuCl_2 + Fe = FeCl_2 + Cu$. The advantage of the revolving tumblers over the launder method is that precipitation is faster and the iron remains cleaner for a longer period. A higher-grade copper (85 per cent) is obtained, owing to its comparative freedom from basic iron salts. The precipitated copper and mother liquor run into a settling pit, the supernatant liquid being drawn off for further processing; the copper, after being given a wash, is filtered, briquetted, and run down in a reverberatory furnace, cast into anodes, and electrolyzed.

A demand exists for cupric oxychloride $[3Cu(OH_2) \cdot CuCl_2]$ as an insecticide and fungicide. It is prepared by treating pregnant liquor with cement copper, which precipitates cuprous chloride. This is dissolved in brine and oxidized. The oxychloride comes down and is filtered off. The supernatant copper-free liquor from the settling pit is next treated by vacuum evaporation for separation of glauber salt. The crystallized salt is removed, heated to convert it to the anhydrous form, and finally separated by centrifuging.

Before the next step (precipitation of cobalt), the iron picked up in solution by the precipitation of copper on scrap iron has to be dealt with. The liquor is submitted to intense air oxidation by circulating in a tank, withdrawing at the bottom, and ejecting at the top through a main fitted with jets, the operation occupying some 30 hr in all. Milk of lime is added to precipitate the iron and calcium sulfate. After filtration, calcium hypochlorite precipitates a cobalt sludge which is filtered off and after further chemical treatment is reduced in an electric furnace. Zinc can be recovered by treating the liquor from cobalt precipitation with lime, when an impure zinc hydroxide separates out which, after filtration and calcining, can be sold as zinc oxide (per cent Zn) to smelters for recovery of zinc.

When appreciable quantities of lead are present, it can be recovered by either of two methods. In the first, the lead is recovered by volatilization during sintering of the purple ore. Salt (1 per cent) is added and, during the course of sintering, lead chloride is volatilized and is caught in an electrostatic precipitator. Lead refiners object to processing the highly corrosive lead chloride and therefore it is transformed into a sulfate containing about 40 per cent lead.

The second method involves leaching. After the extraction of the copper, the purple ore is leached with a hot (70 to 80°C) brine solution, whereby the lead goes into solution. The mixture is allowed to settle and the supernatant lead solution pumped off, evaporated, and passed over scrap iron, the lead being precipitated in a similar manner to that employed in copper precipitation. The lead is washed, collected, and sent to the lead smelters as cement lead containing 85 per cent lead.

From 100,000 tons of cinders, approximately the following amounts of products are obtained:

 1,500 tons of cement copper
 1,350 tons of zinc oxide
    10 tons of cobalt concentrate
 1,200 tons of lead precipitate
    92 lb of gold ⎫
 6,000 lb of silver ⎬ (contained in the copper and lead precipitates)
85,000 tons of iron sinter (65 per cent iron)
 8,500 tons of glauber salt

To obtain the foregoing results, the following amounts of raw materials are required:

   10,000 tons of salt
    5,000 tons of coal
    2,000 tons of iron scrap
3,000,000 kwhr

The recoveries are in the neighborhood of 80 to 85 per cent of the copper, 65 per cent of the cobalt, and the same of silver. These comparatively low extractions are accounted for by difficulty in dissolution.

Roughly speaking, the sale of the nonferrous metals pays all operating expenses, leaving the profit to be extracted from the pig iron. In an effort to decrease costs still further, by-products are produced wherever possible, such materials as cement, fertilizer, and bricks (from blast-furnace slag) being exploited to the full.

PROCESS IN THE UNITED STATES

A very complete description of the treatment in the United States of pyrite cinders at the plant of the Pyrites Co., Inc., Wilmington, Del., has been published.[1] In general the method is similar to that described for England. Tables 59 to 65 are from this description. In these tables, all tons are long tons of 2,240 lb. Present pyrite-cinders leaching at Wilmington is on a scale very much smaller than that described. These tables give data on chloridizing roasting, leaching, copper precipitation, zinc and sodium sulfate recovery, sodium sulfate production and recovery, and lead recovery.

TABLE 60. CHLORIDIZING ROASTING, HENDERSON PROCESS, PYRITES CO., INC.
(Long tons)

	1936	1937
Furnace days run.	2,996	3,506
Cinder roasted, dry tons (2,240 lb).	204,868	234,885
Cinder roasted per furnace day.	68.4	67
Moisture in cinders, %.	10.14	10.24
Salt charged to furnaces, tons.	21,575	32,918
Salt charged to leaching tanks, tons.	2,309	115
Total salt used, tons.	23,884	33,033
Salt used, % of dry cinders.	11.66	14.11
Gas used, million cu ft.	177.57	190.52
Gas used per ton cinders, cu ft.	870	810

At Wilmington three methods of leaching were used: (1) when leaching for copper and silver, (2) when it was desired to extract gold as well as copper and silver, and (3) during the period when zinc was being recovered in addition to copper and silver. These three leaching modifications are shown in Figs. 26, 27, and 28.

The leach slurry used for gold extraction was made by slaking 160 lb of

[1] R. C. Trumbull, W. Hardick, and E. G. Lawfer, Treatment of Pyrites Cinders at the Plant of the Pyrites Co., Inc., *Bulletin of the Institution of Mining and Metallurgy*, December, 1948.

Table 61. Leaching, Henderson Process, Pyrites Co., Inc.

	1936	1937
Tanks charged............................	1672	1910
Tanks discharged.........................	1670	1917
Leaching time per tank, hours.............	64.56	70.12
Volume of pregnant solution, cu m.........	249,000	296,020
Copper in pregnant solution, gpl...........	13.2	13.9
Copper in pregnant solution, total tons.....	3,235	4,049
Analysis of cinders, before leaching:		
Cu, %................................	1.68	1.81
Zn, %................................	2.12	2.30
Pb, %................................	1.26	1.18
Au, dwt per ton........................	0.57	0.56
Ag, oz per ton.........................	1.82	1.84
Analysis of cinders, after leaching:		
Cu, %................................	0.07	0.065
Zn, %................................	0.10	0.215
Pb, %................................	1.32	1.25
Au, dwt per ton........................	0.26	0.29
Ag, dwt per ton........................	0.65	0.49

Table 62. Copper Precipitation and Recoveries, Henderson Process, Pyrites Co., Inc.

	1936	1937
Precipitation:		
Drum hours run........................	14,634	17,410
Solution treated per drum hour, cu m....	17.10	17.0
Scrap iron used, tons...................	3,564	4,791
Precipitate, wet tons...................	5,002	6,100
Moisture in precipitate, %..............	21.46	19.16
Cu in tail liquor to waste, gpl...........	0.029	0.035
Recoveries:		
Cu in cinder to furnaces, tons............	3,441	4,239
Cu in bars produced, tons...............	1,548	
Cu in precipitate shipped, tons...........	1,644	4,098
Cu in bar furnace slag, tons.............	28	
Recovery, Cu, %.......................	93.0	96.6
Ag in cinders to furnaces, oz..............	370,762	430,579
Ag in precipitate produced, oz...........	242,197	334,932
Recovery, Ag, %.......................	65.3	77.6
Au in cinders to furnaces, oz..............	5,824	6,472
Au in precipitate produced, oz...........	2,725	3,102
Recovery, Au, %.......................	47.9	48.0

TABLE 63. ZINC RECOVERY, HENDERSON PROCESS, PYRITES CO., INC.

Operating Data, July, Aug., and Sept., 1931

Cinders leached for Zn, tons............... 46,800
Time running Zn solution, hours........... 1.5
Zn solution treated, cu m................. 6,700
Zn content, 81 gpl, tons.................. 542
Cu content, 14.2 gpl, tons................ 93
Scrap Zn for Cu precipitation, tons........ 160
H_2SO_4 (66°Bé) used, tons................ 139
Final Zn liquor produced, cu m............ 5,450
Zn content, 110 gpl, tons................. 600

Solution Analyses, gpl

	Zn	Cu	SO_4	Fe	H_2SO_4	Cl
Solution from head tanks..........	81	14.2	111.0	0.10	0.58	174.0
Decopperized solution.............	91	0.07	116.4	0.25	0.30	166.2
Final solution....................	110	0.08	51.6	0.46	0.43	198.0

TABLE 64. SODIUM SULFATE PRODUCTION, HENDERSON PROCESS, PYRITES CO., INC.

	Zinc fraction	Glauber fraction
Solution to crystallizers, cu m..................	6,700	6,560
Number of batches cooled.....................	247	244
Initial solution temperature, °F...............	106	123
Final solution temperature, °F.................	51	36
SO_4 in solution, before cooling, gpl..............	116.4	147
SO_4 in solution, after cooling, gpl...............	51.6	79
Brine temperatures, to crystallizers, °F..........	9.2	9.4
Brine temperatures, from crystallizers, °F.......	24.5	24.5

Tons brine circulating per hr............... 296
Quantity brine circulating, gpm............ 1,834
Total compressor hours.................... 3,184
Anhydrous Na_2SO_4 produced, tons.......... 825
Evaporator hours run...................... 1,848
Total glauber salt produced, tons............ 3,325

TABLE 65. SODIUM SULFATE RECOVERY, HENDERSON PROCESS, PYRITES CO., INC.
(Operating data for Oct., Nov., and Dec., 1931, treating glauber-salt liquor only)

Number of batches cooled	785
Volume of liquor cooled, cu m	22,600
Average temperatures before cooling, °F	114
Average temperatures after cooling, °F	38
Glauber salt recovered, tons	5,300
Reagents and filter aids for purification:	
Soda ash, lb	16,300
Caustic soda solution gal	65,854
H_2SO_4 (66°Bé), lb	91,144
Paper pulp, lb	13,250
Evaporator hours run	3,173
Anhydrous Na_2SO_4 produced, tons	1,910
Estimated steam per ton Na_2SO_4, lb	3,700
Fe_2O_3 in glauber salt, %	0.203
Zn in glauber salt, %	0.168
Fe_2O_3 in Na_2SO_4 anhydrous, %	0.0031
Zn in Na_2SO_4 anhydrous, %	0.0050

TABLE 66. LEAD RECOVERY, HENDERSON PROCESS, PYRITES CO., INC.
(Operating data for Aug., 1940, to May, 1941, inclusive)

Cinders brine leached, tons	103,744
Pb recovered, tons	521.7
Pb recovered per ton cinders, lb	11.26
Pb content cinders, lb per ton	25.80
Pb content leached cinders, lb per ton	10.00
Leaching time per tank, hours	60
Pb in precipitate shipped, %	86.96
Moisture in precipitate shipped, %	5.0
Salt used, tons	5,630
Leaching extraction, %	61
Pb recovered and shipped, %	39

quicklime in 500 gal of water and adding 200 lb of chlorine to oxidize the solutions and aid in gold extraction. Gold is readily precipitated as metal by ferrous sulfate, but ferric sulfate and ferric chloride are gold solvents.

Copper was precipitated continuously in steel drums, lead-lined, the lead being protected by wood blocks set edge-wise. The liquor carrying cement copper in suspension was pumped to Dorr thickeners. After thickening it went to flat-bed vacuum filters for washing and dewatering.

A series of launders gave additional settling capacity for finely divided cement.

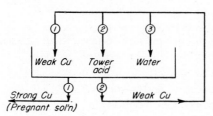

Fig. 26. Modification of the Henderson process for leaching for copper and silver.

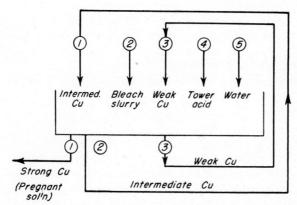

Fig. 27. Modification of the Henderson process for leaching for copper, silver, and gold.

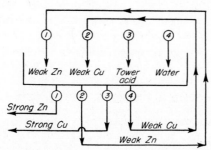

Fig. 28. Modification of the Henderson process for leaching for copper, silver, and zinc.

When zinc is recovered as an oxide precipitate, the steps in the process are

1. Precipitation of copper.
2. Refrigeration of the solution to crystallize out glauber salt.
3. Precipitation of the iron as ferric hydroxide.
4. Precipitation of manganese and cobalt.
5. Precipitation of zinc as hydroxide.
6. Calcination of the zinc precipitate.

The sodium sulfate was produced as anhydrous salt, Na_2SO_4. This was pure, of good color, coarsely crystalline, and commanded a premium over ordinary salt cake.

Lead extraction consisted of the following steps, applied after copper leaching and thorough washing of the residues to remove sulfates:

1. Leaching with hot concentrated brine.
2. Precipitation of the lead as $Pb(OH)_2$ by milk of lime.
3. Repulping this precipitate with tower acid and precipitation of metallic lead by scrap iron.

Figure 29 is a flow sheet showing the lead-recovery procedure.

Corrosion by Henderson process liquors is severe and with the exception of leaching tank outlets, where monel metal lasts fairly well, no metal equipment can be used. All equipment exposed to the solutions must be of wood or rubber or must be lined with rubber or mastic. Where mastic linings are used, they must be covered with wood to prevent sagging.

Leaching was generally in batches. At Wilmington the square tanks were of concrete, lined with a 2-in. layer of asphaltic mastic, supported on the walls by 2-in. wood staves. Launders were of asphaltic mastic construction with a wood lining to avoid erosion. Storage tanks were of wood-stave construction. Solutions for circulating to the leaching tanks were pumped from storage through rubber-lined pipe lines, with rubber-lined valves as needed. All pumps were rubber-lined.

N'CHANGA COPPER MINES, LTD.

The capacity of the mine and plant of N'Changa Copper Mines, Ltd., Northern Rhodesia, was recently extended to enable an annual production of approximately 64,000 long tons of copper. A portion of this production will be from a leaching plant and will be produced at N'Changa in the form of cathodes.[1]

[1] Skinner's *Mining Yearbook*, p. 277, 1949.

The flow sheet of this plant is shown in Fig. 30.   Description of the plant is as follows:

Leaching-plant feed is oxide flotation concentrate filter cake.   The tonnage is 500 dry tons per day, averaging 16 per cent oxide copper, 2 per cent sulfide copper, and 17 per cent moisture.   The specific gravity of the ore is 3.1.   The feed is by belt conveyor to the pulping agitators.

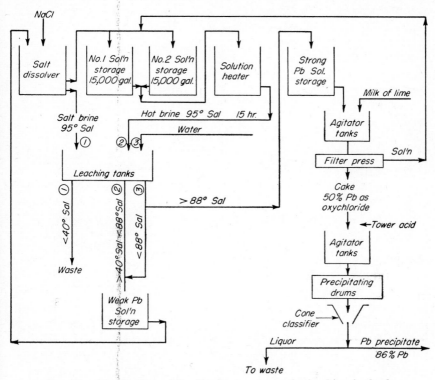

Fig. 29.   Modification of the Henderson process for leaching for lead.

Pulping and mixing are at a ratio of 1:1 with spent solution (1.2 sp gr). This pulp is pumped to the mixing agitator, where more spent solution and sulfuric acid are added.   The specific gravity of the pulp is then 1.290.   A 10-min contact is given, after which the pulp flows by gravity to the leaching agitators.

Leaching agitation is continuous.   The weight loss in leaching is 30 per cent.   A 3-hr contact is given, after which the pulp is pumped to the primary thickener.

Primary thickening of leach residue yields an overflow which is pumped to the clarifying thickeners.   The underflow is controlled by No. 4

Quadruplex Dorrco pump at 55 to 60 per cent undissolved solids and pumped to washing thickeners.

CCD washing of leach residue is done in four steps of CCD decantation. The thickener discharge is 55 to 60 per cent undissolved solids, controlled

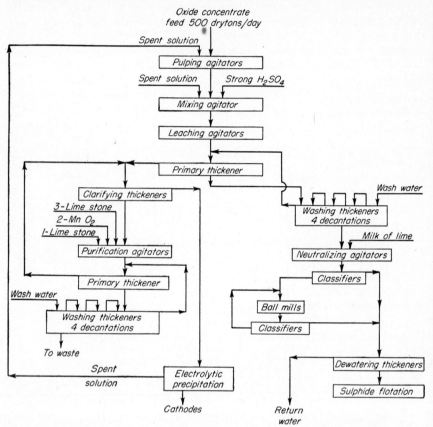

Fig. 30. Flow sheet of copper-leaching plant, N'Changa Copper Mines, Ltd., Northern Rhodesia.

by No. 4 Quadruplex Dorrco pump, handling about 59 gpm pulp at 1.658 sp gr.   Flow is by gravity from Dorrco pump to sump, mixed with over-flow solution or wash water, and pumped to the succeeding thickeners or to a regrind section.   The volume of wash water is about 419 gpm. Washing efficiency is 95 per cent.   The overflow is pumped to the primary thickener and the washed pump residue is pumped to the neutralizing agitators.

Neutralizing agitation feed is about 350 dry tons per day at a dilution of 55 to 60 per cent undissolved solids.   Specific gravity of the solids is

2.9. Milk of lime is added to the agitators to complete neutralization and the pulp is then discharged by gravity to the regrind and sulfide flotation section.

Clarification thickener overflow is pumped to the tank-house storage. The amount of overflow is about 420 gpm at 1.2 sp gr. It contains about 55 gpl copper and 15 to 20 gpl acid. The underflow is controlled by a No. 2 Dorrco pump and goes to the purification section. The underflow varies in amount, the expected maximum being 80 gpm, with undissolved solids nominal and variable, depending on the clarity of the primary thickener overflow and the quantity of solution to be purified.

Purification is continuous on feed from the clarifying thickeners. Ground limestone is added to reduce acidity to pH 1.7 to 1.8. Manganese dioxide (about 14 lb per ton solution) and limestone to pH 3.7 to 3.8 (about $62\frac{1}{2}$ lb per ton solution) are then added. Contact time is about 1 hr in each agitator. The pulp is discharged by gravity to a sump, mixed with overflow from the first washing thickener, and pumped to the primary purification thickener.

The primary purification thickener overflow is pumped to clarifying thickeners. The underflow goes to the purification washing thickeners. There are four stages of decantation. The thickener discharge contains about 30 per cent undissolved solids. It flows by gravity from Dorrco pumps to sumps, is mixed with overflow solutions or water, and is pumped to a succeeding thickener or to waste. The volume of wash water is about 5 gpm. The washed residue pulp is discharged to waste and the first thickener overflow is pumped to the primary thickener.

Electrolysis occupies four sections of 12 cells per section. The cells are 3 ft 6 in. by 3 ft 9 in. by 46 in. inside and have 38 cathodes per cell. The flow per cell is 5 to 10 gpm in parallel. The current density is 16 amp per sq ft and the voltage 1.8 to 2.0. The strong electrolyte has about 55 gpl copper and the spent electrolyte about 30 gpl copper.

Expected acid consumption is as follows:

1. Chemical: 400 lb per ton copper recovered.
2. Mechanical: 300 lb per ton copper recovered.
3. Purification: 250 lb per ton copper recovered.
   Total: 850 to 1,000 lb per ton copper recovered.

CHAPTER 7

OPERATING DATA FROM PRACTICE—ZINC

Although all zinc-leaching and electrolytic plants must make use of the same basic processes, no two of them are exactly alike in their operating problems or their methods of solving them. Some of the similarities and differences in the major electrolytic zinc plants of the world are described in this chapter. Table 67 gives a list of zinc-leaching and electrolytic plants in operation.

GENERAL RELATIONSHIPS

Roasting, as already pointed out in the chapter on that subject, can be observed in several stages of progress in the world's zinc plants. The Wedge, or the Edwards, type of furnace has been favored until recently, when the flash, or suspension, type of roasting was developed. The latter has the advantage of greater capacity over the Wedge, up to twice as much per unit in some cases. Several European plants are now using flash roasting and Risdon, in Australia, has replaced its Edwards roasters with flash furnaces.

Temperatures in the Wedge type run lower than in flash roasters. Maximum in the former is about 750°C, compared with 950°C for the latter. Comparisons made at Trail show that the higher temperature of the flash roaster does not mean greater ferritization.

All plants use cyclones and a Cottrell system for catching roaster dust. Flash roasters lose more dust than Wedge types, 35 per cent as against about 15 per cent. Some plants return this dust to the furnace, even in flash roasters. Trail leaches it directly. Risdon uses scrubbers along with cyclones and a Cottrell plant to catch dust.

As measured by total and sulfide sulfur in the calcine, either type of roaster gives a satisfactorily roasted product. For a more complete discussion of roasting, see Chaps. 1 and 3.

Leaching zinc calcine for electrolysis is done by "single" or "double" leaching in either batch or continuous processes. These methods have already been discussed in Chap. 4 but for convenience will be briefly reviewed here.

Single leaching refers to the practice of adding calcine to spent electrolyte until the acid content is brought as low as possible and still be

able to dissolve zinc. The pulp is then neutralized with lime which precipitates iron and other impurities for removal by thickening. Results
are up to the operator, who must be sure to add no more calcine than

TABLE 67. ZINC-LEACHING AND ELECTROLYTIC PLANTS, 1936–1943*

Company and Location	Rated Daily Capacity, Tons Zinc Cathodes
United States:	
Anaconda C. M. Co., Great Falls, Mont.†	440
Anaconda C. M. Co., Anaconda, Mont.†	213
Sullivan Mining Co., Kellogg, Idaho†	105
American Zinc Co., Monsanto, Ill.†	100
A. S. & R. Co., Corpus Christi, Tex.†	70
Canada:	
Cons. M. & S. Co., Trail, B.C.†	450
Hudson Bay M. & S. Co	150
Europe:	
Norske Zinkompani, Norway†	150
Ordzhonikidze, U.S.S.R.	75
Cheliabinsk, U.S.S.R.	75
G. von Giesche's Erben, Germany	200
Giesche Spolka Akcyna, Poland	66
Slaskiekopalnie Cynkownie, Poland	22
Vielle Montagne, France	110
Vielle Montagne, Belgium†	30
C.I.E. Liguri, Italy	10
Soc. Monteponi, Italy	20
Soc. Min. Met. Pertusola, Italy	36
Soc. Monte Catini, Montevecchio, Italy	60
Rhodesia:	
Rhodesia–Broken Hill Dev. Co.†	70
Japan:	
Nippon Soda	20
Mitsubishi, Hosokura	27
Mitsubishi, Naoshima	20
Australia:	
Electrolytic Zinc Co., Risdon, Tasmania†	225
Total daily rated capacity	2642

* A. A. Center, World Survey of Electrolytic Zinc, 1936–43, *Trans. AIME*, Vol.
159, p. 182.

† Described in this chapter in detail or shown in flow sheet or plant layout.

will be leached. The method is best suited to small plants and batch
operation.

Double leaching refers to the practice of adding excess calcine until all
the acid in the spent electrolyte is used up, and iron and other impurities
have precipitated. This precipitate is then removed by thickening and
leached once more with a low-acid solution. This takes out the zinc but

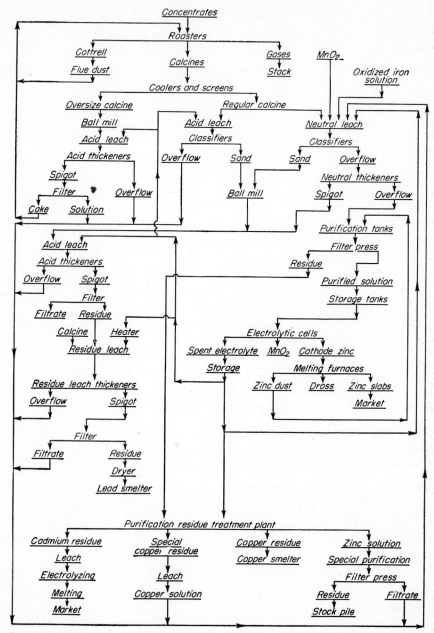

Fig. 31.   Flow sheet of electrolytic zinc plant of Anaconda Copper Mining Co., Great Falls, Mont.

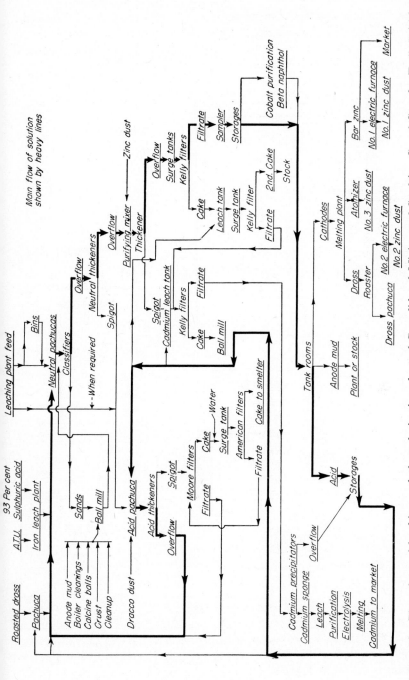

FIG. 32. Flow sheet of leaching and electrolytic zinc plant of Consolidated Mining and Smelting Co. of Canada, Trail, British Columbia.

removes only a small portion of the precipitated impurities.   Following another thickening, and possibly filtration, this solution returns to the first leach (being added to spent electrolyte) and the pulp is discarded. This technique is used in several large electrolytic zinc plants.

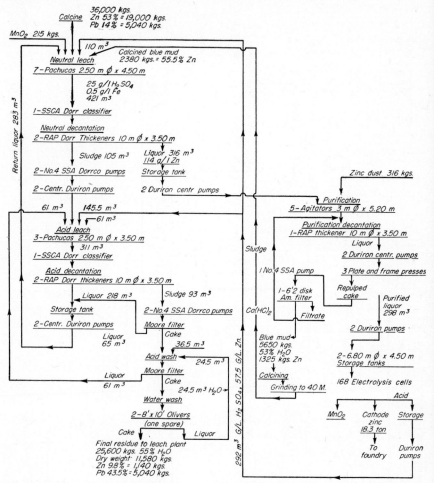

Fig. 33.   Flow sheet of electrolytic zinc plant of the Vielle Montagne company in Belgium.

The processes used by Anaconda at Great Falls, Mont., and by Consolidated Mining and Smelting Co. of Canada at Trail, British Columbia, are shown in the flow sheets appearing herewith as Figs. 31 and 32, respectively.   The flow sheet of the Vielle Montagne electrolytic zinc plant in Belgium is shown in Fig. 33.

A special method, called "reverse" leaching, is used at the Monsanto,

Ill., plant of American Zinc Co. of Illinois. Described in this chapter, page 220, it consists essentially of adding acid to a pulp of calcine, rather than the more conventional methods outlined above. The object is to keep formation of silica gel at a minimum so that later thickening and filtering will not be impeded.

At Risdon, in Tasmania, a similar silica problem was solved by keeping the single-leach pulp acidified until most of the residue had been filtered off. This removed most of the source of silica gel and made possible neutralization and purification in the ordinary way.

Purification practice varies widely from plant to plant, although here again the basic features are the same. Iron, silica, alumina, arsenic, and antimony are removed by precipitation of ferric hydrate. Copper, cadmium, cobalt, nickel, germanium, etc., are removed by precipitation with zinc dust.

A special problem at Risdon is removal of chlorine, which otherwise corrodes anodes and causes sticking of the zinc deposit. At Trail, fluorine causes trouble and requires carrying of two separate circuits.

Power supply is different in all plants, both in original source and in conversion for use in electrolysis (see the discussion in Chap. 4). Current densities vary from 30 to 40 amp per sq ft of cathode area for low-density plants, through 60 to 68 amp for intermediate density plants, to about 100 amp for the only high-density plant in operation (Bunker Hill at Kellogg).

Current efficiencies vary from about 85 to 94 per cent. Power use runs from 1.4 to 1.8 kwhr per lb of zinc. With the exception of Risdon, the usual deposition period is 24 hr for each set of cathodes. At Risdon, conditions are such that the longest deposition period in the industry (72 hr) also gives the highest current efficiency recorded. It does not follow, however, that long deposition periods mean high efficiency. The contrary is usually true.

All plants plate their electrolytes down to about 55 gpl of zinc. Leaching for low-density plants builds it up again to 110 to 135 gpl. Intermediate and high-acid plants run their solutions up to about 160 to 180 gpl.

Detailed descriptions of several typical electrolytic zinc plants follow. Tables 68, 69, and 70 condense certain of these details for reference.

AMERICAN ZINC CO. OF ILLINOIS, MONSANTO, ILL.
(A LOW-DENSITY PLANT)

The original electrolytic zinc plant of American Zinc Co. of Illinois was described by L. P. Davidson, general superintendent, in 1944.[1] It is an example of plants using a low-current density process.

[1] L. P. Davidson, New Electrolytic Zinc Plant of American Zinc Co. of Illinois, *Trans. AIME*, Vol. 159, 1944.

TABLE 68. ROASTING FOR ZINC LEACHING, INDUSTRY PRACTICE

	Anaconda, Great Falls	A. S. & R. Co., Corpus Christi	Cons. M. & S. Co., Trail, B.C.	Electr. Zinc Co., Risdon	G. Von Giesche, Madgeburg	Norske Zinkompani, Norway	Sullivan Co., Kellogg, Idaho	Giesche Spolka Akeyjna, Poland	Hudson Bay M & S. Co., Flin Flon, Man.
Type of furnace	Wedge type 25 ft diam, seven hearths	Skinner suspension type, 20 ft diam	Suspension type, 25 ft diam	Modified Skinner type	Humboldt nine hearth, 6,500 mm diam	Wedge remodeled for flash roasting	Wedge seven hearth, 25 ft diam	Suspension	Modified Wedge "split draft," 25 ft diam, seven hearths
Capacity, tons per 24 hr per furnace	40–60	70–120	50–130		64		40–50		50
Fuel	Natural gas			Small amount of oil	Industrial gas		Fuel oil		Powdered coal
Feeder	Apron feeder	Feeder belt	Feeder belt		Feed hoppers		Scraper feeders		Feeder belt
Shaft speed, rpm	1 in 4 min, 1 in 2 min				1 in 1–2 min				1 in 3½ min
Temperatures, °C	Gas over hearth No. 1: 438 No. 2: 560 No. 3: 626 No. 4: 650 No. 5: 622 No. 6: 622 No. 7: 543	Roaster combustion chamber, 930	Roaster combustion chamber, 900–955				Max temp. on any floor, 750		Gas temp. No. 1: 450–470 No. 2: 620–650 No. 3: 710–720 No. 4: 740–750 No. 5: 730–780 No. 6: 730–800 No. 7: 670–700
Dust, quantity		35 % of calcine	40 %	13 % of feed	13 % of feed		ca. 15 %		18 % of charge

Dust, collection	Flues and Cottrell	....	Flue and Cottrell	Cyclones and Cottrell	Cyclones, flue, and Cottrell	Cyclone, scrubber, and Cottrell	Cyclones and Cottrell	Cyclones and Cottrell	Flues and Cottrell
Dust, disposal	To re-treatment roaster	....	Returned to roasters	....	To furnace, leaching, and residue plant	Returned to furnace	Direct to leaching	Returned to No. 3 roaster hearth	Returned to special furnace
Gas, % SO_2	To stack	....	....	....	6 %	0.5–0.7 %	9 %	9 %	2.5–3 %
Gas temperature to boilers							1500°F	....	
Gas temperature from boilers							500–600°F	320°C	
Steam produced							200 lb per 100 tons concentrate at 200 lb	0.7 lb steam per lb concentrate	
Calcine sulfide S	0.4 %		0.47 %		0.3 %		0.6 %	0.1 %	
Calcine sulfate S	3.4 %		2.63 %		1.0 %		1.7 %	0.73 %	
Cooling and conveying	Cast-iron rotary conveyors to trommels, fines to leaching, size to ball mill, and back to re-treatment		Chute, grizzly and Jacoby conveyor		Water-cooled chute, screens, and conveyor		Jacoby rotary conveyor	Water-cooled screw conveyors to ball mill; Fuller-Kinyon pumps to bins	

TABLE 69. LEACHING OF ZINC, INDUSTRY PRACTICE*

	Anaconda, Great Falls, Mont.	A. S. & R. Co., Corpus Christi	Amer. Zinc Co.	Cons. M. & S. Co., Trail, B.C.	Electr. Zinc Co., Risdon	G. Von Giesche, Madgeburg	Norske Zinkompani	Sullivan Co., Kellogg, Idaho	Hudson Bay M. & Sm. Co., Flin Flon
Leaching method	Double	Single batch	Single, continuous	Double, continuous	Single, continuous	Double batch	Double	Single batch	Double
Leaching equipment	Pachucas for neutral and acid leach	Wooden tanks 20 ft diam by 10 ft lead- and brick-lined, mechanical agitation, wooden arms and shaft	Wooden tanks, lead- and brick-lined; wooden paddle agitators	Pachucas for neutral- and acid-leach	Pachucas, calcine feed, screened	Tanks, conical bottoms, lead- and brick-lined, special M.A.N. agitator	Pachucas 3 m diam by 6 m	Wooden lead-lined tanks, mechanical agitation	Pachucas
Settling and washing equipment	Neutral leach: classifiers, ball mill thickeners, Dorr thickeners, filters Acid-leach: thickeners, filters	Agitated pulp storage tanks, 27¼ ft ID by 10 ft deep; Worthite pump, Burt filters solution and wash and storage tanks; Dorr thickeners for Burt residue, 30 ft diam. by 8 ft Uf.; Oliver filters, cake to dryer, cake to smelter	Dorr thickeners of to purif. u.f. to Eimco drum filters cake to Ruggles-Coles dryer, dried cake shipped	Neutral leach: classifiers, ball mill thickeners; Acid leach: Dorr thickeners, 50 ft diam, Moore filters, Surge tank, American filters, cake to smelter	Dorr classifiers, lime precipitation tanks, Dorr thickeners, pulp to tanks	Thickeners 18 m diam by 4 m, ball mill thickener, lead-lined rubber-covered mechanical pressure filters, rotary dryer, cake to residue plant	Dorr classifiers, Dorr thickeners, 15 m diam by 5 m, thickeners, Moore filters, Oliver filters, cake to smelter	Launder to storage tank, Burt filters, 5 ft diam by 40 ft, Dorr thickener, Ruggles-Coles dryer, cake to smelter	

TABLE 69. LEACHING OF ZINC, INDUSTRY PRACTICE.*—(Continued)

	Anaconda, Great Falls, Mont.	A. S. & R. Co., Corpus Christi	Amer. Zinc Co.	Cons. M. & S. Co., Trail, B.C.	Electr. Zinc Co., Risdon	G. Von Giesche, Madgeburg	Norske Zinkompani	Sullivan Co., Kellogg, Idaho	Hudson Bay M. & Sm. Co., Flin Flon
Purification	....	Two-stage wood stave, unlined tanks, covered and vented, 20 ft diam by 10 ft 6 in. steam coil; mechanical agitation, first stage 5-6 hr. Shriver presses temperature 90°C+; second stage 4-5 hr; Shriver presses, Cu cake to smelter, Cd cake to treatment	o'f to surge tank, Gould centrifugal pumps to wood tanks, paddle agitator, Shriver filter presses, cake to Skinner roaster; filtrate to cells; cake leached with spent electrolyte and Cu and Cd products shipped; Co precipitated	Cu and Cd precipitated in batches, tanks mechanically agitated, temp 40°C, mixers 10 ft diam by 18 ft wide, wood agitator, wood stem, Kelly filters, neutral storage tanks, 60 ft diam by 12 ft, unlined					

* For details of leaching, see flow sheets.

TABLE 70. ELECTROLYSIS OF ZINC, INDUSTRY PRACTICE

Zinc

	Anaconda, Great Falls, Mont.	A. S. & R. Co., Corpus Christi, Tex.	Amer. Zinc Co., Monsanto, Ill.	Cons. M. & S. Co., Trail, B.C.	Electr. Zinc Co., Risdon, Tasmania	G. Von Giesche, Madgeburg, Germany	Norske Zinkompani, Eitrheim	Sullivan Co., Kellogg, Idaho	H. B. M. & S. Co., Flin Flon, Man.
Power equipment	....	Steam-turbine-driven generators for d-c C.D. 60 amp per sq ft	Power bought 13,800 volts, two 5,500 Mercury-arc rectifiers, two 5,000-amp 600-volt d-c generators	Motor-generator sets; rotary converters; mercury-arc rectifiers; average C.D. 40 amp per sq ft	Power bought at 11,000 volts three-phase 50-cycle a-c rotary converters to 440 volts; C.D. anode 30 amp per sq ft, cathode 27 amp per sq ft	750-850 volts per cell groups; C.D. 67-68 amp per sq ft	C.D. 38 amp per sq ft	2 d-c generators driven by synchronous motor in series to give 500 volts C.D. 100 amp per sq ft	D-c m-g sets 6,000 amp at 500 volts, C.D. cathode 35.2 amp per sq ft, C.D. anode 32.8 amp per sq ft
Current efficiency	....	88.5%	88.5%	91-92.3%	92%				
Kwhr per lb Zn	....	1.50	1.419 d-c	....	1.41 d-c	1.8			
Deposition period	....	24 hr	....	24 hr	72 hr	24 hr	24 hr	2	24 hr
Cell feed, gpl Zn	....	172	135	127-120	111.9	160	....	....	123.4
Spent electrolyte, gpl Zn	....	60	35	57-54	50	55-60	....	....	52.5

TABLE 70. ELECTROLYSIS OF ZINC, INDUSTRY PRACTICE.—(Continued)

Cadmium

	Anaconda, Great Falls, Mont.	A. S. & R. Co., Corpus Christi, Tex.	Amer. Zinc Co., Monsanto, Ill.	Cons. M. & S. Co., Trail, B.C.	Electr. Zinc Co., Risdon, Tasmania	G. Von Giesche, Madgeburg, Germany	Norske Zinkompani, Eitrheim	Sullivan Co., Kellogg, Idaho	H. B. M. & S. Co., Flin Flon, Man.
Current density per sq ft	10	....	....	4	11.0	23.2	....	10	
Current efficiency	....	....	....	85–90%	88.7%				
Deposition period	12 hr	....	48 hr	48–96 hr	4 days	....		12 hr	
Cell voltage	....	....	Shipped to Fairmont plant	....	3.5	9.65–2.7			
Cell type	Same as for zinc	....	....	Same as for zinc	Rotating cathodes	Rotating cathodes	....	Similar to zinc cells	
Cell feed, gpl Cd	200	....	....	177	150.7				
Spent electrolyte, gpl Cd	100	....	....	104	68.2				

Since publication of this paper, considerable improvement and enlargement have taken place.   These developments are described in two papers, one of which has not been published.[1]   The following description is abstracted from these papers.

The plant was designed for the treatment of roasted zinc concentrates by "reverse" leaching, settling, filtering, washing and drying of residue, and continuous purification, followed by clarification in filter presses. Electrolysis is carried out in lead-lined concrete cells using Tainton alloy anodes and aluminum cathodes.   Power is purchased from the Union Electric Co. and converted to direct current by mercury-arc rectifiers. Cathode zinc is melted in a gas-fired furnace and cast in the usual way.

In general, the original simple flow sheet was not changed.   The principal changes were the treatment of purification cake for the recovery of copper, cadmium, and zinc; the filtering, drying, and reclaiming of leach residue; "reverse" leaching; continuous purification; and melting furnace-fume collection.

The plant is divided into seven major divisions: (1) calcine unloading and storing, (2) leaching, (3) residue filtering and drying, (4) purification, (5) cake treatment, (6) electrolyzing, (7) melting and casting.   No attempt is made to give tabulated data except the general operation results.   The present flow sheet is shown in Fig. 34.

1. Calcine Unloading.   Roasted zinc concentrates or calcines are received at the electrolytic plant in box and hopper railroad cars.   Each car is drill-sampled before unloading.

The calcine unloading facilities consist of two 75-hp Rootes Blower Dracco pneumatic unloaders, one track hopper, and a gasoline-driven scoop truck.   The pneumatic unloaders can be used for both box and hopper cars.   Calcine is conveyed to any one of 10 feed bins or to two large storage bins.   Calcine from the track hopper, at the east side of the plant, is conveyed to the same bins by a screw conveyor and elevator system.   The gasoline-driven scoop truck can be used to unload box cars from either side and dumps directly into the same bucket elevator used in conjunction with the track hopper.   The two large calcine storage bins have a capacity of 630 tons each.   The 10 feed bins have a total capacity of 870 tons.

Calcine is recovered by a 6-in. variable-speed screw feeder in each feed bin.   These screw feeders discharge into one of two 10-in. screw-collecting conveyors, which carry the calcine to a Merrick Feedoweight.   This

[1] L. P. Davidson, R. K. Carpenter, and H. J. Tschirmer, Reverse Leaching of Zinc Calcine, *Trans. AIME*, Vol. 101, 1951; also unpublished paper by T. J. Moore, L. A. Painter, and H. J. Tschirmer.

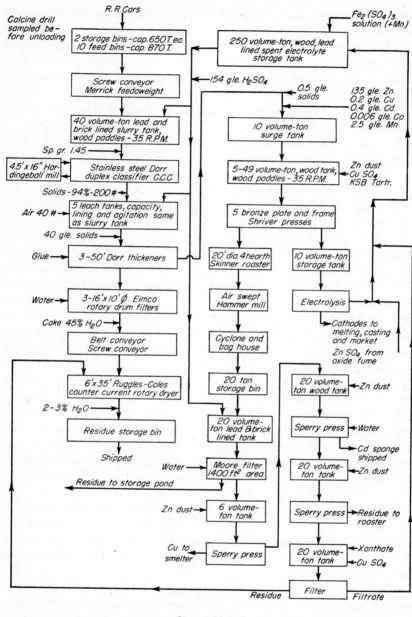

Calcine drill sampled before unloading

R.R. Cars

2 storage bins −cap. 650 T. ea.
10 feed bins −cap. 870 T.

Fe₂(SO₄)₃ solution (+Mn)

250 volume-ton, wood, lead lined spent electrolyte storage tank

Screw conveyor
Merrick feedoweight

154 gle. H₂SO₄

0.5 gle. solids

135 gle. Zn.
0.2 gle. Cu
0.4 gle. Cd
0.006 gle. Co
2.5 gle. Mn

40 volume-ton lead and brick lined slurry tank, wood paddles − 35 R.P.M.

10 volume-ton surge tank

Sp. gr. 1.45

4.5' x 16" Hardingeball mill

Stainless steel Dorr duplex classifier C.C.C.

5-49 volume-ton, wood tank, wood paddles − 35 R.P.M.

Zn dust
Cu SO₄
KSB Tartr.

Solids - 94%-200#

Air 40 # →

5 leach tanks, capacity, lining and agitation same as slurry tank

5 bronze plate and frame Shriver presses

40 gle. solids

Glue

3−50' Dorr thickeners

20' dia. 4 hearth Skinner roaster

10 volume-ton storage tank

Water

3-16' x 10' Ø Eimco rotary drum filters

Air swept Hammer mill

Electrolysis

Cake 45% H₂O

Belt conveyor
Screw conveyor

Cyclone and bag house

Cathodes to melting, casting and market

Zn SO₄ from oxide fume

6' x 35' Ruggles-Coles counter current rotary dryer

20 ton storage bin

20 volume-ton wood tank ←Zn dust

2-3% H₂O

Residue storage bin

20 volume-ton lead & brick lined tank

Sperry press ←Water

Cd sponge shipped

Shipped

Water →

Moore filter 1400 ft² area

20 volume-ton tank ←Zn dust

Residue to storage pond

Zn dust →

6 volume-ton tank

Sperry press →Residue to roaster

Cu to smelter

Sperry press

20 volume-ton tank →Xanthate
→Cu SO₄

Residue   Filter   Filtrate

Plant divisions

1. Calcine unloading and storing
2. Leaching
3. Residue filtering and drying
4. Purification
5. Purification coke treatment
6. Electrolysis
7. Melting and casting (pumps not shown)

Fig. 34. Flow sheet of the "reverse" leaching electrolytic zinc plant of American Zinc Co. of Illinois, Monsanto, Ill.

system makes possible the blending of various calcines to obtain the most desirable feed.

2. Leaching.   After the plant was expanded in 1943 to produce 100 tons of slab zinc daily, operating difficulties in the leaching section prevented reaching rated capacity.   The leaching plant simply could not produce enough electrolyte.   The so-called "reverse" leach was developed and several other operating problems solved so that the 100-ton capacity could be reached.

The reverse leach runs as follows: All calcine to be leached is fed continuously to a slurry mixing tank.   About one-third of the total acid used goes to this tank with the calcine.   The slurry goes into a classifier and the oversize is ground.   Classifier overflow goes to leaching tanks, where the leach is completed.   Leached pulp is thickened, the overflow is purified, and the underflow is filtered.

Two factors caused trouble in the original plant.   One, the presence of ferrous iron in the calcine, was eliminated by better control of roasting. The other, the large amount of silica that went into solution, was eliminated by the reverse-leach technique.   The large amount of silica in solution caused slow settling in the thickeners, which in turn made it hard to filter the purified thickener overflow.   The leach residue (thickener underflow) was also hard to wash and filter.   So much zinc was tied up in residues that at times they could not be discarded but had to be stored in makeshift ponds.

Attempts to reduce the soluble silica by intensive roasting failed because silicates, probably zinc, formed that were readily soluble.   Various coagulants were tried and all manner of leaching and thickening controls were attempted, but without success.   It was suggested finally that dissolution of silica could be controlled by careful control of acid concentration.   This could be most easily done by adding acid to a calcine slurry, rather than by the usual addition of calcine to an acid pulp.   Hence the term, "reverse leach."

This method increased thickening rate five times.   The volume of residue came to about 10 per cent of the total leach pulp whereas under former conditions the residue had sometimes amounted to 95 per cent of the original pulp.   The thickened pulp filtered well and could be dried after washing.

However, when the reverse leach was first tried, calcine slurry was made, using purified solution carrying about 135 gpl of zinc sulfate. Despite all precautions, the piping carrying this slurry cemented shut, except for vertical sections, within 24 hr after the plant began running. A slurry of zinc oxide and zinc sulfate solution quickly forms a cement, even faster than had been expected.

This difficulty was avoided by making the slurry with calcine and spent electrolyte. This required replacing the conventional Dorr classifier by one with stainless steel rakes, and finally all exposed parts of the classifier and other equipment were made of stainless steel.

Spent electrolyte at approximately 130 gpl sulfuric acid flows from the cell room through wooden lead-lined launders to two 150-volume-ton[1] concrete lead-lined acid sumps, from which it is pumped intermittently to a 250-volume-ton wood-stave lead-lined storage tank. This storage tank is situated at a higher level than the leach floor and spent electrolyte flows through a lead line to the slurry-mixing tank and the leaching tanks.

Calcine, fed by a Merrick Feedoweight, and spent electrolyte are added continuously to the stainless steel slurry-mixing tank. The amount of calcine and acid are so proportioned that a specific gravity of about 1.5 is maintained. The slurry is discharged through an air lift into a stainless steel duplex Dorr classifier in closed circuit with a 4 ft 6 in. by 16 in. Hardinge conical ball mill. The solids in the classifier overflow are about 94 per cent minus 200 mesh.

Ground slurry carrying 4.5 to 5 tons of equivalent calcine is pumped by a 125-gpm vertical-type pump to any one of six leaching tanks which have the same capacity, construction, and agitation as the slurry tank. Each leaching tank has a 1-in. copper line delivering air at 40 psi to a point at the bottom center of the tank. This air in conjunction with the copper in solution (from the spent electrolyte) serves to oxidize any ferrous sulfate formed in the leaching operation.

The leaching procedure in these tanks is as follows:

1. Addition of 5 volume-tons of spent electrolyte.
2. Addition of approximately 14 volume-tons of slurry.
3. Addition of more spent electrolyte until a test for acid is obtained on methyl orange spot paper.
4. The "finishing" of the leach which consists of small acid additions followed by continued agitation until the maximum amount of acid has been added that is consistent with complete precipitation of ferric hydroxide.
5. The "finished" leach is discharged through either of two vertical slurry pumps.

To ensure the complete precipitation of the iron group impurities, enough ferric sulfate solution is added to the spent electrolyte to maintain a concentration of 0.5 gpl of iron. Ferrous sulfate is made by digesting scrap iron in spent electrolyte. This solution is pumped to a 20-volume-

---

[1] A volume-ton is 32 cu ft of pulp. Solution assays reported in grams per liter can be converted to pounds per volume-ton by multiplying by two.

ton air-agitated tank and the iron is oxidized to the ferric state by manganese dioxide. The ferric sulfate solution is pumped as needed into the spent electrolyte storage tank. The use of manganese dioxide results in a rather constant manganese content of 2.5 gpl in the feed to the cell room.

Leach pulp containing an average of 40 gpl of solids is pumped to the first of the three 50-ft Dorr thickeners, where the bulk of the settling takes place. Glue in a water solution is added (150 lb per day) to the feed to these thickeners as a coagulant. The overflow from the first thickener is pumped to two thickeners in parallel. Here the settling of the finer particles takes place and the clear overflow (0.5 to 1.0 gpl of solids) is pumped to the purification tanks.

3. Residue Filtration and Drying. Underflow from the three Dorr thickeners is pumped by air-actuated diaphragm pumps of 75 gpm maximum capacity to three 16- by 10-ft Eimco rotary drum vacuum filters.

The filter cake is washed on the filters by water sprays which are capable of reducing the water-soluble zinc in the residue by about 65 per cent. The cake from the filters, averaging about 45 per cent moisture, is carried by belt conveyor, then by a screw conveyor into a 6- by 35-ft Ruggles Coles direct-fired, countercurrent, rotary dryer. The interior of the dryer is equipped with lifting flights and approximately 700 ft of ¾-in. steel chain. The chains increase the drying efficiency and prevent the formation of rings. The discharge from the dryer, averaging 2 to 3 per cent water, is transported by bucket elevator to a 50-ton residue storage bin. The dried residue from this bin is shipped to other plants for treatment.

4. Purification. Overflow from the secondary thickeners contains an average of 135 gpl of zinc, 2 gpl of copper, 4 gpl of cadmium, and 0.006 gpl of cobalt. This solution flows through a wooden, lead-lined, open launder to a 10-volume-ton concrete surge tank. Two 500-gpm Gould centrifugal pumps take the solution from the surge tank to five 49-volume-ton wood-stave tanks agitated by wooden paddle mixers rotating at 35 rpm.

Originally about 225 lb of zinc dust was added per tank, which was about four times the theoretical amount necessary to precipitate copper and cadmium completely. It was felt that some reduction in the use of zinc dust was possible. Tests indicated that purifying continuously would reduce the amount of zinc dust needed without increasing the impurity content. To try this on a plant scale three of the purification tanks were connected in series. Thickener overflow was added continuously to the first tank. An 8-in. copper pipe, 6 in. from the bottom, connected the first to the second tank; a 6-in. copper pipe, 2 ft above the middle, connected the second to the final tank. The final tank discharged through the existing copper line at the bottom of the last tank. The other two purification tanks were used as surge tanks for the thickener overflow in order to assure a more constant rate of feed to the continuous purification. Zinc dust and copper sulfate were added continuously by two hopper-fed, variable-speed belt feeders. Potassium antimony tartrate was mixed into the copper sulfate before its addition to the hopper of the feeder.

A substantial saving of zinc dust was realized, amounting to between 15 and 30 per cent, depending on the cobalt content of the calcines treated. Reagent addition is governed by the purification solution volume rate from the filter presses as measured by a weir in the discharge launder.

The approximate reagent consumption, per 100 tons of cathodes, is 3.5 tons of zinc dust, 1.3 tons of copper sulfate, and 23 lb of potassium antimony tartrate. The retention time in the series of tanks ranges from 2 to $3\frac{1}{2}$ hr. The cadmium and copper in solution are removed and from 2 to 5 mg per l of cobalt are removed, depending on the cobalt concentration in the feed to purification. Five bronze plate-and-frame Shriver presses filter the solution from the final purification tank.

Purification cake is charged into the Skinner roaster in the purification-cake treatment department. The filtrate flows through a lead-lined wooden launder to a 10-volume-ton surge tank from which it is pumped to storage tanks for the cell room.

5. Purification-cake Treatment. Purification cake from the Shriver presses contains copper, cadmium, cobalt, and the unused portion of the zinc dust used in precipitating these elements. The proportions are roughly as follows:

	Per Cent
Cadmium	13
Copper	8
Zinc	78
Cobalt	0.4

The purpose of the purification-cake treatment is the selective removal of the copper and cadmium as by-products and of the cobalt as an impurity. All filters used in this department are 24-in. Sperry plate-and-frame presses. All tanks, with the exception of the cadmium-precipitation tank, are agitated by wooden paddle mixers. The cadmium tank is agitated by a Patterson inverted cone mixer.

The purification cake is fed by a variable-speed belt conveyor into a 20-ft-diameter, four-hearth Skinner roaster where the moisture is removed and the metallics roasted to oxides. The roaster product is put through an air-swept hammer mill and collected by a cyclone and bag house which discharges into a 20-ton storage bin.

The roaster product is batch-weighed by a Richardson scale which dumps into a 20-volume-ton acidproof brick- and lead-lined leaching tank filled with spent electrolyte. Additions of roasted purification cake are made until the acid is neutralized. The finished leach is filtered through a Moore filter of 1,400 sq ft filtering area and the washed residue is pumped to the residue storage pond.

The filtrate is treated in a 6-volume-ton tank with enough zinc dust to precipitate the copper, which is separated in a Sperry press and stored for shipment to a copper smelter. The filtrate from the copper precipitation is treated in a 20-volume-ton wood-stave tank with enough zinc dust to precipitate only the major portion of the cadmium. The cadmium sponge is separated in a Sperry press and thoroughly washed with water. The washed sponge, averaging 65 per cent cadmium, is shipped by truck to the Fairmont plant for reduction to cadmium metal.

The filtrate from the cadmium precipitation tank is treated with an excess of zinc dust in a 20-volume-ton tank in order to complete the removal of cadmium from the solution. This tank is discharged through a Sperry press and the residue charged to the Skinner roaster. The filtrate is agitated with potassium ethyl xanthate and copper sulfate in a 20-volume-ton tank for from 4 to 5 hr. The average proportion of reagents used is 90 lb of potassium ethyl xanthate and 30 lb of copper sulfate per tank. This treatment lowers the cobalt content to about 3 mg per l. The solution is filtered, the residue being put through the rotary dryer with the leach residues and the filtrate being returned to the zinc circuit by way of the spent electrolyte sumps.

6. Electrolysis—Power Conversion. Power for electrolysis and for auxiliaries throughout the plant is purchased from the Union Electric Co. system. There are 8,000-kva underground three-phase 60-cycle 13,800-volt cables, and a 7,500-kva overhead emergency transmission line. Power for auxiliaries is transformed by three 1,000-kva 13,800/400-volt transformers.

Electrical conversion equipment for electrolysis includes four 12-anode 5,500-amp 700-volt water-cooled mercury-arc rectifiers, and two 5,000-amp 600-volt d-c generators driven by an 8,400-hp 13,800-volt synchronous motor, the latter unit being used primarily to replace the rectifiers when they are removed from the line for repairs.

The station arrangement places the oil-insulated, self-cooled type transformers outdoors, with the outdoor 13,800-volt switchgear. The rectifiers, regulating heat exchangers and metal-clad oil circuit breaker, are on the first floor of the station directly below the rectifiers to which they are connected. The rectifiers, anode breaker, cathode breakers, disconnect switches, duplex control panels, individual control panels, and motor-generator set are mounted on the second floor at about the same elevation as the transformer secondary connection. Bus connection to the individual rectifiers is made below the rectifier assembly. The neutral or negative connection from the interphase transformers is carried across the station directly below the rectifier assembly.

For normal operation the four rectifier units are paired on both the a-c and d-c sides of the station. There are two three-phase autotransformers, one with $7\frac{1}{2}$-deg lead and the other $7\frac{1}{2}$-deg lag, with the load ratio control feature, each connected to two six-phase transformers, making a 12-phase unit for a paired rectifier assembly and 24-phase for the entire station.

Current efficiencies for each cell room are determined by integrating the daily recorded ampere charts traced by two Leeds-Northrup recording potentiometers connected to their respective calibrated shunts in the cell circuits.

Electrolysis—Equipment. Two units of 180 and 192 cells in series comprise the electrolyzing circuits.

Twelve cells arranged in two adjacent rows of six cascading cells are an operating unit or cascade. A 20-in. working space is between adjacent cascades. A stripping floor 44 ft by 300 ft is between the ends of the 15 cascades of unit 1 and the 16 cascades of unit 2.

Cells are lead-lined 4-in. reinforced concrete; interior dimensions are 7 ft 10 in. by 3 ft by 5 ft 2 in. deep. All concrete surfaces are coated with "Vinaline," a plastic acid-resistant paint. Each cell is mounted on six lead-capped, standard 5-ft by 5-ft by 3-in. solid glass blocks and supported on reinforced-concrete piers.

Lead-lined Proderite cells, previously used, failed because of both inadequate reinforcement and the temperature difference between inside and outside walls during winter months.

Current is conducted to and from each unit by twenty-one 2,000,000-circular-mil overhead copper cables equivalent to 33 sq in. of conductor. Electrodes rest on tapered bus bars 2 in. wide, designed to carry 330 amp per sq in. cross section. Anode and cathode bus bars are on the same side of each cell, supported on brackets fastened into the cell wall. Phenolic resin-impregnated Fiberglas insulating blocks are between the bars and brackets.

Purified solution for the cell room is stored in two 200-volume-ton stave tanks. Two 300-gpm Gould centrifugal pumps withdraw solution from the bottom of the tanks to a constant head cone about 23 ft above the cell room floor. A 6-in. rubber hose from the bottom of the cone delivers solution to two 6-in. lead lines. Each line supplies one unit. Glue solution is pumped into the cell feed by a small Lapp Pulsafeeder.

Feed, for all except the bottom cells of a cascade, flows through a $1\frac{1}{2}$-in. iron manifold 12 in. above the center of the cascade. A $\frac{3}{4}$-in. branch and valve are provided for each cell. The iron manifold is connected to nipples in the 6-in. lead line by a $1\frac{1}{2}$-in. rubber hose.

Spent electrolyte is returned to surge sumps from each unit by a covered, lead-lined, wooden launder at the foot of the cascades.

Twenty-seven aluminum cathodes, $\frac{1}{4}$ in. by 3 ft 6 in. by 24 in., and twenty-eight 1 per cent silver-lead grid anodes, slightly smaller than the cathodes, operate in each cell. Cathodes are positively spaced on 3-in. centers by indentations in glazed-porcelain insulating blocks. Anodes are provided with three glazed-porcelain cone separators, one at the center and one at each lower corner of the sheet. Cathode edges are covered by GRS rubber channels. These channels are adequate to minimize edge corrosion and less than 1,000 new channels are used each month. The consumption of wood strips formerly used had been about 2,000 per day.

Cathodes are made and repaired in a plant shop. Rolled and polished aluminum sheets are welded to extruded aluminum bars. Two lifting lugs are provided for each bar. A 3-in. section of $\frac{5}{8}$-in. by $\frac{1}{2}$-in. copper channel is welded to the bar for the electrical contact. The interior surface of the contact is cadmium-plated for welding.

The present cathode design was evolved after experience with sheets cast into header bars and cast-in copper contacts. No consistent bond was made between the cast header bars and sheet. The cast bars were replaced by extruded bars welded to the sheets. The uniform size, greater mechanical strength, and corrosion resistance of the extruded bars have been most advantageous. One bar can be used for two new sheets before it is scrapped.

A change in contacts was necessary and ends of the extruded bars were first metallized with copper. Results were erratic. It was found that cadmium-plated copper could be readily welded to aluminum by an arc with standard eutectoid rods. Adequate ventilation is provided, where this welding is done, to remove cadmium fumes. The welded contacts fail under severe mechanical shock, but have been more successful and less expensive than any previous design.

Anodes are $\frac{1}{4}$-in. rolled and perforated 1 per cent silver-lead alloy sheets. These are burned to chemical lead header bars cast around a copper bar. The lower edge of one end of the bar is exposed for bus bar contact. The sheet perforations are $\frac{3}{8}$ in. square and spaced on $\frac{7}{8}$-in. centers.

Nine adjacent cathodes are lifted from the cells at one time by a $\frac{1}{2}$-ton chain hoist hung on a strain insulator. Transport to the stripping floor is on an overhead monorail.

Two lead coils per cell, one at each end, cool the electrolyte, and 2,400 gpm of cooling water is pumped to the cell room from wells on the plant property.

Positive air pressure is maintained in the cell room to dissipate fumes by forcing in 200,000 cfm of fresh air.

Electrolysis—Operation. Rated cathode zinc production is 112 tons daily with an average current of 10,000 amp. About half of this meets ASTM special high-grade-zinc specifications.

Electrolysis is carried on at an average anode current density of 35 amp per sq ft. The electrolyzing solution contains about 135 gpl zinc, and is fed to the upper ten cells of each cascade to maintain the acid concentration between 100 and 110 gpl sulfuric acid. The tail cells are stripping cells and the spent electrolyte leaving them contains about 125 to 135 gpl sulfuric acid. Acid concentration in each cell is tested nine times daily by measuring the conductivity of the solution. Manganese depletion in the cells is about 0.5 gpl. Cell temperature is normally maintained below 40°C.

Aqueous glue solution at the rate of 1 lb of glue per ton of cathodes is pumped continuously into the feed to improve the character of the cathode deposit.

Cathodes are removed for stripping once each day and returned to the same cell. Nine adjacent cathodes, one-third of the number in a cell, are removed at one time and transported to the foot of the cascade. Zinc deposits are stripped from the aluminum by inserting the edge of a floor chisel under one corner of the deposit. Normally, the entire sheet can then be pulled off. Very strong adherence has occurred at times. When reasonable prying will not loosen the deposit, the cathode is removed from service and cleaned with spent electrolyte in a separate cell. Cathodes last about 18 months and usually fail because of corrosion of the sheet above the solution line. The corroded portion and edges are sheared off, the surface of the header bar is milled, and the sheared plate is again welded to it.

Twenty-one men are engaged in cleaning cells and anodes five days a week. One cascade is cut out each day, the electrodes removed, and electrolyte pumped out with a self-priming centrifugal pump. Anodes are trucked to a cleaning floor to be scraped and straightened. Cooling coils are removed, scraped, and flushed with spent electrolyte. Cell walls are scraped clean and the accumulated cell sludge is shoveled out to be returned to the flash roaster.

The present cleaning process is laborious. Plans are being made to mechanize this work so that more cleaning can be done with the same or less labor. Hand hoists used for lifting anodes from the cells will be replaced by electric hoists. Methods of eliminating the hand-scraping of anodes are being studied.

Each cascade is cleaned every 43 days. Tests have proved that both the cascade ampere efficiency and lead content of the metal depend on the cleanliness of the anodes.

7. Melting and Casting—Oxide Recovery. Zinc oxide in the melting furnace gases is recovered by water scrubbing. This method is a radical departure from the more conventional cooling-flue and bag-house system for the recovery of oxide from zinc-melting furnace gases. The unit was constructed after tests by the plant staff and is, as far as is known, the first instance of the use of water-spray jets for this purpose. It offers the advantages of relatively low initial cost, low cost in maintenance and operation, simplicity, and small space requirements.

A 24-in. brick-lined flue connects the furnace to a vertical spray cooling tower of the recovery unit. A 24-in. and a 30-in. water-jet fume scrubber are in series with the spray tower. These are mounted on the flat top of a 14-ft-diameter cone-bottomed steel tank. Two parallel baffles in the tank extend from the top into liquid in the body of the cone and divide the upper section into three chambers. The cooling tower is on the first chamber. A 24-in. duct leads from this to the 24-in. scrubber on the second chamber. A 30-in. duct connects this to the 30-in. scrubber on the last chamber. Cleaned gas leaves the last chamber through a 30-in. steel stack.

Oxide washed from the flue gas collects in the lower part of the cone. The thickened pulp is withdrawn to a 27-volume-ton lead-lined stave holding tank by an Olivite diaphragm pump. The light pulp near the top of the cone is recirculated through the cooling tower and scrubbers by a 1,000-gpm centrifugal pump.

Solids settle in the holding tank and the excess water is decanted daily. The zinc oxide is washed with hot water to remove chlorine and is then dissolved in sulfuric acid. The resulting zinc sulfate solution is pumped to a spent electrolyte launder in the cell room.

AMERICAN SMELTING & REFINING CO., CORPUS CHRISTI, TEX.
(AN INTERMEDIATE-DENSITY PLANT)

The following is a description of the zinc leaching and electrolytic plant of the American Smelting & Refining Co. at Corpus Christi, Tex., abstracted from the article by Cunningham and Jephson.[1]

[1] J. H. Cunningham and A. C. Jephson, Electrolytic Zinc at Corpus Christi, Texas, *Trans. AIME*, Vol. 159, pp. 194–209.

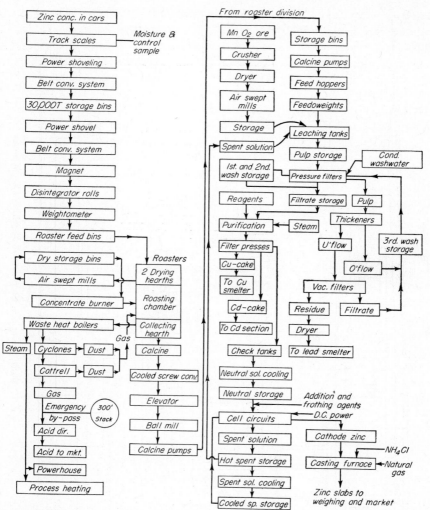

FIG. 35. Flow sheet of electrolytic zinc plant of American Smelting & Refining Co., Corpus Christi, Tex.

The original article has been corrected by Jephson for any changes in operating details since publication. The description therefore represents present practice in this intermediate-density plant. The flow sheet (Fig. 35) has also been checked and is up-to-date. Plant layout is shown in Fig. 36.

The plant for production of electrolytic zinc, erected by the American Smelting & Refining Co. in 1942, is situated on Nueces Bay on the Gulf

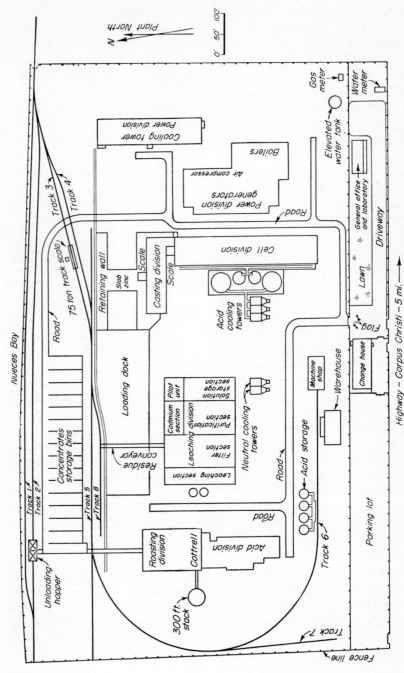

Fig. 36.   General layout, electrolytic zinc plant, American Smelting & Refining Co., Corpus Christi, Tex.

Coast, some 5 miles west by rail and highway from the city and port of Corpus Christi.

Factors leading to the establishment of this plant in the area were ample supplies of natural gas for the generation of electric power, advantageous shipping lanes, favorable market for acid, adequate supply of labor, and moderate climate.

The design of the plant includes the use of Trail suspension roasting equipment, contact acid equipment, batch leaching in mechanically agitated tanks, pressure filtering and washing of leach pulp, batch purification in mechanically agitated tanks followed by clarification in filter presses, and cooling of purified solution by evaporation. Electrolysis is performed in cells using Tainton alloy anodes and aluminum cathodes. Cathode current density is 60 amp per sq ft. Except for the portion returned to the leaching division, the cell solution is continuously flowing in closed circuit through the cells to cooling towers, which hold cell temperatures within desired limits. Direct current for electrolysis is supplied by generators driven by steam turbines. The cathode zinc is melted in a gas-fired furnace and cast in the usual way into slabs for shipment.

The plant divides into five major divisions: concentrate storage, roasting and acid preparation, leaching, electrolysis, melting and casting.

The concentrate storage consists of 15 bins of 2,000-ton capacity each, or a total of 30,000 tons. The bins provide a ready means of storing various grades or shipments separately.

Concentrates are reclaimed by 1-yd shovels, delivering to a belt conveyor which leads to 100-ton feed bins in the roasting division.

Roasting and Acid Preparation. The roasting and acid division comprises the roasting of the zinc concentrates and the recovery of the sulfur from resultant gases in the form of acid.

Concentrates are roasted in two Skinner suspension-type roasters. These furnaces are 20 ft ID, have two upper drying hearths, a combustion chamber 24 ft high, a third hearth which is the bottom of the combustion chamber, and a lower or fourth hearth from which gases and calcine leave the furnace. The capacity of these furnaces is 70 to 120 tons of concentrates each per day.

From the 100-ton wet-concentrate bins above each furnace, a 30-in. feeder belt discharges to No. 1 drying hearth of the roaster. On No. 2 hearth the drying is completed and the concentrate rabbles outward, discharging down a chute into a ball-mill feed bin. Under average conditions the moisture of concentrate reaching the mill feed bin is 0.5 per cent or less.

The product, ground in two 7-ft by 36-in. Hardinge air-swept ball mills,

is carried by air to classifiers in closed circuit with the mill.   Each classified product, 98 per cent minus 200 mesh, is air-borne to a 9-ft cyclone
dust collector which discharges into an 80-ton dry feed bin for the concentrate burner.

This bin discharges through a 24-in. gate valve and a closed-type
rotary feeder to a 24-in. belt, which feeds the concentrate burner.   Air
is supplied to the burner by a fan at 15,000 cfm and the fan also draws a
controlled quantity of hot gas from the roasting chamber into and across
the No. 2 drying hearth.   This hot gas, after being used for drying, is
discharged back into the roasting chamber through the concentrate
burner.   A regulated amount of atmospheric air is mixed with this gas
after it leaves the No. 2 drying hearth.   The quantity of atmospheric air
taken into the burner is controlled to suit the roasting operation.

Calcine settles on the bottom of the roasting chamber, or hearth No. 3,
is rabbled to the center, and drops to hearth No. 4, where it is rabbled
outward and is discharged through a chute to a 19-in. screw conveyor
39 ft long.   Calcine in the screw conveyor is transferred to another 18-in.
screw conveyor 70 ft long.   These conveyors are water-cooled both on the
shaft carrying the screw and on the jacket.

From the screw conveyor, the calcine is elevated 44 ft by a steel chain-
and-bucket elevator of 15 tons per hr capacity.   The elevator discharges
through a chute to a 5-ft by 22-in. denodulizing ball mill of 2 tons per hr
capacity or, in case of emergency, to a small storage bin which discharges
through a 14-in. rotary valve to the boot of the elevator again.   The ball
mill discharges through a chute to Fuller-Kinyon pumps which carry the
calcine through a 4-in. calcine-conveying pipe line 475 ft long to storage
bins at the leaching division or directly to the leaching charge bins.

Gas from the No. 4 hearth of each roaster is conducted through a short
suspended-arch brick flue to waste-heat boilers.

The steam generated is about 0.7 lb per pound of concentrate roasted,
and is used for solution heating in the leaching division.   Gases from
each boiler go to two cyclone units in parallel.   Gas volume is 8,500 to
10,500 cfm each, at 320°C maximum gas temperature.   The gas is drawn
from each cyclone unit through a 36-in.-diameter steel flue by a hot-gas
fan at 320°C at the rate of 10,000 cfm.   The gas is delivered through a
common steel flue to the Cottrell dust precipitators.   Rated capacity per
precipitator is 18,500 cfm at 260°C.   From the Cottrells the gas passes
through a 36-in.-diameter steel duct to the acid section.   The original
three-unit Cottrell proved insufficient at increased loads and an additional
three-unit Cottrell was installed.

All dust, about 25 per cent by weight of the calcine, is handled in a closed system and ultimately returns to the No. 3 hearth of either roaster. Dust from the waste-heat boilers drops through a hopper to a 10-in. screw conveyor. Cyclone dust drops through a sealed feeder to the same conveyor. Cottrell dust discharges into a 6-in. screw conveyor and is conveyed to a convenient point where it discharges into a 10-in. screw conveyor handling waste-heat boiler and cyclone dusts. For roaster data and analyses, see Chap. 3, Tables 14 and 15.

The sulfuric acid section consists of a standard Leonard-Monsanto contact unit. The acid unit was designed to have a capacity of 125 tons of 100 per cent sulfuric acid daily, but has on occasion produced more than that amount. The unit also produces 25 per cent of the acid output as oleum. There is storage for 3,000 tons of acid. Shipments are regularly made by rail in tank cars.

Leaching Division. The leaching division includes the leaching operation, filtering, washing, residue drying, purification, cooling of purified solution, and production of cadmium.

Calcine from the roasting division is generally stored in two bins of 500 tons capacity each, from which it is handled by a Fuller-Kinyon pump to individual 20-ton charge bins over the four leaching tanks. Each calcine charge bin discharges through a 12-in. screw conveyor and a Merrick Feedoweight to one of the leaching tanks at a maximum rate of 48 tons per hr.

The leaching tanks are wood-stave construction, measuring, inside the lining, 20 ft in diameter by 10 ft deep. They are lined with 10-lb sheet lead and 4.5 in. of acidproof brick. Agitation is provided by horizontal wooden stirrer arms attached to a wooden shaft with Worthite bolts. The arms are placed 10 in. above the bottom of the tank. The agitator is driven at 8 rpm by a 15-hp motor. Each tank has a 1-in. resin-pressed plywood cover and plywood ducts for ventilation.

A leach is started by pumping in 18,000 gal of spent electrolyte containing 195 gpl of sulfuric acid and 60 to 65 gpl of zinc. The electrolyte is delivered through an 8-in. diameter lead pipe line from the cell division. To this is added 1,500 gal of strong wash water from the Burt filter wash storage. Sufficient calcine is then added to drop the acidity to 5 gpl after a 2-hr agitation. Finely ground manganese dioxide is added during this first stage to oxidize the ferrous iron in solution, 200 lb per leach usually being enough.

Acidity and ferrous iron are checked at the end of the 2-hr period, and during the following 1 to 2 hr the leach is completed by the addition of successively smaller amounts of calcine and of manganese dioxide, as needed. The filtration rate is watched carefully, and the final, very small additions of calcine are governed by the filtration rate rather than by the pH of the solution, once the solution has become neutral to methyl orange.

Each leaching tank is discharged through a 6-in. opening in the tank bottom controlled by a rubber plug with a ceramic seat, and also by a 6-in. rubber-lined valve. The pulp drops directly through a 6-in. rubber hose to pulp storage.

The finished leach is dropped into one of two agitated pulp-storage tanks, which are 27 ft 3 in. ID by 10 ft deep and of the same general construction as the leaching tanks. Working capacity of each pulp tank is 40,000 gal. Pulp is pumped from the tanks through a 5-in. lead pipe by 4-in. Worthite pumps, which deliver to the Burt filters through a 4-in. combination Everdur and rubber pipe header.

Filtration. There are eight Burt filters, each 5 ft in diameter by 40 ft long. Each filter is rotated at a speed of 6 rpm by a 15-hp motor. The filter shell is steel, copper-, or rubber-lined. The interior is fitted with wooden filter boards of triangular cross section, spaced symmetrically around the inside circumference and extending half the filter length from each end, there being a total of 32 boards per filter.

The time needed for a complete filter cycle on a full charge is 3 to 4 hr, of which about $1\frac{1}{4}$ hr is occupied in filtration proper, the remainder by charging, three washings, repulping, and discharging.

Filtrate and washes are discharged from the nipples into a copper-lined catch pan. This pan discharges into a Haveg launder, which may be swung by hand to discharge into either the filtrate launder or one of the wash-water launders. In turn, the filtrate launder discharges into any one of three storage tanks for impure solution.

These tanks are unlined wood-stave construction, 20 ft in diameter by 9 ft. 6 in. deep, having a capacity of 18,000 gal.

The wash-water launders discharge into first and second wash storages. The three wash-storage tanks are unlined wood-stave construction, 12 ft in diameter by 8 ft 6 in. deep, having a capacity of 6,700 gal each, in which are stored strong, medium, and weak wash water.

The filtration cycle is started by filling a filter with pulp from the pulp-storage tanks. The filter is then rotated and air pressure is turned on. The clear solution is forced through the canvas covering the filter elements, follows the grooves in the boards, and escapes through the discharge nipples. The solids build up on the canvas inside the filter. When the filtration is finished, air and steam escape through the nipples and the pressure inside the filter shows a drop on the pressure recorder. The air is now turned off and strong wash water is pumped in by one of the two 3-in. wash-water pumps, delivering at a rate of 250 gpm. When sufficient water has been added, the valve is closed and air turned on again. This enriched, strong wash water is discharged to the impure-solution storage.

In similar fashion, one charge of medium wash water is advanced to the strong-wash-water tank, and one charge of weak wash to the medium-wash tank. At the end of this third washing, more weak-wash, or condensate water, as the case may be, is pumped into the filter and the vacuum is turned on with the filter rotating. After a few minutes the residue and water become a heavy slurry, which is discharged through four ports in the discharge end of the filter into a residue launder. More weak wash water is used toward the end of the discharging period to flush the remaining residue out of the filter, after which the ports are closed and the filtration cycle is completed.

Solution from the strong-wash-water tank is partly used in the leaching tanks, as previously mentioned. The water thus removed from the wash-water circuits is balanced in the weak-wash-water tank, which receives residue thickener overflow, filtrate from thickener underflow, and condensate water, as needed. The bulk of the condensate water used is pumped from the power house into a storage tank, which also collects condensate from the steam-heating coils in the purification tanks.

The residue slurry discharged from the Burt filters is carried by launder to two Dorr thickeners connected in series. The thickeners are 30 ft in diameter by 8 ft deep, with standard arms rotating at 0.2 rpm. The overflow returns to Burt-filter weak-wash storage. The underflow is handled by two Duplex diaphragm lead pumps with a capacity of 100 gpm, to two Oliver vacuum filters, 8 ft in diameter by 12 ft long. The filtrate is returned to Burt-filter weak-wash storage.

The residue cake from the vacuum filters, containing about 50 per cent moisture, is delivered by belt conveyors to one of two gas-fired rotary dryers, 6 ft in diameter by 35 ft long and revolving at 6.4 rpm. The partly dried residue from the dryer contains about 30 per cent moisture. It discharges through a chute to chain-bucket elevators which lift it 29 ft to a conveyor belt that delivers it 180 ft away to a hopper over the railroad siding, where it is loaded into cars for shipment to the lead smelter.

Purification. Solution is handled from the three storage tanks for impure solution by two 4-in. Worthite pumps, each rated at 500 gpm. The pumps deliver to four purification agitator tanks through 4-in. rubber hoses. The 4-in. copper pipe suction lines are provided with valves, so that either pump may handle the solution. All purification tanks are covered with 1-in. resin-pressed plywood and are ventilated through plywood ducts connecting with a fan in the building roof.

Two-stage purification of the zinc sulfate solution is employed, the first stage removing the copper, cobalt, arsenic, and antimony; the second removing the cadmium.

Zinc dust is stored in a four-compartment 10-ton bin on the purification floor. Spent electrolyte is stored in a 3,200-gal lead-lined tank, from which it is distributed as needed through rubber hoses to any purifier tank.

During the first stage of the purification, in which copper, cobalt, arsenic, and antimony are removed, spent electrolyte is added continuously, while zinc dust, copper, and arsenic reagents are added at intervals. The temperature is raised to 90°C or higher. The first stage is completed after 5 to 6 hr and the solution is then pumped by 4-in. Worthite pumps through one of two 36-in. 36-plate bronze Shriver filter presses into one of the four cadmium-removal purifiers. Kraft paper is used over the filter canvas to ensure a clear filtrate. The copper cake is dropped through chutes into hand carts, which are emptied into an outdoor storage bin. The cake goes to a copper smelter.

During the second stage of the purification, the removal of cadmium, spent electrolyte and zinc dust are added and the temperature is allowed to drop to 75°C. After 4 to 5 hr, the solution is pumped by 4-in. Worthite pumps through one of three additional 36-in. bronze Shriver presses to one of four wood-stave check tanks of the same dimensions and capacity as the purifiers.

To handle solution from each purification stage, a set of three Worthite pumps is provided, two in operation and one spare, interconnected so that any pump may be cut out for repairs. Rubber hoses are used on delivery lines to give flexibility of discharge and to avoid valves.

The cadmium filter cake from the final filtration is taken to the cadmium section for further treatment. The purified solution, to which a small amount of spent electrolyte has been added in order to minimize precipitation of basic salts, is stored in the check tanks until the purity of the solution has been checked. Provisions are made for returning for repurification any batch of solution that is found by control checking to be unsatisfactory.

Solution from the check tanks is handled in copper piping by 4-in. Worthite pumps of 500 gpm capacity, two of which are installed. They deliver through a common header either direct to pure solution storage or first over the cooling tower and then to storage. Cooled solution flows from the tower in a launder which discharges into the neutral storage tanks or by-passes into two 24,000 sump tanks, from which the solution may be returned to the tower for further cooling when desired. Pure solution storage consists of three wood-stave, unlined tanks, with inside dimensions of 30 ft in diameter by 10 ft 6 in. depth, each holding 50,000 gal. The purified and cooled solution is now pumped by two Worthite pumps of 200 gpm capacity to a lead-lined launder 215 ft long, which delivers the solution to the cell division.

Electrolysis. The overflow solution from the 320 cells is collected in two storage tanks for hot spent solution, from which a portion is pumped over a cooling tower and another portion goes to the leaching division. To the cooled spent solution are added controlled amounts of cooled purified solution returned from the leaching division. This mixed cell-feed solution is stored in two solution-storage tanks, from which it is pumped continuously to the cell-feed launder system where reagents are added. The solution then flows in parallel through the cells and is returned to the hot spent storage tanks.

The 320 cells are divided into electrical circuits each with 160 cells in series, placed in 16 banks of 10 cells each. Each cell contains 25 anodes and 24 cathodes in parallel. The current path for one circuit is from the positive conductor bar through the anodes and electrolyte to the cathodes in cell 10 of bank 1, through the next 9 cells in bank 1 to the cathode bar at the rear of bank 1, through a connecting bar to the anode bar at the rear of bank 2, through the 10 cells in bank 2, to the cathode bar at the front or stripping-floor end of bank 2, through a connecting bar between banks 2 and 3 to the anode bar at the front of bank 3, etc. The current leaves the unit through the cathode bar at the front of bank 16. Alternate cell banks not connected by permanent bars at the front end are provided with movable cut-out bars. By means of these bars 20 cells at a time are cut out for cleaning and repairing.

The cells are constructed of 4-in. reinforced concrete with 8-lb lead or acidproof brick lining. Inside they are 7 ft long, 2.5 ft wide, and 4.5 ft deep. For electrode details, see Chap. 5, page 128.

In the stripping operation, every other one of the 24 cathodes in a cell is removed at one time and placed in a stripping rack so designed as to make both faces of each cathode readily accessible. The 24-hr zinc deposits are easily removed by the use of a stripping knife and a mallet. The zinc sheets are stacked in racks from which they are picked up by a Hyster gasoline truck fitted with a lifting fork. The zinc is carried to scales, weighed, and then taken to the charging platform at the melting furnace.

Solution Flow. The two wood-stave lead-lined cool storage tanks are 50 ft ID by 10 ft 6 in. deep and have a capacity of 150,000 gal each. Condensate water is added here when needed to adjust the gravity of the electrolyte. Four Worthite 6-in. pumps, rated at 1,500 gpm each, pump the solution to the main cell-feed launder, which extends the full length of the cell room. The conditioning reagents are added to the 50 ft tanks. The solution then flows into 32 individual feed launders, one for each bank of cells, from which each cell receives solution at a regulated rate of about 10 gpm. A by-pass allows any excess of solution in the main feed launder to be returned to the hot spent storage.

The cell overflow is collected in individual launders for each bank of cells. These discharge through a main return launder into the two wood-stave lead lined hot spent tanks, which are 30 ft ID by 10 ft 6 in. deep and have a capacity of 55,000 gal each. From the hot spent storage, two Worthite 6-in. pumps, rated at 900 gpm each, deliver solution to the leaching division through an 8-in.-diameter lead pipe line. Four other Worthite 6-in. pumps, rated at 1,500 gpm each, handle hot spent solution to the three-section cooling towers, from which it returns to the cool storage for recirculating to the cells. The total volume of solution in the cell circuit is about 350,000 gal. About 40,000 gal of water per day is evaporated from the cooling tower.

Anodes and cells are cleaned at regular intervals. The anodes are scraped, brushed, straightened, and repaired as necessary before being replaced. A vacuum-cleaning system is used to remove solution and suspended manganese slime from the cells.

The main bulk of the solids is cleared from the cell by the vacuum system, and cell cleaning is finished by scraping caked sludge from sides and bottom and shoveling it into carts for removal.

A froth is maintained at all times on the solution surface in the cells by the use of frothing agents, added by two small cup-type feeders. This froth largely eliminates the mist caused by the escape of gas bubbles formed during electrolysis.

The power for electrolysis and for auxiliaries throughout the plant is developed from steam generated in three Erie City Iron Works boilers fired with natural gas. The direct current is supplied by five Westinghouse d-c generators of 2,500-kw capacity, which are geared to steam turbines. Auxiliary power is supplied by two Westinghouse a-c turbo-generators of 2,000 kw each. Marley towers with induced draft are used for cooling condenser water. The switchboard and circuit-breaker equipment are General Electric.

The following data are typical of a semimonthly period during 1947:

Zinc cathodes produced, tons	1,400
Total current, amp per circuit	11,500
Average volts at power house per circuit	485
Average current efficiency, %	84.7
Average kwhr per lb zinc	1.50
Average current density, amp per sq ft	60
Temperature of electrolyte, °C	36

Typical spent electrolyte analyses: H_2SO_4, 1.95 gpl; Zn, 60 gpl; Mn, 5 gpl; Cu, Cd, Co, As, Sb, Pb, 1 mg per l or less.

Melting and Casting. The weighed cathode zinc is transferred from the stripping-floor level with a gasoline truck into a 140-ton gas-fired reverberatory furnace with a flat suspended-arch top. The inside dimensions of the furnace are 12 ft wide by 21 ft long with 2 ft 4 in. average depth of metal bath.

The oxide fume in the furnace gases is recovered in a bag house. Molten zinc is removed from the furnace in two 500-lb capacity ladles and poured into molds placed on two parallel benches opposite the two dipping wells. The benches have 44 molds each. The slab zinc produced is over 99.99 per cent pure.

Cadmium Production. The press cake and cleanings from the second-stage zinc-solution purification tanks are leached with fresh strong acid and zinc electrolyte in a wood-stave lead- and brick-lined tank, which is 15 ft in diameter by 10 ft 6 in. deep, and has a working capacity of 12,000 gal. This and all other agitator tanks in the cadmium section are covered and ventilated. The wooden agitator of the tank rotates at 15 rpm. After 12-hr agitation, the cadmium and zinc are taken into solution. The present practice is to make two 12,000-gal leaches per week.

Leaches are discharged through a 2-in. Worthite pump of 150 gpm capacity to a hand-closed 36-in. bronze Shriver press with 24 plates. The cake from this filtration, containing copper, is stored for shipment. The filtrate, containing about 120 gpl of cadmium and 110 gpl of zinc, is pumped to an unlined 15-ft-diameter by 10-ft 6-in.-deep sponge-precipitation agitator tank having 14,000 gal capacity. The agitator rotates at 8 rpm and is placed well above the tank bottom to provide space for a large quantity of cadmium sponge. Sponge precipitation with zinc dust is carried out in one stage.

The cadmium-free solution is then pumped through a filter press to the cobalt-purification tank of the same specification as the sponge tank, except that the agitator revolves at 15 rpm. By means of the usual reagents, the cobalt content of the solution is lowered to 10 mg per l or less. The filtrate from filter pressing is sent to zinc leaching and the cake is shipped with the zinc residues.

The washed sponge contains an average of less than 5 per cent zinc. It is now placed in seven steam-heated drying pans for oxidation, prior to leaching with cadmium-spent solution. About five days is required to oxidize the sponge sufficiently for satisfactory leaching.

Sponge leaching is performed in two lead-lined tanks, 8 ft in diameter by 8 ft 6 in. deep, having a capacity of 3,000 gal each. The wooden agitators rotate at 15 rpm. Cadmium-spent solution, strong sulfuric acid, and condensate water are added to dissolve the sponge.   The leach is filtered in a 36-in. bronze Shriver press having 24 plates.   The filtrate is delivered to two lead-lined cell-feed tanks of 3,000 gal capacity each, which discharge by gravity to the cadmium-cell launder, where it mixes with circulating spent solution and glue solution.   Cadmium-cell over-flow solution flows by launder to two lead-lined spent-solution storage tanks of 3,000 gal capacity each.   From these tanks part of it is pumped to a small cooling tower and then returned to the cells, and part to various tanks where it is used for cadmium leaching and acidification.   The cooling tower may be by-passed if desired, and then recirculated cadmium-spent solution goes directly to the cell-feed launder.

There are 10 cells of the same size and construction as those used in the zinc plant.   The anodes are solid sheets of chemical lead and the cathodes are aluminum, as in the zinc plant.   Both are fitted with wooden strips. Current is supplied by a 50-kw motor generator, which delivers 2,000 amp at 25 volts.   Current density is 10 amp per sq ft.

Cathodes are stripped every 12 hr.   They are folded into bundles, washed, and dried.   When dry they are melted in an iron pot under a rosin flux.   The metal is cast into balls and ingots, weighed, and boxed for shipment.   Typical analyses are given in Table 71.

TABLE 71.   TYPICAL ANALYSES FROM CADMIUM PLANT, A. S. & R. CO., CORPUS CHRISTI, TEX.

Product	Cd	Zn	H_2SO_4
Cd cake from Zn plant, %	20	55	
Leach residue, %	1	10	
Cd sponge, %	80	5	
Cell-feed solution, gpl	2000		
Spent electrolyte, gpl	100	30	120

SULLIVAN MINING CO., KELLOGG, IDAHO
(A HIGH-DENSITY PLANT)

Because it is the only electrolytic zinc plant in the world making use of a high-current-density, high-acid process, the Sullivan plant in Kellogg, Idaho, makes a most interesting comparison with low-density and inter-mediate-density plants.   Working successfully with the process devel-oped some years ago in Kellogg by U. C. Tainton, the plant offers some marked differences from practice in other electrolytic zinc plants.[1]

As in most plants, however, the major divisions of the Sullivan plant

[1] Abstracted from W. G. Woolf and E. R. Crutcher, Electrolytic Zinc Plant of the Sullivan Mining Co., *Trans. AIME*, Vol. 121, p. 527; brought up to date by W. G. Woolf in 1951.

include (1) roasting, (2) leaching, (3) purification, (4) electrolysis, (5) melting and casting, (6) cadmium recovery. These will be discussed in that order.

Roasting. Although the Sullivan zinc plant accepts custom concentrates, its most important sources of raw material are the Bunker Hill Mine and the Star Mine of the Coeur d'Alene mining district of Idaho, together with that from another affiliated company, the Pend Oreille Mines & Metals Co., operating in the Metaline district of Washington. These supply zinc concentrated from complex zinc-lead-silver ores. The plant feed, therefore, has approximately the following composition:

	Per Cent
Zinc	51
Lead	3
Iron	10
Sulfur	31
Water	9.5
Copper	0.2
Insoluble	3.0

Concentrates are delivered to the plant in railroad cars, which discharge into bins beneath the track. There are eight storage bins of about 300 tons capacity each. There are individual belt feeders at the bottom of each bin which feed a collecting conveyor leading over a Weightometer.

After addition of roaster returns, sweepings, and roaster cleaning, the material goes through a 30- by 12-in. set of rolls and on into a bucket elevator into which flue and Cottrell dust are added. The elevator leads to a tripper conveyor feeding any of eight 25-ton roaster feed bins, one to each roaster.

Wedge roasters, 25 ft. in diameter, are used. There are seven hearths below the drying hearth. Eight roasters are operated. Each furnace has two Mahr-type oil burners on the bottom hearth. Each hearth has two air-cooled rabble arms, and on hearths 3, 4, 5, and 6 there are also two air arms used to distribute air that has just served to cool the rabble arms on the hearth immediately below.

Roasted calcine discharges at the periphery of the bottom hearth into duplicate Jacoby conveyor systems. A grizzly here removes lumps too coarse to go through the conveyor. The Jacoby conveyors are 14-in. cast-iron tubes about 150 ft long, rotating on trunnions. Cast integrally with the tubes is an inside helix that advances the calcine along the tube as it rotates. In traversing the conveyor, the calcine cools from about 400 to 100°C.

Leaving the conveyors, calcine is elevated to a storage bin from which it is passed over a 20-mesh screen. Oversize goes back to the roaster feed, along with lumps removed by the grizzly mentioned previously, and goes through the crushing rolls and the roaster once more.   Undersize goes to one of six main calcine storage bins from which leach plant feed is drawn. Each bin holds about 125 tons.

Roaster gas discharges through two uptakes on the top hearth of each roaster.   These enter a balloon flue that leads 1,100 ft to the Cottrell plant which is 400 ft higher than the roaster plant.   Dust gates along this flue permit cleaning.   Flue dust averages about 20 per cent of the raw concentrate; Cottrell dust, about 5 per cent.   Samples of dust give about the following range of assays:

	% Zn	% Acid-soluble Zn	% Water-soluble Zn	% Fe	% S
Flue dust............	43–49	25–40	7–12	6–9	1–12
Cottrell dust........	20–45	15–25	9–20	2–7	2–12

The objective of the roasting step, of course, is to render as much as possible of the zinc in the calcine soluble in the spent electrolyte that is used for leaching.   Because a dead roast requires a degree of heat that in turn increases formation of insoluble ferrites, and because any sulfide sulfur left in the calcine ties up twice its weight of zinc, the roasting procedure demands a nice balance between sulfide sulfur left in the calcine and ferrite produced in it.

In addition, roasting must be adjusted to produce a certain amount of zinc sulfate that replaces the sulfate lost in solution in various ways.   To hold down ferrite formation, a maximum temperature of 750°C has been set for any hearth.   Individual roasters have at times handled as much as 65 wet tons of concentrates per 24 hr, and the roasters have also been kept going on as little as 18 tons per day.   The optimum rate appears to be about 40 to 50 wet tons daily.

Best operating procedure seems to be to provide equipment at the roaster floor to enable operators to run regular water-soluble zinc and sulfide sulfur assays themselves.   For a recent year, average calcine assays were: total zinc, 56.0 per cent; acid-soluble zinc, 50.7 per cent; water-soluble zinc, 3.4 per cent; total sulfur, 3.1 per cent; sulfide sulfur 0.05 per cent; iron, 9.2 per cent; insoluble, 4.1 per cent.

Leaching.   Calcine is carried from the storage bins through a series of conveyors and elevators to two calcine weighing hoppers over each of six agitator tanks.   There is also a manganese dioxide weighing hopper over each agitator.

The agitators are 20 ft in diameter by 13 ft deep, wood-stave, lead-lined tanks, with an inside lining of acidproof brick.   Agitating mechanism is a series of lead-covered 3-in. pipes hung from radial arms extending from a central shaft just above the pulp.   Each pair of these pipes is joined by a heavy cast-iron lead-covered shoe.

The batch system of leaching is used.   A measured amount of spent electrolyte is pumped into the tank and heated, if necessary, to about 60°C by steam coils placed in the tank.   Two-thirds of the quantity of calcine required for complete neutralization is then added.   Agitation proceeds for 3 to 5 hr.   Very good extraction is obtained on this portion of the leach because the minimum acid strength is about 40 to 60 gpl. Heat released during the reaction raises the pulp in the agitator to the boiling point, 104 to 106°C in this case.

The remaining acid is then neutralized by adding small, carefully measured increments of calcine.   The leach is then reacidified with about 20 to 25 gpl of sulfuric acid by adding more electrolyte.   The acid is then again carefully neutralized with calcine, the objective being to avoid adding excess calcine that will go undissolved, and to make sure that all iron is precipitated.   This repeated neutralization improves filtration of the pulp.   About ¼ lb of glue per ton of pulp is also added for this purpose.   Manganese dioxide is added as needed to oxidize any ferrous iron in the pulp.

The tanks are discharged through 6-in. lead pipes to either of two storage tanks, constructed similarly to the leach tanks, ahead of the Burt filters.   There are fourteen Burt filters, 5 ft in diameter and 40 ft long. The pulp is filtered and washed three times.   Vacuum is applied to dislodge the cake, and water is added to form a pulp, which is discharged to Dorr thickeners.   Thickener overflow is used over again for repulping. Underflow is filtered in Oliver filters, dried, and shipped to the Bunker Hill lead smelter for recovery of lead, gold, and silver.

The Burt filters, used here and at the Corpus Christi zinc plant of A. S. and R., prove particularly useful because filtration takes place without crystallization of zinc sulfate from the nearly saturated solution being filtered, and because it is possible to wash the cake thoroughly with a minimum of water.[1]

Purification.   Zinc sulfate solution produced in the leaching department contains, in addition to the dissolved zinc, a number of impurities, among them being copper, cadmium, cobalt, antimony, arsenic, nickel,

[1] W. G. Woolf and A. Y. Bethune, The Burt Filter, *Trans. AIME*, Vol. 187, page 585.

and germanium. The solution contains about 220 gpl of zinc, 300 mg. per l of copper, 600 mg per l of cadmium, 15 to 30 mg per l of cobalt, 3 to 8 mg per l of antimony plus arsenic, as well as manganese and magnesium which do not need to be removed.

The solution is drawn from storage tanks through 6-in. copper pipes, fitted at the discharge end with rubber hoses and pinch cocks. These empty into unlined, thick-stave, wood tanks, 22 ft in diameter by 15 ft high, which contain paddle agitators. The tanks are fitted with steam coils.

Enough zinc dust is added to each charge of solution to precipitate all the copper. This charge is filtered through Shriver plate-and-frame filter presses, then discharged into another similar agitator. Cobalt removal is aided by a small amount of copper in solution. Therefore a little raw solution is added to this second purification step. The temperature in the batch is raised with steam to 75°C or above, and more zinc dust is added until cobalt, antimony, and cadmium are reduced to 1 mg per l or less. Nickel is presumed to be gone when cobalt is, and no test for it is made.

The final filtrate, which carries 225 gpl of zinc, goes to a check tank where it is held until the operators make final assay checks on its purity. Simple but accurate tests have been devised that the operators can run themselves. As a further check, a sample is taken and assayed in the laboratory. The residue from purification is treated in a separate cadmium plant.

In the filter presses, 30-lb kraft paper is used over 10-oz canvas duck. When the filter is opened, the paper is peeled off, leaving the canvas clean. The used paper is thrown into the leach agitators, where it disintegrates.

Electrolysis. In the cell room there are four circuits, two of 150 cells each and two of 160 cells each, in series electrically, but parallel with regard to solution flow.

Each unit is supplied with power from a motor-generator set consisting of a synchronous motor direct-connected to two d-c generators, the smaller circuits being 4,000 amp and 500 to 550 volts each, the two larger 5,000 amp and 500 to 585 volts each. Each pair of generators is connected in series to give 8,000 and 10,000 amp of direct current, respectively. Current density is about 100 amp per sq ft of submerged cathode area.

Each cell contains 14 cathodes and 28 anodes. Electrodes are held in place by lead-covered wooden frames. Cathodes slide into the cell in wooden guides that also serve as spacers for the anodes. Distance between faces of anode and cathode is only ⅝ in., which accounts for the necessity of holding accurate spacing.   Wooden guides are replaced about every 60 days.

Cathodes are of $\frac{1}{8}$-in. aluminum plate, with an aluminum header bar welded to it by hydrogen welding.   Cathode contact is obtained by using a copper clip, attached to the bus bar, into which the header bar slips. Because the header bar is itself copper-plated, a copper-to-copper contact is obtained.   There is no exposed copper over the cell proper.

Cells are not cascaded, but are set up in two rows of 75 cells each in each circuit.   The cells are side to side, not end to end.   The 1- by 2-in. copper bars that connect the pairs of cells are supported independently of the cells.   They act as the cathode bus for one cell and the anode bus for the cell adjoining.   Copper tie-up is therefore relatively small, considering the amperage carried in the circuit.   Current efficiency is approximately 90 per cent and voltage drop across each cell is 3.4 volts.

Solution circulates at a rate of about 10 gpm per cell.   Overflow drops into sumps through hard-rubber pipes.   The sump below each row of cells extends the full length of the row.   From the sumps, the solution is pumped up to cooling cells from which it flows back to the electrolytic cells by gravity.

There are seven cooling cells, each containing 98 rectangular cooling units made of lead, through which cold water is circulated.   The electrolyte flows around these cooling units.   They are in series to solution flow.   A total of about 5,000 gpm of water is circulated.

Neutral solution is delivered to the cell building as required through an iron launder.   Electrolyte is pumped back to the leaching department through stainless steel centrifugal pumps.

The neutral solution is fed to the cell circuit in batches instead of continuously.   For example, if the acid content of the cell-room electrolyte has reached 27 to 28 per cent sulfuric acid, a portion of it, say one-fifth, is pumped from the cell room to the leaching department, and an equal amount of neutral solution is drawn from the purification storage tanks to the cell-room circuit.   This reduces the acid content to about 22 per cent.   When the acid again reaches 28 per cent, the cycle is repeated.

Because the zinc content of the neutral solution is so much higher than is in general use in electrolytic zinc plants, a relatively small tonnage of solution is required to produce the zinc.   About 6 tons of pure solution is required per ton of zinc cathodes produced.

Cathodes are pulled every 8 to 12 hr.   One cathode is pulled at a time and when each one is withdrawn, a clean cathode is immediately dropped into its place.

Melting and Casting.   Cathodes are melted in two oil-fired reverberatory furnaces, 15 by 28 ft, with an inverted arch hearth.   There are two ladling wells in the end opposite the firebox, separated from the main bath by a bridge wall.   The wells are heated with oil burners.   The furnaces hold about 100 tons of molten metal.   The ladle, supported on a crawl, and handled by one man, carries 350 to 400 lb of metal.   Molds for standard slabs or special shapes are placed in a line reached by the ladle.

Cathodes are charged in bundles of 700 to 800 lb, sliding down a trough through a swinging door into the furnace.   The furnace is drossed after 80 tons of cathodes have been melted.   Once each month wall and arch accretions are barred down.   Zinc produced at the plant is all "Special High Grade" according to ASTM specifications.[1]

Cadmium Plant.   Purification residue is sampled, weighed, and stored for re-treatment.   In the cadmium plant, it is ground in a ball mill to produce a fine sludge, then sent to a lead-lined agitator for leaching with spent electrolyte from the zinc tank house.   Cadmium dissolves, leaving cement copper, which is filtered off and sent to a copper smelter.   The solution carrying cadmium and other impurities goes to an agitator like those in the main purification room.   Zinc dust is added to bring down cadmium as a sponge.   This is filtered off in Shriver presses and the solution pumped to storage.   The cadmium precipitate is heated on a steam platform, where it oxidizes in a short time, becoming readily soluble in the return solution from the cadmium electrolytic cells.   All the cadmium is not oxidized, and the small amount remaining insoluble serves to remove residual copper and other impurities.

The neutral solution carrying the dissolved cadmium goes to the cadmium cells.   These are of the stationary cathode type, similar to the zinc cells.   Current density is about 10 amp per sq ft.   Circulation and regeneration of electrolyte proceed as they do in the zinc circuit.   Impurities tend to build up in time, and they are removed by using the fouled solution for the cadmium purification step instead of electrolyte from the zinc circuit.

Cathodes are stripped every 12 hr and the cadmium melted in an electric melting pot under fused caustic soda.   The metal is cast into the required market shapes.   A separate motor-generator set supplies the cadmium plant with its own power.   Cadmium produced is of high purity, assaying 99.99+ per cent.

ELECTROLYTIC ZINC—ITALIAN PRACTICE

The following notes on zinc leaching and electrolysis in Italy are by Prof. L. Cambi of Milan, Italy (private communication, 1949):

"The most important ore deposits worked at present in Italy are those

[1] A. Y. Bethune and W. W. Schmittroth, Spectrographic Analysis of Special High Grade Zinc, *Trans. AIME*, Vol. 182, p. 248, 1949.

of zinc, and recent prospecting has revealed further important ore bodies, especially of the sulfide type.

"Italian zinc ore production is considerably greater than the internal consumption, or even the capacity of metallurgical treatment plants now operating or projected. In 1947 the production was 97,000 tons of concentrate, averaging 52.5 per cent zinc, in addition to about 10,000 tons of low-grade oxidized ore, averaging 18 per cent zinc. During the same year, about 17,000 tons was exported.

"The average production from 1910 to 1914 was 140,000 tons per year. After the postwar depression, it reached in 1928 a maximum of 220,000 tons, with an average zinc content of 38.4 per cent.

"In spite of this situation Italy had no zinc metal industry of its own at the beginning of the First World War. In 1917 a distillation plant, using Belgian-Silesian retorts, of the old mining company Societa di Monteponi started production at Vado Ligure near Savona.

"On account of the high cost of fuel and the comparatively low cost of water power, it was obvious that a proper solution could only be found in the electrolytic zinc process.

"Various attempts were made to apply the electric furnace, but had to be abandoned owing to the same type of difficulties encountered everywhere else. An electrolytic process after the principle of chlorinating the oxidized ore and then electrolyzing the chloride, similar to the old Höpfner process, was investigated. It proved uneconomical.

"At the end of 1916, it was finally decided to abandon the thermoelectric and the chloride electrolytic processes and to direct research work toward sulfuric acid leaching with subsequent electrolysis. The test work on an industrial scale was, at that time, financed by the well-known power-distributing company Societa Edison of Milan.

"At that time no information was available in Italy on the work done along similar lines by the large metallurgical companies in North America, such as Anaconda, Trail, etc. The ore extracted was predominantly of the oxidized type, as the extraction of sulfide ore on a large scale began only several years later, as it did in the rest of the world, with the introduction of the flotation process. My research work was therefore directed primarily toward the oxidized ore of the two important districts of Monteponi in Sardinia and of the Brembo and Serio Valleys around Bergamo in Northern Italy.

"Decision was made in favor of the low-grade calamine of Sardinia with low silica content, primarily on account of the ease with which it could be leached with sulfuric acid. At the present time, the calamines of the Bergamo district, some with higher silica content, are also being considered for treatment in the Italian electrolytic plants.

"By the end of 1917, I had already established the processes best suited for the sulfuric and electrolytic treatment of the Italian calamines.

"After the first attempt of the Siemens Co. at Lipine (Poland) in 1911–1912, no more work had been done in Europe on an industrial scale on the sulfuric leaching of zinc ores.   While the research work on calamine was in progress, the Societa Elettromineraria of Genoa resumed production of blende with quartz gangue at their mine of Vallauria near Tenda, and approached the Societa Edison with the suggestion of constructing a plant for the electrolytic treatment of this ore.

"The blende in question was obtained from the concentrator, annexed to the mine, as a concentrate with 40 to 42 per cent zinc and 20 per cent sulfur.   The electrolytic zinc plant was designed for a capacity corresponding to the production of the mine, or about 10 tons of metal per day.   It was to be considered as a pilot plant for the further development of the electrolytic treatment of Italian ore.

"I completed this project in 1918, but on account of the general situation at the time, it could not begin operation until 1921.

"This operation also involved a problem new to Italy at that time— roasting the blende.   The choice fell upon mechanical furnaces of the Huntington-Heberlein or Herreshof type, and of the retort type heated with generator gas.   This constituted the first European installation of this kind and was followed by the modern plants with Wedge and similar furnaces.   Two units, each having a capacity of about 20 tons ore per day, were installed.

"Roasting the blende from Vallauria presented, from the point of view of leaching, the difficulty common to all blendes with quartz gangue. They form comparatively large quantities of zinc silicate in the calcined product, which in turn is responsible for the formation of colloidal silica during the leach.

"The large amount and the nature of the residue made it necessary to apply equipment for continuous decantation and continuous filtration. In Europe at that time, these methods and equipment were practically unknown.   My project was established with the help of the Dorr and the Oliver companies, and in the small plant of S. Dalmazzo di Tenda were installed, for the first time in Europe, Dorr thickeners of 21-ft diameter and Oliver drum filters of about 130-sq-ft filter area in acidproof construction.

"The pilot plant at S. Dalmazzo was shut down in 1930 on account of the exhaustion of the mine.   It was then adapted for another electrolytic process, but it had set the pattern for the larger electrolytic zinc plants built later in Italy.

"In view of the research done in the years 1916 to 1918 on the Sardinian calamine, the Societa di Monteponi decided to build a semi-industrial plant, after my project, for the electrolytic treatment of the low-grade iron-bearing calamine of the Campo Pisano mine near Cagliari in Sardinia. This semi-industrial plant was built at Vado Ligure near Savona and functioned from 1919 to 1922, acting as a pilot plant for the large installations built later at Monteponi, with a capacity of 120 tons per day of low-grade calamine. This installation started operations in 1926 and has operated continuously since then, even through the last war.

"This is a comparatively modest installation, having a capacity of 20 tons of metal per day, but it presents considerable interest from a metallurgical standpoint. The low-grade calamine, averaging today about 18 per cent zinc, was considered a waste product, although after the construction of the electrolytic zinc plants, it proved to be a valuable raw material. The high-grade calamine is exported or sent to distillation. The electrolytic treatment was made possible from an economic point of view by the very low cost of the raw material, and from the metallurgical point of view by the nature of the ore, which consists exclusively of basic zinc carbonate embedded in limonite, which is insoluble in the electrolyte.

"The large quantity of insoluble residue made it necessary to install a large number of Dorr classifiers, Dorr thickeners (eight of 40-ft diameter) and continuous Oliver filters (seven of 25 sq m each).

"In 1936, the electrolytic zinc plant at Porto Marghera (Venice) started operations with the treatment of blende from the Montevecchio mine in Sardinia, which belongs jointly to the S. A. Montevecchio and to the Societa di Monteponi. This plant has a capacity of 50 tons of zinc per day.

"At the present time the construction of another plant at Ponte Nossa near Bergamo has been started by S. A. Piombo e Zinco (AMMI group), which will treat the calamine from the Serio and Brembo Valleys and will have a capacity of 50 tons of zinc per day. It may safely be stated that the work begun in 1916 is reaching its final results with this last installation.

"In closing, I would like to point out that Italian zinc hydrometallurgy has followed two lines, one for the blende, the other for the calamine. The treatment of the calamine, which is considered of lower value than the blende, is of considerable economic and social interest and requires on a large scale the application of the continuous equipment which we owe to J. V. N. Dorr."

DET NORSKE ZINKOMPANI A/S

Det Norske Zinkompani A/S was founded in 1923 on the initiative of the Belgian company, Compagnie Royale Asturienne des Mines, which owns large zinc mines in Northern Spain.

The plant at Eitrheim operates under patent licenses from the Anaconda Co. It was started in 1929 and is one of the largest and most modern of European electrolytic zinc plants. The flow sheet is shown in Fig. 37.

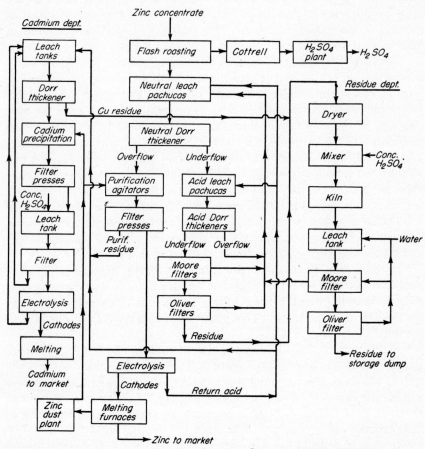

FIG. 37. Flow sheet of electrolytic zinc plant of Det Norske Zinkompani A/S, Eitrheim, Norway.

A few months after it started, the plant reached an output of 40,000 metric tons of zinc per year. Prior to the Second World War, output had climbed to 45,000 metric tons per year.

The raw material is sphalerite flotation concentrates from mines in Spain, Newfoundland, Mexico, South America, Jugoslavia, and other countries. Norwegian zinc ores from Sulitjelma and Moi Rana have also been used. The ores treated average:

	% Assay
Zn	45–58
S	30
Pb	0.5–4.0
Cu	0.05–2.0
Cd	0.1–0.5
Fe	3–15
Ag, oz per ton	0.34–15.9

There are small quantities of other metals, such as Co, Ni, As, Sb, and Ge, and silica, aluminum oxide, lime, and magnesia.

On account of conditions in the electrolysis, the chlorine content of the roasted ore must not exceed 0.002 per cent.

The ore is delivered in boats in amounts up to 8,000 tons. It is transported on conveyor belts to silos 500 m from the quay. These silos hold 30,000 metric tons of ore and are divided into pockets for different ores.

Roasting Department. Two Wedge furnaces have recently been reconstructed for flash roasting, resulting in three times the original capacity and a higher sulfur dioxide content in the gases than before. The gases are vented through cyclones and a Cottrell plant to the sulfuric acid plant built on the Pettersen intensive chamber system. The sulfuric acid produced has a concentration of 58 to 60°Bé or about 75 per cent H_2SO_4 and the output is about 100 tons of this acid per 24 hr. The capacity for acid can be doubled with only small alterations.

Leaching. The roasted ore from the silos or from the roasting plant is transported by an electric train to the leaching department, where the ore is treated with return sulfuric acid formed in the electrolysis of the zinc sulfate.

The return acid from the electrolysis carries about 100 gpl free sulfuric acid and about 140 gpl zinc sulfate (55 to 60 gpl zinc). A part of this return acid is mixed with overflow from the thickeners for "acid" leaching and with filtrates from the residue filters, so that the mixture contains 5 to 10 gpl free sulfuric acid. Ferric sulfate solution is also added to this mixture in order to bring the iron content up to about 0.7 per cent ferric iron. Some manganese dioxide is also added from the electrolytic cells or from imported pyrolusite in order to oxidize bivalent iron.

An excess of roasted zinc ore is added to this mixture, neutralizing the sulfuric acid and precipitating dissolved trivalent iron as ferric hydroxide together with the impurities, arsenic, antimony, and germanium.

Ferric sulfate solution is produced by dissolution of scrap iron in warm return acid and oxidation of bivalent iron to trivalent with manganese dioxide.

The leaching is carried out in a series of wooden Pachuca tanks agitated by compressed air (at about 45 psi). The Pachuca tanks are 3 m in diameter by 6 m high (*ca.* 9 ft 11 in. by 19 ft 8 in.).

The solution overflows through two series of five Pachucas each and then through two Dorr classifiers which separate undissolved particles of sand. (These classifiers are not shown on the flow sheet.)

The solution is then distributed to five Dorr thickeners or clarifying tanks, each 15 m in diameter and 5 m deep. The mechanism rotates once in 4 min. The residue is drawn from the bottom of these tanks at intervals of a few minutes.

The clear solution overflows to a collecting tank for the five thickeners and is pumped up to eight wooden tanks, 3 m in diameter and 6 m deep, equipped with agitators driven by electric motors. Each of these tanks is filled in turn with 38 cu m zinc solution, and 60 to 100 kg zinc dust is added to precipitate copper, cadmium, and other impurities, such as cobalt and nickel.

Before purification, the neutral zinc sulfate solution contains: 110 to 130 gpl zinc, 0.1 to 0.2 gpl cadmium, 6 to 12 mg per l cobalt, 0.2 to 0.8 mg per l nickel, and 5 to 10 mg per l ferrous iron.

The following maximum percentages of impurities are permitted in the purified solution to electrolysis: 1 mg per l cadmium, 0.5 mg per l copper, 0.1 mg per l nickel, arsenic, antimony, and germanium. The cobalt content preferably should not exceed 10 mg per l and is at present kept at 5 to 7 mg per l.

When a purification tank has been filled with solution and agitation with zinc dust has proceeded for 1 hr, a rapid test for copper and cadmium is carried out and, if this is satisfactory, the solution is filtered through filter presses with cotton filter cloth covered with paper. Eight presses are employed for this filtration. The filtrate from the presses is pumped to two large surge tanks each taking 700 cu m.

The residue in the presses contains undissolved zinc dust together with copper, cadmium, and other impurities, and it is treated in the cadmium department.

The residue with undissolved zinc oxide from the five Dorr thickeners for neutral leaching is withdrawn continuously and conveyed by a bucket elevator to acid leaching, where the sludge passes three Pachuca tanks in series in two steps, return acid being added meanwhile for dissolution of zinc oxide. The overflow from the last Pachuca in the series is maintained at 0.5 to 2.0 gpl free sulfuric acid and flows to two Dorr thickeners.

The overflow from these last two thickeners flows to a collecting tank and is pumped from there to neutral leaching.

The residue from the last acid leach is dropped to a Moore vacuum filter, consisting of 30 filter bags 2.4 m wide and 1.9 m high, suspended in a frame which can be moved from the filter tank to the washing tank with an overhead crane.

The residue gathers at the bottom of the washing tanks, where it is drawn out and pumped to two rotating Oliver vacuum filters, from which a residue with 30 to 35 per cent moisture is obtained. The filtrates and wash filtrates from these filters are pumped to neutral leaching.

The object of the acid leaching is to dissolve as much of the acid-soluble zinc in the ore as possible, but at the same time one must avoid dissolving too much of the precipitated impurities, arsenic, antimony, and germanium.

The residue from the Oliver filter, which amounts to about 100 metric tons dry weight per 24 hr, contains when dried 15 to 20 per cent zinc, 4 to 6 per cent lead, 2 to 3 per cent copper, some silver and gold, 25 to 35 per cent ferrous oxide, and the gangue. From the cadmium department there is also obtained a copper-bearing residue with 15 to 20 per cent copper.

The present procedure for the treatment of these three valuable residues is shown in the flow sheet.

Cadmium Recovery.   The residue from the purification, when it comes from the filter presses, is treated in the cadmium department. Cadmium and excess zinc dust are dissolved in dilute sulfuric acid. The leaching is completed at about 20 gpl free sulfuric acid, the solution is neutralized with roasted zinc ore, and run to a Dorr thickener. The insoluble copper residue is drawn from the bottom of this thickener and pumped to the dryer in the residue department.

The overflow, which is a neutral solution of zinc and cadmium sulfates, is filtered through a filter press and cadmium is precipitated by cementation with just about the theoretical quantity of zinc dust. Filtration through a filter press yields a zinc sulfate solution, which is pumped to the leaching department, and a concentrate containing 60 to 70 per cent cadmium.

This concentrate is dissolved in strong sulfuric acid and after the precipitation of iron, copper and nickel, and their removal by filtration, the cadmium sulfate solution is fed to electrolytic cells where cadmium is deposited on cathode plates of aluminum. Lead plates are used as anodes.

The coating of cadmium is removed from the aluminum plates once in 24 hours. It is weighed, dried, and melted in electrically heated cast-iron crucibles under a layer of caustic soda.

The metal is guaranteed to have a purity of 99.95 per cent cadmium and contains 0.005 to 0.015 per cent lead and 0.002 to 010 per cent copper.

The output of cadmium is at present 500 to 600 kg per 24 hr. The total output in 1937 was 154.2 tons, out of a world production of about 3,000 tons.

Electrolytic Department. The tank house has an area of 3,700 sq m. There are three series, each of 144 cells, in which the zinc is precipitated out of the zinc sulfate solution at a current strength of 12,000 amp per series. The voltage per cell is 3.6 to 3.7 and the current density is about 38 amp per sq ft. Each cell has 27 cathode plates of aluminum and 28 lead anodes.

The deposited zinc is removed from the cathodes after 24 hr. The cells are fed continuously with neutral zinc sulfate solution containing 110 to 130 gpl zinc. The discharge from the cells, the so-called return acid, contains 100 gpl of free sulfuric acid and 55 to 60 gpl of zinc, and is recirculated to the leaching department for the treatment of fresh calcine. The total volume of zinc sulfate solution in circulation throughout the plant is 9,000 cu m.

The direct current for electrolysis is obtained through rectification, each series having its own rectifier with a tension of 400 per 580 volts. Of the 30,000 to 35,000 hp used in the plant, 90 per cent is for electrolysis.

Zinc dust for purification is produced through dispersion of a thin jet of molten zinc with compressed air. The dust is trapped in a chamber from which it is raked out and screened. The output is about 7,000 kg per 24 hr.

The plant output of electrolytic zinc is 125 tons per 24 hr or 45,000 tons per year.

Det Norske Zinkompani employs a staff of 100 technicians and 700 workmen. It imports annually, in metric tons:

Zinc ore	about 90,000
Manganese dioxide	700
Cinders	20,000
Crushed ore	6,000
Limestone	10,000

and exports

Zinc	45,000
Cadmium	150

ELECTROLYTIC ZINC CO. OF AUSTRALASIA, LTD.

The plant and process of the Electrolytic Zinc Co. of Australasia, Ltd., at Risdon, Tasmania, were described in 1936.[1] Since that time a number

[1] W. C. Snow, Electrolytic Zinc at Risdon, Tasmania, *Trans. AIME*, Vol. 121, p. 482.

of important changes have been made.   These are described by Ross,[1] from whose paper the following is abstracted.

The major changes have been

1. Replacement of two-stage roasting by a preliminary roast followed by the flotation of all the leach residue and the roasting of the flotation concentrate.
2. Screening of all calcine fed to the Pachucas.
3. Continuous leaching of calcine and improved classification of Pachuca discharge.
4. Close pH control during purification for iron removal.
5. Recovery of cobalt as a good-grade oxide.
6. Production of part of the zinc in the form of "4-mines" metal (99.99 per cent purity).

Changes planned and on which construction is proceeding involve

1. Two suspension roasters.
2. A contact acid plant to produce 150 tons (2,240 lb) of acid per day and replacing the existing Mills-Packard chamber plant.
3. Extra power-station capacity.   This will increase the output of cathode zinc from about 245 to 290 tons per day.

An ammonium sulfate plant and improved treatment of zinc-plant residues for recovery of zinc, lead, and other metals are also planned.

Figure 38 shows approximately the present flow sheet.   In this several steps have been omitted for the sake of clarity.   Among these omitted steps are the treatment of the cobalt and cadmium precipitates and the method of precipitation of chlorine from the solutions.   This last is done with silver sulfate.   For details, see the original article describing the plant in 1936.

The plant output of cathode zinc in 1936 was about 200 tons per day. This has since been increased to about 245 tons per day, and plant extensions that are practically complete will permit of an output of about 290 tons per day in the near future.

New Roasting Practice.   A major change has been made in the roasting policy.   In 1936, the calcine, partially preroasted in Australia for acid making, was roasted in modified Leggo furnaces using coal as fuel, sulfur being reduced from about 6 to about 0.8 per cent.   The bad feature was the need for spending money on fuel to oxidize only about 5 per cent of sulfur.   It was recognized that if the preroast calcine, as received, were

[1] S. W. Ross, Electrolytic Zinc at Risdon, Major Changes since 1936, *Trans. AIME*, T.P. 2524D.

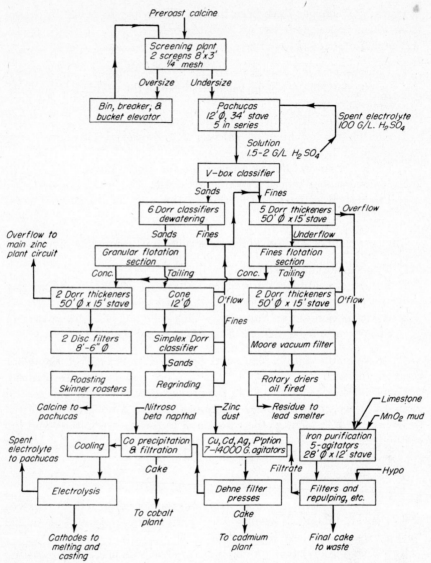

FIG. 38.   Flow sheet of electrolytic zinc plant of Electrolytic Zinc Co. of Australasia, Ltd., Risdon, Tasmania.

leached and if a process could be developed for zinc sulfate recovery from the leach residue, this small quantity of sulfide concentrate would probably roast autogenously.   This would virtually eliminate fuel cost for roasting, as well as greatly increasing the weight of sulfur oxidized per square foot of hearth area.

Flotation of sand leach residues worked quite successfully, but the slime portion was difficult to float. This fact had held up preroast calcine direct leaching for many years, but successful flotation of this slime fraction was finally achieved. Direct leaching of the preroast concentrate and flotation of granular and slime leach residues were accordingly started in 1940. The mixed concentrate from flotation is roasted for the most part in modified Skinner furnaces. The flotation tailing, filtered and dried, becomes the final zinc plant residue.

Continuous Leaching. In order to make the change from batch to continuous leaching, preliminary screening of the preroast calcine was

TABLE 72. LEACHING DIVISION, ELECTROLYTIC ZINC CO. OF AUSTRALASIA, LTD.

New calcine leached, tons	11,660
Circulating load calcine and dross leached, tons	3,909
Total calcine leached, tons	15,569
Assay calcine leached:	
Sulfate S, %	1.38
Sulfide S, %	5.79
Total Zn, %	56.6
Soluble Zn, %	42.1
Pb, %	1.0
Fe, %	9.2
Cu, %	0.18
Cd, %	0.31
Ag, oz	4.3
Au, oz	0.017
Spent electrolyte, acid, gpl	90.5
Acid added to circuit, tons	283
Granular residue to flotation, % of total calcine leached	24.2
Slime residue to flotation, % of total calcine leached	26.8

necessary for the removal of larger lumps impossible to feed through the continuous Pachuca series.

There was somewhat restricted space for building new Pachucas for increased production and this, together with savings in labor and time and improved classification, led to the adoption of continuous leaching.

It has been found that five Pachucas in series, used continuously, leach as well as 10 employed in batch work. In normal present practice, the 10 original Pachucas are arranged in two groups of five in series, only one group being used at a time.

Classification has been improved by the addition of a V-shaped box, into which the Pachuca discharge enters and through which it flows. The overflowing fine fraction goes to Dorr thickeners, the underflow from which is delivered to a pulp-holding tank for the slime flotation plant. The granular fraction from the V-box is dewatered in duplex Dorr classifiers, the overflow from which goes to the thickeners, the underflow being delivered to the granular flotation section.   Tailing from this section is reground and goes to the slime flotation section.

Flotation tailing flows to two 50-ft diameter by 15 ft deep Dorr thickeners, the overflow from which is returned to the flotation circuit, the underflow being filtered, dried, and shipped to the lead smelter.

TABLE 73.   FLOTATION SECTION, ELECTROLYTIC ZINC CO. OF AUSTRALASIA, LTD.

Granular residue treated, tons.................. 3,696
Assay sulfide S, %............................   17.52
Slime residue treated, tons..................... 4,095
Assay sulfide S, %............................   8.02
Combined concentrate, tons..................... 4,041
Slime tailing or final residue, tons............... 3,028
Slime tailing, % of new calcine leached........... 26.0

	Combined concentrate	Slime tailing
Sulfide S, %..............................	22.5	1.99
Total Zn, %..............................	49.4	22.3
Pb, %....................................	0.88	4.0
Cu, %....................................	0.21	0.14
Cd, %....................................	0.70	0.13
Ag, oz...................................	10.2	6.5
Au oz....................................	0.03	0.026

Addition agents	Xanthate, %	Eucalyptus	Cresylic acid
Granular circuit, lb per ton......	Nil	0.35	Nil
Slime circuit, lb per ton..........	0.04	0.04	0.03*

* Cresylic acid was not added throughout the year.   This figure represents the normal addition when it was used.

The overflows from the five primary thickeners dealing with Pachuca discharge combine and go forward for removal of iron, silica, arsenic, antimony, and germanium.   This procedure is essentially the same as described in the original article but proper and careful pH control during the precipitation has greatly improved the filtration rate of the iron precipitate.

It is believed that the presence of at least 1 gpl and preferably 1.3 gpl of silica in the solution going to iron precipitation is effective in controlling germanium.   This metal, if not removed almost completely, increases the reversion of cadmium during the filtration of the copper-cadmium precipitate, and also reduces current efficiency during subsequent electrolysis.

Cobalt separation by the use of nitroso-β-napthol is unchanged, except in minor detail, from the practice previously described. However, cobalt oxide is now recovered from the cobalt precipitate which was formerly wasted.

In the electrolytic cells, the original anode spacing varying between $3\frac{1}{2}$ and 4 in. has been reduced to 3 in., center to center. For this purpose a suitable double-cone, porcelain spacing insulator was developed and two of these were fitted to each anode.

TABLE 74. IRON PURIFICATION, ELECTROLYTIC ZINC CO. OF AUSTRALASIA, LTD.

Solution treated, gal per day..................... 800,000

	Solution composition	
	Before treatment	After treatment
H_2SO_4 gpl......................	1.95	Neutral
Total Fe, mg per l...............	470	0.3
Ferrous Fe, mg per l.............	290	
Silica, gpl......................	1.65	0.112
As, mg per l....................	2.65*	0.2
Sb, mg per l....................	0.44*	0.1*
Limestone used, tons†............	.....	600
Fe precipitate, tons†............	.....	1200
Total Zn, %.....................	.....	7.0
Water-soluble Zn, %.............	.....	3.5

* These figures are representative but are not necessarily yearly averages.

† The figures for limestone used and weight and composition of iron precipitate are typical but due to minor changes in procedure during the year do not depict the year's average work.

A minor difficulty has come about from fluorine in the electrolyte, which has increased from about 15 to 20 mg per l up to 30 to 35 mg. This has resulted in increased solution-line cathode corrosion and an increased cathode cost per ton of zinc.

Closer electrode spacing and greater current flow have called for more cell cooling. In practice an endeavor is made to keep the electrolyte temperature below 35°C. For removing a quickly deposited, thin, hard scale from the cooling coils, a system of electrolytic cleaning has been developed in which the coils are made cathodic in a dilute solution of sulfuric acid.

As addition agents in electrolysis about 24 mg per l of glue and 10 mg

TABLE 75.   PURIFICATION, ELECTROLYTIC ZINC CO. OF AUSTRALASIA, LTD.

Zn dust used, tons... 71
Zn dust used, lb per ton cathode Zn............................ 26.7
Zn dust used, % of chemical equivalent of Cu plus Cd............. 298

	Solution composition	
	Before treatment	After treatment
Cu, mg per l.................................	112	0.1
Cd, mg per l.................................	176	1.8
Cu-Cd precipitate, tons......................	...	192

	% Zn	% Pb	% Cu	% Cd	Ag, oz
Assay Cu-Cd precipitate.....	33.6	0.6	6.7	10.35	2.3

Co removed, lb... 1,801
β-Naphthol used, lb per lb Co......................... 10.0
NaNO₂, lb per lb Co................................... 6.9
Caustic soda, lb per lb Co............................ 3.17
Lime, lb per lb Co.................................... 14.2
Cl removed, lb.. 1,090
Ag loss, oz per lb Cl removed......................... 0.99

TABLE 76.   COBALT REMOVAL, ELECTROLYTIC ZINC CO. OF AUSTRALASIA, LTD.

Co precipitate treated, tons................................. 42.5
Co content of crude precipitate, %........................... 1.93
Acid used, tons.. 2.47

	% Ca	% SiO₂
Co concentrate assay.........................	0.023	0.151

Oil used in roasting, tons..................................... 11
Finishing temperature, °C (approximate)...................... 750
Output of oxide, tons... 1.0

	% Co	% Fe	% Zn	% Ca	% SiO₂
Co oxide assay........	64.3	2.5	1.6	0.50	6.77*

* This figure is abnormally high.   It is usually about 2%.

TABLE 77. ELECTROLYSIS, ANALYSIS OF FEED SOLUTION, JUNE, 1947, ELECTROLYTIC ZINC CO. OF AUSTRALASIA, LTD.

	Grams per Liter		Milligrams per Liter
Zn	111.9	Total N	142
Mn	20.8	NH₄ N	138
Ca	0.44	Nitrite N	3
Mg	1.77	Nitrate N	Possible
Na	3.7		trace
K	1.36	Phosphate	Trace
Sulfate	219.4	Al	0.44
	Milligrams per Liter	Pb	0.07
		Bi	0.001
Co	9.4	Ni	0.2
Cu	0.11	Se	Nil
Cd	1.6	Te	Nil
Silica	102	Sn	0.065
Total Cl	139	Ag	0.35
Chloride Cl	99	Fe (total)	1.2
Chlorate Cl	Nil	Fe (after filtration)	< 0.1
Perchlorate Cl	40		
Fl	32	Solids in suspension	74
As	< 0.1	Specific gravity	1.344
Sb	0.09		

TABLE 78. ELECTROLYTIC PLANT DATA, ELECTROLYTIC ZINC CO. OF AUSTRALASIA, LTD.

Output of cathode Zn, tons (four weeks)	5,917
Anode current density—amp per sq ft	
At 12,000 amp	28.3
At 18,000 amp	32.1
Cathode current density, amp per sq ft	
At 12,000 amp	26.2
At 18,000 amp	29.4
Voltage per unit at 12,000 amp	502
Voltage per unit at 18,000 amp	507
Current efficiency, %	92.0
Zn deposited, lb per d-c hp-day	12.59
Zn deposited, lb per a-c hp-day	11.47
Glue, lb per ton cathode Zn	0.84
β-Naphthol, lb per ton cathode Zn	0.33

per l of β-napthol are used. Current efficiency averages about 92 per cent, with a 72-hr stripping period. The accompanying tables of operating data refer to average figures for a 4-week period during the year ended June 30, 1948.

Feed solution was taken for analysis in June, 1947. During the year ended as above, average cathode zinc output was 211.2 tons per day, although it rose to about 245 tons at the close of the year.   A full description with flow sheet of the cadmium recovery plant was given in a separate paper, which is abstracted in Chap. 8.

TABLE 79.   MELTING AND CASTING, ELECTROLYTIC ZINC CO. OF AUSTRALASIA, LTD.

Cathode Zn melted, tons (4 weeks)............:.... 5,877
Proportion of scrap therein, %.................. 2.02
Zn slabs cast, tons............................ 5,658
Dross produced, tons........................... 272
Flue and baghouse dust (estimated), tons......... 37
Zn content of dross, %......................... 79.4
Zn recovery as slab zinc, %.................... 96.27
Oil consumed, % of zinc fed.................... 2.29
Ammonium chloride, lb per ton feed............. 1.32

Analyses of Products

	High-grade slab Zn, %	Four Nines cathode Zn, %
Zn...............................	99.9838	99.9918
Pb..............................	0.0116	0.0048
Cu..............................	0.0012	0.0011
Cd..............................	0.0025	0.0023
Fe..............................	0.0009	0.00001
As..............................	0.00001	0.00001

RHODESIA-BROKEN HILL DEVELOPMENT CO.

This African low-density plant produces about 1,900 tons of electrolytic slab zinc per month.   It is particularly notable for its handling of difficult purification problems, including the control of soluble silica.

The company operates a lead-zinc flotation mill and a leaching plant for vanadium, the latter being described in Chap. 8.   Lead concentrate goes to a lead smelter and the zinc concentrate goes to the electrolytic zinc plant.   Flow sheets for crushing and sorting, flotation, and zinc leaching and electrolysis are given in Figs. 39, 40, and 41, respectively.

Roasting and Leaching.   Production of zinc concentrate comes to about 95 long tons daily.   Average assays are 57 per cent zinc and 4 per cent lead.   The concentrate is dry-ground to 95 per cent minus 325 mesh and is then flash-roasted.   In addition, the tailing from the lead-zinc sulfide flotation is also leached.   This product amounts to about 75 long tons daily, averaging 27 per cent total zinc, 25.5 per cent oxide zinc, 10.5 per cent total lead, 9.5 per cent oxide lead.   This material is pulped with unpurified zinc sulfate solution and is pumped to storage. The pulp carries about 10 lb of undissolved solids per gal.

Manganese ore carrying 10 to 20 per cent manganese dioxide, and anode mud carrying 60 to 65 per cent of the same material, are ground in a ball mill with impure zinc solution and pumped to storage.

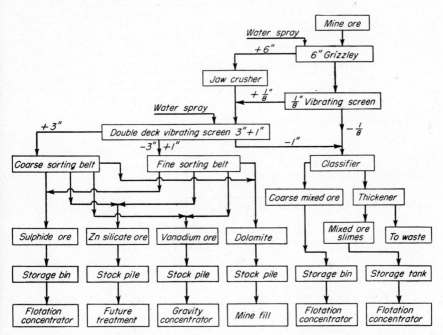

	Lead %		Zinc %		V₂O₅
	Total	Oxide	Total	Oxide	%
Sulphide ore	21.7	3.7	36.2	10.9	
Zn silicate ore	7.3	4.9	27.0	26.6	
Mixed ore and slimes	15.7	7.2	26.2	16.4	
Vanadium ore					2.0 –5.0

FIG. 39.   Flow sheet of crushing, washing, and sorting plant, Rhodesia-Broken Hill Development Co., Ltd.

Calcine from roasting the sulfide ore is leached by batch agitation in five flat-bottomed redwood leaching tanks, 15 ft in diameter by 17 ft deep. The tanks are lined with lead, protected by a high-silica brick lining. The tanks have two impellers each, plus Pachuca-type air-lift columns. There are 10 to 12 charges treated daily.

The leach begins by running into the tank about 1 to 1¼ tons of 90 per cent sulfuric acid (200 to 300 gal). To this is added 7 tons of the sulfide tailing pulp mentioned previously. The oxides in this pulp react easily with the sulfuric acid and the pulp has to be added slowly to avoid excessive frothing.

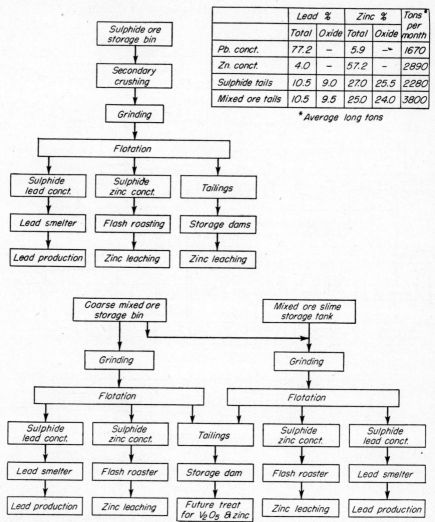

	Lead %		Zinc %		Tons* per month
	Total	Oxide	Total	Oxide	
Pb. conct.	77.2	–	5.9	–*	1670
Zn. conct.	4.0	–	57.2	–	2890
Sulphide tails	10.5	9.0	27.0	25.5	2280
Mixed ore tails	10.5	9.5	25.0	24.0	3800

*Average long tons

FIG. 40. Flow sheet of flotation plant, Rhodesia-Broken Hill Development Co., Ltd.

Thereafter, 15,000 gal of spent solution is run in. This solution contains about 35 gpl zinc and 135 gpl sulfuric acid. The mixture is then agitated for about ½ hr.

When a check of free acid shows that it is down to about 80 to 100 gpl

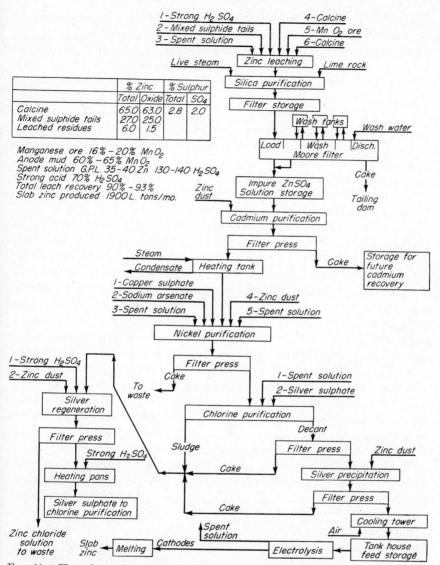

FIG. 41. Flow sheet of zinc-leaching and electrolysis plants, Rhodesia-Broken Hill Development Co., Ltd.

of sulfuric, dry calcine is slowly added until the free acid content is down to 10 to 15 gpl. This takes about 180 lb of calcine per gpl of sulfuric acid, or about 7 tons of calcine. Agitation continues about 1½ hr, after which the ferrous iron content of the pulp is determined. It is usually about 1 gpl.

Manganese-bearing pulp, as mentioned previously, is then added to the extent of 160 lb of manganese dioxide per 100 mg per l of ferrous iron. The manganese pulp is added at this low-acid strength at a slow rate in order to prevent a reaction between manganese dioxide and any sulfide zinc, which would decrease the efficiency of iron oxidation. After another half-hour of agitation, calcine goes in until the free acid is brought down to 1 to 3 gpl. Another 2 hr of agitation and the pulp is ready for silica precipitation. By the time the pulp is pumped to the silica precipitation tanks, the acid content is down to 0.1 to 1.5 gpl and the temperature is down to 60°C. The impurities now in solution are silica, phosphorus, cadmium, nickel, etc.

Silica Precipitation. The objective of the silica purification step is to bring down all the silica in a granular filterable form. It is done by batch agitation in precipitation tanks of the same number, type, and size as the leaching tanks. The pulp is agitated and heated by steam coils while the tank is being filled. Ground limestone is then added to give an excess of about 2 gpl, usually 600 to 800 lb of limestone being required. Ferrous iron is then determined and about 25 lb of manganese dioxide added per 100 mg per l of it. Temperature is brought up to 70°C and the pulp agitated for at least 1 hr for silica conditioning. During this period, ferric sulfate reacts with phosphorus pentoxide and vanadium oxide, forming iron complexes. The excess iron precipitates as ferric hydrate and the silica changes from a gel to a granular form.

A test for granulation of silica is then made by filtering 250 cc of the pulp through a 4-in. Buchner funnel until the cake cracks. Filtration time and filtrate volume are noted. If the filtration time is less than 8 min, granulation is assumed satisfactory. If filtration is too slow, agitation is continued until the test shows the proper result.

Tests are also made for ferrous iron and residual phosphorus pentoxide. Ferrous iron should be less than 25 mg per l and the residual phosphorus pentoxide only a trace. If all tests are finally satisfactory, the pulp discharges by gravity to a filter.

Filtration. Moore filters are used to filter the pulp. There are four stages of countercurrent washing. Three filters are available, one as a spare. Each has forty 6- by 10-ft leaves, totaling 4,000 sq ft of filter area per basket.

The filters are of wood construction with grooved wood panel backing and cotton duck cloth. The filter vats are of concrete and are lead-lined. There are 18 to 20 filter cycles per day, including cake formation, taking 60 to 90 min; washing and transfer, taking about 1 hr; and cake discharge, about ½ hr. The filtrate and first wash carry 120 to 125 gpl zinc. This solution is pumped to impure zinc solution storage consisting of two 30,000-gal tanks. The usual advancing wash system is used, the fourth wash solution generally carrying 1.0 to 1.5 gpl zinc. The filtrate volume is approximately 10,000 gal per charge to purification.

The washed residue going to the tailing dam carries 6 per cent total zinc, 1.5 per cent acid-soluble zinc, and 16 per cent lead.

Cadmium Purification. Cadmium is removed by batch agitation in four 17- by 17-ft tanks, lead-lined, but without brick lining. Mechanical agitation is by two impellers in each tank. The purification cycle is as follows:

About 18,000 gal is drawn from the impure zinc sulfate storage. This solution carries 120 to 125 gpl of zinc and is at a temperature of 45 to 50°C. About 30 lb of zinc dust is added, and the solution is agitated for a maximum of 2 hr, a limit set because longer agitation tends to redissolve cadmium. The cadmium content of the solution is then determined and more zinc dust is added if required; otherwise the solution is pumped to the cadmium filters.

The filters used are five 40-ft frame, 42- by 42-in. Dehne pressure filters, of iron construction and using double twill filter cloth. About 4,000 lb. of cadmium, as a cake containing 10 to 12 per cent cadmium, is produced per month. This cake is stored for future cadmium recovery. The filtrate is pumped to two 30,000-gal heating tanks in which the solution is heated to 75°C by steam coils.

Nickel Purification. Nickel is removed by batch agitation in tanks of the same number, size, and type as the cadmium-purification tanks. While the heated solution from the cadmium purification is entering the nickel tanks, about 20 lb of copper sulfate per charge is added, along with 10 lb of sodium arsenate. The mechanism of the action of the sodium arsenate is not known, but experience has shown it to be beneficial to the condition of the copper-zinc couple.

Spent solution is then added in sufficient amount to bring the solution nearly to neutrality, while leaving it still slightly basic. The purpose of this step is to dissolve any precipitated basic salts. When the tanks are nearly full, about 300 lb zinc dust is added, which precipitates copper, nickel, and arsenic. Enough spent solution also goes in to bring the pulp to neutral, the object of this addition being to keep the copper-zinc-arsenic couple clean. The full charge is about 20,000 gal and agitation is continued for about 1 hr, after which the solution is tested for nickel and arsenic. Nickel content is reduced to less than 1 mg per l and arsenic to less than 0.5 mg per l.

The solution is then pumped to one of four filter presses of the same construction as the cadmium presses.   The cake from these is discharged to waste and the solution, which carries 100 to 150 mg per l free chlorine, is pumped to the chlorine-purification section.

Chlorine Purification. Chlorine is removed by batch agitation in tanks of the same size, number, and construction as the cadmium tanks. The tanks are half-filled with filtrate from the nickel purification presses, and spent solution is added to acidify to about 0.1 to 0.2 gpl sulfuric acid. Silver sulfate (45 per cent silver) amounting to 150 lb per mg per l of chlorine is then added and the tanks filled with solution from the nickel purification.   A charge is about 18,000 gal and about 10 charges per day are run.

The charge is agitated for about 1 hr and then settled and decanted. The decanted solution is pumped to filter presses and the sludge (silver chloride) is pumped to the silver regeneration section.   The filters used are two Dehue pressure filters.   The cake discharge from these (one a day) goes to the silver-regeneration section and the filtrate, with less than 20 mg per l of chlorine, and with a trace of silver both as sulfate in solution and as suspended chloride floc, is pumped to the silver-precipitation section.

Silver Precipitation. Silver is recovered by batch agitation in two tanks of the same size and construction as the cadmium tanks.   A charge is 18,000 gallons and about 50 lb of zinc dust per charge is added, the excess zinc being used to neutralize free acid.

After zinc dust addition, agitation is continued for 2 hr and the solution is then pumped to filter presses, which are the same number, size, and construction as the chlorine presses.   The cake (5 per cent silver) goes to the silver-regeneration section and the filtrate, carrying 40 to 50 gpl zinc, is pumped to cooling towers.   In the towers, it is cooled to 40°C and goes to one of two pure solution storage tanks.

The silver chloride sludge from the chlorine purification and the cake from the silver precipitation are agitated with strong sulfuric acid and zinc dust.   The pulp is then filter-pressed, the filtrate (zinc chloride) going to waste.   The cement silver cake is heated in cast-iron coal-fired heating pans with strong sulfuric acid and stirred until completely sulfated.   The resulting silver sulfate is ground, weighed into batch lots, and reused in the chlorine-purification section.

Zinc Electrolysis. The zinc tank house has two units of 72 cells each. The units have 12 cascades of 6 cells each.   The cells are water-cooled with lead coils.   Each cell has 40 cathodes and 41 anodes.   The power per unit is about 19,000 amp at about 265 volts.   The current density is about 30 amp per sq ft of cathode surface and the voltage drop per gap about 3½ volts.   Solution is fed to each cell to hold sulfuric acid at 130 to 150 gpl.   Cathodes are stripped after 48 hr deposition.

Zinc Melting.   Zinc is melted in a standard reverberatory furnace with a bath of 125 tons of molten zinc.   The melting efficiency is 94 per cent. About 1,900 long tons of slab zinc are produced per month.   Average analysis of this zinc is

	Assay, %
Zinc	99.9734 (by difference)
Lead	0.0220
Iron	0.0010
Copper	0.0006
Cadmium	0.0030

The over-all zinc recovery, slab zinc sold divided by zinc in the plant feed, is 90 to 93 per cent.   Zinc dust is made for the purification sections. The zinc dross is ground in a ball mill, leached in separate leach tanks, and pumped to the spent solution storage.

CHAPTER 8

OPERATING DATA FROM PRACTICE—MISCELLANEOUS

A brief description of leaching methods for nickel, cobalt, manganese, tin, cadmium, and vanadium and abstracts of published accounts of methods for treating uranium and radium are here presented.

NICKEL

Most of the world's nickel is produced by pyrometallurgical processes. There are, however, a number of localities in which garnierite, $H_2(NiMg)SiO_4 \cdot nH_2O$, occurs, the ores of which, especially when low-grade, are not well adapted to fire metallurgy, due largely to the lack of sulfur required for matte formation in smelting. In all these ores the quantity of magnesium present is too great for economical acid leaching.

NICARO NICKEL CO.

The Caron ammonia process is adapted to the treatment of these and similar ores. The method was employed during the Second World War by the Nicaro Nickel Co., a subsidiary of Freeport Sulphur Co., to extract nickel from the lateritic iron ores of Oriente province on the North coast of Cuba. The process consists essentially of roasting to reduce nickel to metal, leaching with an ammoniacal solvent, precipitation of nickel and evolution of ammonia by solution heating, and recovering the ammonia for solvent regeneration.

After about six months of operation of a 1-ton-per-day pilot plant (capacity of roaster) to verify certain basic facts and to establish best working conditions, design and construction of a plant to treat 3,000 tons ore per day were decided upon.

Equipment used in this plant is shown in the flow sheet, Fig. 42, the main steps of the process being:

1. Wet-ore storage and handling.
2. Drying.
3. Grinding.
4. Reduction.
5. Leaching and washing.
6. Product precipitation and ammonia recovery.

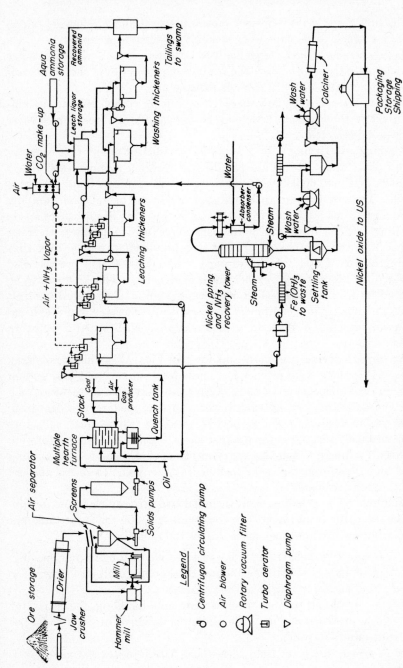

Fig. 42.   Nickel-recovery flow sheet, Nicaro Nickel Co., Cuba.

The first three steps represent purely physical and mechanical operations, for which pilot-plant work was not considered necessary.

Based on the use in the large plant of 12 furnaces, each with an average capacity of 300 tons per day, the ratio of expansion over the pilot-plant scale was actually 300:1 in a single furnace.

Notes in regard to the flow sheet follow, but for complete plant description refer to the excellent article by Dufour and Hills[1] from which these notes are abstracted.

Crushing and Drying.   In order to have sufficient ore-storage capacity at the plant and to facilitate blending, a working storage area with a capacity of about 60,000 tons, serviced by two gantry cranes, was provided.   The cranes were to handle the ore from the railroad dumping track and to load the ore from the track into two Stephens-Adamson traveling feeders, feeding a 36-in. belt conveyor.   A primary crushing unit of a Jeffrey double-roll crusher was provided to reduce rock to a maximum size of 4 in.   Inside storage of about 5,000 tons ore was also provided for use in rainy weather and emergencies.   This area was to be serviced by a P. & H. traveling crane capable of feeding each dryer unit directly.   The feeding equipment for each dryer consisted of a Stephens-Adamson traveling feeder and an automatic Richardson batch-weighing feeder.

Concurrent drying was used and for this four Allis-Chalmers rotary dryers 135 ft. long were provided.   These have an enlarged feed section 14 in. in diameter, the main body of each unit having a diameter of 11.5 in.   The discharge end of each dryer was equipped with a Hardinge rotary table feeder to get a positive seal.   Cyclone dust collectors removed dust from the dryer exhaust gases.   Duplicate conveyors were provided for transporting the ore from the drying plant to the grinding plant and Weightometers were included at this point to record the ore feed through the plant.

Grinding.   The grinding plant included two primary elevators for lifting the discharge from the hot-ore conveyors to a 200-ton surge tank and three grinding circuits, each consisting of the following:

1. A Pennsylvania hammer mill, type C-430, with $\frac{3}{8}$-in. bar spacing.
2. A secondary elevator for handling the hammer-mill discharge.
3. A 16-ft-diameter Sturtevant air separator.
4. A 3- by 9-ft Hardinge conical ball mill handling the separator rejects in closed circuit.   The unit was designed to grind to 95 per cent minus 80 mesh.

[1] M. F. Dufour and R. C. Hills, Nickel from Cuba, *Chemical Industries*, p. 621, October, 1945.

Eight concrete silos with a capacity of 10,000 dry tons were provided as emergency storage and for final ore blending and maintenance of uniform plant feed.

Twelve Herreshoff roasting furnaces were built, each 22.5 ft in diameter with 11 hearths, in which steam-cooling was used. The roast is a reduction roast. Spare roasting capacity was provided by a rotary kiln.

Jacoby conveyors were chosen for handling the hot ore from the furnaces, discharging to Hardinge rotary coolers, 9 by 6 ft, partially immersed in water and revolving at 6 rpm.

Leaching. After cooling, the ore was conveyed by inclined screws to tanks where it was mixed with liquor from the leaching plant and then pumped to the leaching plant.

For the aeration units in the leaching plant, Turbo-mixers were chosen. The leaching plant was designed as three parallel lines, each with three stages. The Turbo-mixers for each individual step were built in blocks of three to minimize short-circuiting and limit the size of each unit. A suitable scrubbing system was provided to recover ammonia from the exit air used in the agitation process.

The thickeners in the leaching plant were 75-ft-diameter Dorr torque type S units. Similar units were used in the washing plant but this washing section was designed in two parallel lines of four stages each, and these units were 110 ft in diameter. These sizes were based on unit area determinations made on a laboratory scale. The layout of the leaching and washing sections of the plant was carried out by J. D. Grothe of the Dorr Co.

Tanks in the leaching and washing sections were of prestressed concrete construction with dome-shaped roofs to prevent atmospheric ammonia losses.

In the product-precipitation and ammonia-recovery sections of the plant, stills similar to the units used in the Calumet & Hecla plant were adopted, with standard condensing, absorbing, and cooling equipment.

Recovery. Filtration of the basic nickel carbonate was by 8- by 8-ft Oliver vacuum filters. An intermediate thickener step, previous to filtration, was used to lighten the load on the filters.

An F. L. Smidth "Unax" kiln was chosen for calcining the wet nickel carbonate. The unit was 10 by 132 ft and was brick-lined for 80 ft. A dry cyclone dust collector removed most of the oxide dust from the kiln gases, this being recycled to the kiln feed. A wet collector removed all final traces of oxide, its discharge going to the thickener handling the slurry from the product-distillation columns.

Cooled oxide from the kiln was transported by screw conveyor and

Bulk-Flo elevator to the nickel oxide warehouse where it was bagged for shipment.

Problems. Various operating difficulties were encountered in the initial operation. Some of these included: handling the wet sticky ore, especially during heavy rainfalls; flooding characteristics of the ore during grinding; cooling troubles due to tendency of the reduced ore to stick to the cold surfaces of the dryer shell, resulting in higher temperatures of ore discharge; accumulation of "oversize" material in parts of the leaching circuit; unsatisfactory aeration performance resulting in low nickel recoveries; deposition of magnesium–ammonium carbonate scale.

Serious corrosion was experienced only in certain equipment handling the strong liquor from the ammonia distillation operation. All iron was of a 24–20 nickel-chrome alloy, which showed no sign of corrosion after a year's service. The tubes in the heat exchanger gave the most serious corrosion trouble. Aluminum tube bundles proved a satisfactory answer to this problem.

Generally speaking, such alterations and additions as were found necessary were confined to accessory equipment and did not result in any fundamental change in the flow sheet of the basic processing units. For cost data, see Chap. 9.

MANGANESE

Leaching methods for manganese ores may be classified as processes for production of

1. Manganese metal.
2. Manganese dioxide (MnO_2).
3. Manganese oxide (Mn_3O_4).

Brief descriptions of some applications of these procedures are given in the following pages.

1. Manganese Metal Production

There is only one process in operation for electrolytic production of manganese metal. Preliminary and test-plant work on the development of this process by metallurgists of the U.S. Bureau of Mines and the Electromanganese Corp., Knoxville, Tenn., is described in a number of publications of the Bureau and elsewhere.[1]

Electrolytic manganese is comparatively a high-cost metal, although the price was reduced from 40 cents (carload delivered basis) in 1942 to

---

[1] G. D. Van Arsdale and C. G. Maier, *Transactions of American Electrochemical Society*, Vol. 33, pp. 109–129, 1918.

A. J. Allen and A. M. Campbell, *Transactions of Faraday Society*, Vol. 19, p. 559, 1924.

S. M. Shelton, Electrolysis of Manganese Solutions, *U.S. Bureau of Mines Report of Investigation* 3322, 1936.

S. M. Shelton *et al.*, Electrometallurgical Investigations, *U.S. Bureau of Mines* the 1952 price of 28 cents.   It seems improbable that costs will ever approximate those of standard-grade blast-furnace or electric-furnace products.   The reasons for this are as follows:

1. Manganese has a high negative value with respect to hydrogen in the electromotive series.

2. Current losses from solution heating and evolution of cathodic hydrogen will never be low.   However, current efficiency at the Knoxville plant of Electromanganese Corp. has been raised from the low fifties to the high sixties.

3. A high content of buffer solution (ammonium sulfate) must be carried for conductivity and prevention of precipitation of manganese dioxide in the cell.   Together with the other salts present, this means virtually saturated solutions, requiring great care in temperature control to prevent crystallization.

4. Re-solution of manganese in the cell, due to its high activity, can take place very rapidly from a number of causes.   Power interruption causes the plates to "go black," requiring their removal.

5. Power requirements for manganese deposition are higher than for plating any other metal commercially from water solution.   The a-c over-all power consumption at Knoxville is between 5.0 and 5.5 kwkr per lb of finished manganese metal.

6. Reducing roasting is required for most available manganese ores and this type of roasting is difficult.   It required the development at Knoxville of special equipment and methods.

7. The electrolyte must be kept pure.   Currently, less than 1 mg per l of any impurity is contained in the catholyte, with the exception of some elements of the alkaline earth and alkali groups.

8. The present electrolytic manganese process is necessarily a two-solution system.   This arises from the obvious fact that manganese cannot be plated from an acid solution and cannot be dissolved from its

Report of Investigation 3406, 1938.

J. Koster and S. M. Shelton, Engineering and Mining Journal, pp. 137, 510, 1936.

F. W. Woodman and J. H. Jacobs, Studies in the Electrodeposition of Manganese, U.S. Bureau of Mines Report of Investigation 3681, 1943.

C. G. Fink, Anodes for Electrowinning Manganese, Electrochemical Society Reprint 76-5, September, 1939.

J. H. Jacobs et al., Two Years Operation of the Bureau of Mines Electrolytic Manganese Pilot Plant, Trans. AIME, Vol. 159, p. 408, 1944.

E. M. Wanamaker, Discussion, Trans. AIME, Vol. 159, p. 428, 1944.

C. L. Mantell, Commercial Production of Electrolytic Manganese, Transactions of Electrochemical Society, Vol. 94, p. 232, 1948.

R. H. Bennett, A Decade of Electrolytic Manganese, Engineering and Mining Journal, Vol. 150, No. 10, p. 80, 1949.

reduced ores by a basic solution.　A diaphragm cell must therefore be used and is always more expensive than a single-compartment cell.

9.　Corrosion problems are very severe in the process; preferred construction materials are stainless steel, lead, wood, and rubber.

With the exception of manganese metal, pyrometallurgically produced (which now seems to have been relegated to a minor role), electrolytic manganese is at a price disadvantage which ranges from 2 cents per lb (packed and delivered) in the case of low-carbon special grade, to 13.25

TABLE 80.　COMPARISON OF ELECTROLYTIC MANGANESE WITH OTHER SOURCES
(April, 1949)

Items	Mn %	Fe %	Si %	P %	C %	Selling price per lb, Mn content, carloads*			Remarks
						Bulk	Packing	Total	
Electrolytic Mn	Min. 99.98	Max. 0.001	Not found	Not found	0.004	....	......	$0.28	Packed, steel drums, delivered Eastern zone
Mn metal, Thermit process	95–98	2–2.5	1–1.5	......	0.06–0.20	$0.355	......	0.355	Packed, delivered
Low-carbon ferromanganese, special grade	90	Balance	1–2	Max. 0.06	Max. 0.07	0.2525	0.0075	0.26	Delivered
Low-carbon ferromanganese, regular grade	80–85	Balance	1–2	0.18	0.10	0.2475	0.0075	0.2550	Delivered
Medium-carbon ferromanganese	80–85	Balance	Max. 1.5–2.5	......	Max. 1.5	0.1815	0.0075	0.1890	Delivered
Low-iron ferromanganese	85–90	Max. 2.0	Max. 3.0	......	7.0	....	......	0.1475	Delivered
Standard ferromanganese	78–82	Balance	Max. 1.0	Max. 0.35	7.0	0.0965	......	0.0965	Fob plant

* Carloads 56,000 lb except electrolytic manganese, which is 40,000 lb.

cents in the case of low-iron ferromanganese.　Nevertheless, the electrolytic metal is used in competition with all these lower-priced grades. Electrolytic manganese is used almost exclusively in stainless steels, tool steels, and special-alloy steels.　It is also used in various nonferrous alloys.　Table 80 shows composition and prices of electrolytic manganese in comparison with other manganese products.

Much confusion has existed concerning priority of discovery and the relative roles of the U.S. Bureau of Mines and the Electromanganese Corp. in developing the electrolytic manganese process.　The facts are as follows:[1]

[1] R. H. Bennett, A Decade of Electrolytic Manganese, *Engineering and Mining Journal*, Vol. 150, No. 10, p. 80, 1949.

The Knoxville plant was originally designed by Bureau of Mines personnel, following extended laboratory experiments. Its proposed capacity was 2,400 lb of metal per day. Construction was completed in June, 1939.

Unfortunately, many unforseen difficulties appeared on an operating scale. The original plant was an almost complete operating failure. It had to be entirely redesigned and rebuilt, after a period of new research and engineering. This was done by the technical staff of the Electromanganese Corp. All funds for development work and plant construc-

TABLE 81. PRODUCTION OF ELECTROLYTIC MANGANESE IN THE UNITED STATES,
1939–1948
(In pounds)

Year	Electro-manganese Corp.	U.S. Bureau of Mines	Totals
1939	43,669	....	43,669
1940	418,837	....	418,837
1941	1,190,042	....	1,190,042
1942	1,305,310	149,380	1,455,690
1943	2,385,486	464,690	2,850,176
1944	3,308,071	476,200	3,784,271
1945	3,398,569	280,336	3,678,905
1946	2,120,943	127,614	2,248,557
1947	3,499,181	....	3,499,181
1948	4,523,097	....	4,523,097
Totals.....	22,194,205	1,498,220	23,692,425

tion at Knoxville were furnished by private investors and early operating losses were made up by them.

In the new plant, the only features of the original design by the Bureau that were retained were the addition of sulfur dioxide gas to the catholyte (which was discovered by Shelton and associates in the Bureau of Mines); the dimensions of the electrolytic cells; the use of sulfate electrolyte and of ammonium sulfate as a buffer. The last two steps had been developed before the Bureau undertook its electrolytic research program: the use of manganese sulfate by Van Arsdale in 1918, and of ammonium sulfate by Allmand and Campbell in 1924.

The installed monthly capacity of the Knoxville plant is now 450,000 lb of metal of about 99.97 per cent purity. Table 81 gives production of the Knoxville and Bureau of Mines plants through 1948.

The processes in present use for electrolytic manganese at Knoxville were developed by the technical and engineering staff of the Electro-

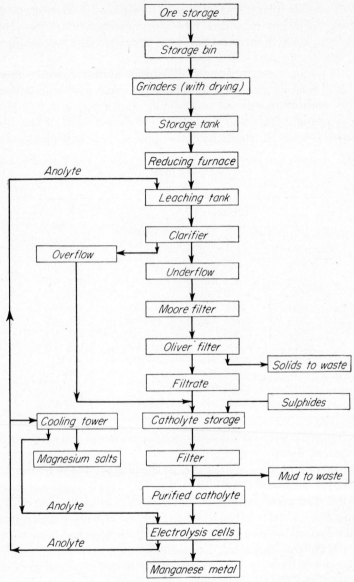

Fɪɢ. 43.   Electrolytic manganese flow sheet, Electromanganese Corporation, Knoxville, Tenn.

manganese Corp. and are based on 14 United States and numerous foreign patents owned by the corporation.   Figure 43 shows a flow sheet of the plant operations and Table 82 gives operating details.

TABLE 82.   DATA ON PRODUCTION OF ELECTROLYTIC MANGANESE BY ELECTRO-
MANGANESE CORP.

Average Mn in ore, %	48
Coarse grinding	Jaw crusher and gyratory
Fine grinding	Raymond mill
Reduction furnace	Two 12-in. ID alloy-steel tubes 15 ft long with 15 ft cooler
Heating methods	Resistance by Nichrome units
Furnace capacity, tons ore pre day	15
Reduction, %	99
Thickeners, Dorr	Two 40-ft diam, 90,000 gal each
Leaching tanks	Six, 8,000 gal each
Purification tanks	Eight, 10,000 gal each
Anolyte:	
Mn, gpl, as $MnSO_4$	10–18
H_2SO_4, gpl	25–35
$(NH_4)_2SO_4$, gpl	120–140
pH	1–1.4
Catholyte feed:	
Mn, gpl, as $MnSO_4$	25–35
$(NH_4)_2SO_4$, gpl	125–135
pH	7.2–7.6
Anodes:	
Composition	Lead base, with Sn, Sb, and Co
Anodes per cell	21
Cathodes:	
Composition	Stainless steel, 18% Cr, 12% Ni, 25% Mo
Size	36 in. by 18 in. by $\frac{1}{16}$ in.
Number per cell	20
Cell amperage	6,000
Cell temperature, °C	35–40
Cathode C. D. amp per sq ft	40
Diaphragm material	Woven textile
Cell voltage	5
Current efficiency, %	65–70
Recovery to metal, %	87
Operating time for cathodes, hr	24–40
Kwhr per lb Mn, d-c	4–4.5
Kwhr per lb Mn, a-c, over-all	5–5.25
Purity of Mn, %	99.97

The product is a very pure metal, average shipments being of the order of 99.97 per cent manganese or better.   Analysis of the metal is as follows:

Mn......................... 99.9+%

NONMETALS

C......................... 0.004%
S......................... 0.0135%
SO$_2$............. Not found, 25-g sample
Sulfates.......... Not found, 25-g sample
P............... Not found, 25-g sample

METALS PRESENT

Ca......................... < 0.001%
Cu......................... < 0.001%
Fe......................... < 0.001%
Mg......................... < 0.001%
Ag......................... < 0.001%

METALS ABSENT BY SPECTROSCOPIC ANALYSIS

Al	Cr	Ni	Ti
Sb	Co	K	W
As	Pb	Si	V
Cd	Mo	Su	Zn

For reduction, the Knoxville plant uses two special furnaces, described as follows: each furnace includes a pair of 12-in. ID alloy-steel tubes, 15 ft long, joined at one end to a 15 ft length of ordinary 12-in. ID wrought-iron pipe. The alloy tubes pass through a chamber heated electrically by Nichrome resistance elements.

The wrought-iron extension is sprayed with water for cooling the reduced ore. Ore and reduction material are fed in at the open end of the alloy tubes and advanced by rotation of the tubes through the heating section and into the cooling chamber. The reaction gases leave each tube at the feed end. The exit end is housed to prevent access of air, the reduced ore dropping to a Redler conveyor, which delivers to the storage bin. Each furnace has a capacity of from 12 to 18 tons of ore daily. Temperature is closely controlled. Reduction is consistently of the order of 98 per cent or better, and there has been no trouble from reoxidation.

In the leaching section lime is used for pH adjustment after agitation, up to the point at which oxidized iron precipitates.

For solution separation and washing, two 40-ft Dorr thickeners are in use, followed by a Moore filter, which in turn is followed by an Oliver filter. Settling and washing are satisfactory, the loss being about 3.25 per cent of the manganese to the process. This is the total mud-residue loss. Washing efficiency is high, and the soluble manganese loss is of the order of 0.30 per cent of the manganese to the system.

The ferrous sulfate step for purification is not used; it is replaced by special procedures for removing impurities not precipitated as sulfides. Ammonium sulfide instead of hydrogen sulfide is employed for this step.

The cell room contains 70 cells in series, each with 21 anodes and 20 cathodes. Current is supplied by a 1,500-kva and a 720-kva motor-generator set, normally operating at 6,000 amp and 270 volts, and 6,000 amp and 120 volts, respectively. Voltage per cell is about 5.6 volts. Current density is 40 amp per sq ft of cathode surface.

The cell used has diaphragms around the cathodes and the anolyte fills the cell around the diaphragms. The anode used has a lead base and contains tin, antimony, and cobalt. These anodes have a life of over 18 months. Formation of manganese dioxide at the anode is low, about 2.5 per cent of the manganese to the plant, and much of this is recovered by reuse in the process.

Practical problems were (1) control of magnesium in the electrolyte, (2) cell cooling, (3) evaporation of electrolyte to make room for the leach residue wash waters.

These three problems were solved by means including direct evaporation of solution, for which a large quantity of cell anolyte was circulated over cooling towers. This provided adequate evaporation, sufficient cooling for holding the cell temperatures at 38 to 40°C, and convenient means for crystallizing and removing a complex sulfate of magnesium, calcium, ammonia, and manganese, which can be collected periodically and sold as a fertilizer for citrus fruit. About 100 tons of this complex salt was produced in two months.

Rubber-covered steel agitators, made by the New England Tank and Tower Co., have given good results. Numerous T-4MC Durimet pumps have served well in circulating the electrolyte, and the rubber-lined Allen-Sherman-Hoff pumps work efficiently in moving leach slurry to the Dorr thickeners. Only a few materials are satisfactory in resisting the corrosive electrolyte, for instance, rubber, stainless steel, lead, and wood.

Electrolytic manganese is finding increased acceptance in both ferrous and nonferrous metallurgy. Because of its high purity, large amounts are consumed by the stainless steel industry and its use in the chemical field is mounting rapidly.

2. Manganese Dioxide Production

There have been many processes proposed for manganese dioxide production from ores. These are reviewed by Hersam.[1]

An important use of MnO_2 is as a depolarizer in dry batteries. Although several chemical processes have produced MnO_2 of quite high purity, their physical properties have not always been suitable for such use. As a matter of fact, the suitability of manganese ores or chemical

[1] E. A. Hersam, "Metallurgy of Manganese," in D. M. Liddell's *Handbook of Nonferrous Metallurgy*, McGraw-Hill Book Company, Inc., New York, 1945.

products for dry batteries can usually be determined only by making them up into commercial cells, which are then subjected to long and elaborate electrical tests under precise conditions. For this reason, and because of low price, the larger part of the supply of battery-grade MnO_2 in normal times has been from natural ores of suitable chemical purity and physical properties. Much of it is imported.

The electrolysis of solutions of $MnSO_4$ to produce anodic MnO_2 suitable for dry-cell use was proposed and investigated a number of years ago on a laboratory scale by Van Arsdale and Maier. The Dorr Company later made a thorough test-plant investigation of this process. During the Second World War it became evident that imports of African, Caucasian, or Brazilian ores would undoubtedly slow up or stop. The war was also expected to bring about a drop in grade of ore from domestic sources. To meet this situation, a high-grade dioxide could be used as a "sweetener" for mixing with lower-grade material. Batteries thus produced would meet standard specifications.

Accordingly, a dry-battery company installed a small pilot plant for production of electrolytic MnO_2 and for the elaborate commercial tests of its suitability. Preliminary work indicated the following conclusions:

1. Production of an anodic manganese product (MnO_2) as outlined is possible, using lead or graphite anodes and lead cathodes. In order to obtain practical current efficiencies (50 to 70 per cent), the cell temperature should be maintained above 70°C, the maximum cell acidity below 50 gpl sulfuric acid, cell-feed concentration of about 60 gpl Mn, and current density of about 12 amp per sq ft of anode surface.

2. Neither of the above anodes is ideal. Graphite tends to disintegrate if insufficiently depolarized, and the product is difficult to remove, owing to its hard, adherent character. The lead anodes contaminate the product with lead, probably as PbO_2, in varying amounts. Preliminary tests did not indicate that a small content of lead in the MnO_2 was detrimental.

3. By controlling the character of the surface of the lead anodes, it is possible to produce deposits varying greatly in apparent density. Rough surfaces yield a hard adherent deposit, which gives a product of high apparent density. Smooth surfaces yield a soft, flaky, nonadherent deposit which continuously sloughs off and gives a product of low apparent density. This same phenomenon was observed with platinum, 6 per cent antimony-lead, and 2 per cent silver-lead. Indications are that possibly these two product types of different apparent density will find optimum application in different types of battery service.

4. Based on a voltage requirement of 3.0 volts (current density of 10 amp per sq ft) and a current efficiency of 50 per cent, it appears that

the cell power requirement will be about 1.7 kwhr per lb MnO_2, equivalent to about 1.4 kwhr per lb of product, assuming a grade of 82.8 per cent MnO_2.

5. Preliminary tests indicated that all samples presented were suitable for battery use and some were exceptionally good.

Notes in regard to the process steps are as follows:

Reducing Roast. The ore is mixed with about 10 to 20 per cent of finely ground coal and heated for 1 hr at about 1500°F under reducing conditions. By this roast the acid-insoluble MnO_2 is reduced to acid-soluble manganous oxide, MnO. After roasting, the calcine must be cooled in the presence of carbon dioxide to 100°F or below, in order to prevent re-oxidation.

Leaching. The MnO content of the calcine can be readily dissolved in H_2SO_4 to give a $MnSO_4$ solution up to about 70 gpl in strength. Above this concentration, the solutions become quite viscous, presenting handling and filtration difficulties. In continuous operation, the calcine is leached with spent electrolyte. The acid in this is neutralized by the calcine and the manganese content of the solution replenished. With good agitation, 1 hr of leaching yields a good extraction. Iron is objectionable in the solution and MnO_2 must be added to ensure oxidation of all the iron, whereupon a pH adjustment to about 6 readily eliminates iron and aluminum. Lime is used for pH adjustment. If the pH is raised to about 7.5, a loss of about 10 per cent of the manganese present is incurred. The procedure therefore is to neutralize, usually to a pH of 6, and only occasionally raise to 7.5, thus periodically removing any impurities which precipitate at this point.

Residue Filtration. The residue after leaching can be easily removed from solution by vacuum filtration. This is more satisfactory than settling, which is slow due to the viscosity of the solutions. Some wash water is used to minimize loss.

Cell Operation. The purified electrolyte is electrolyzed and MnO_2 deposited at the anode, H_2SO_4 being produced in equivalent amounts. The electrolysis limits are not critical and the manganese reduction during electrolysis may be from 70 to 60 gpl, resulting in acidity increase to roughly 20 gpl H_2SO_4. Plating down to about 50 gpl of course reduces the rate of recirculation. Circulation or agitation in the cells is also desirable. Current density between 10 and 15 amp per sq ft is satisfactory. The temperature should be kept at 70°C or above.

Either graphite or lead anodes are used. Neither is entirely satisfactory. The graphite tends to disintegrate, and the removal of the deposit is difficult due to the hard, adherent nature of the deposit on this material.

Under the cell conditions already described, the MnO_2 at the anode is a hydrated product, approximately corresponding to H_2MnO_3. Since anodic electrolytic reactions tend to produce acid, it is probable that this is an acid compound of manganese.

Anode Cleaning. Obviously the flaky nonadherent type of deposit presents no difficulty in anode cleaning, since it can be removed by continuously circulating the electrolyte to a thickener or filter and back to the cells. With this type of deposit, anodes may be kept in service for a week or two without removing. For the hard deposit, the anodes must be lifted from the cells and the deposit removed. However, since the hard adherent deposit may be plated out to a thickness of 1 in. or more, there may be several alternative ways of handling the deposit.

Treatment of Finished Product. The anode product is ground to 100 per cent minus 150 mesh in a pebble mill and then washed to the desired sulfate content by decantation. The sulfate content is obstinately held and lengthy washing is required, since sulfate is objectionable in dry cells. It seems probable that the sulfate in the product is present as either magnesium or calcium sulfate, the latter of course being difficult to remove by water washing.

Qualitative spectographic analysis of the product from graphite anodes gave the following figures:

Manganese	Major
Magnesium	Minor
Aluminum	.OX
Silicon	.OOX
Iron	.OOX
Zinc	Not found
Titanium	.OOX
Copper	.OOX
Lead	.OOX
Chromium	Not found
Nickel	Not found
Tungsten	Not found
Cobalt	Not found
Arsenic	Not found
Antimony	Not found
Germanium	Not found

Calcium is not mentioned in this spectrographic analysis, although its presence is probable.

3. Manganese Oxide Production

During the war, there was considerable interest in various methods for producing high-grade manganese oxide, (Mn_3O_4), from domestic low-grade manganese ores. Several processes were proposed and tested on various scales.

Among these were the Wilson Bradley process, A. T. Weet's proposal, various methods proposed for treating the large amounts of extremely low-grade material of the Chamberlain district, S.D., the Ryerson and other processes for sulfur dioxide leaching, and experiments by the Bureau of Mines on leaching with nitrogen dioxide.

In 1940, the government requested the M. A. Hanna Co. to develop a source of high-grade manganese oxide to be blended with low-grade ores to furnish feed for ferromanganese furnaces.   Following a study of various processes it was decided to concentrate on further development of the sulfur dioxide process, first patented by Van Arsdale and Maier in 1918.

Pilot-plant investigation on a scale of 3 to 5 tons of 10 per cent manganese ore daily was carried on at the plant of the Pan-American Co., Berkeley, Calif.   Plans were then drawn for a plant located near Las Vegas, Nev., to treat 1,000 tons per day of 20 per cent manganese ore from the Three Kids mine.   The plant was built by Defense Plant Corp. and operated by the Manganese Ore Co., created by Hanna.   This plant and its operation have been described by D. N. Vedensky.[1]   The flow sheet is shown in Fig. 44.

Many difficulties were met, the plant never approached rated capacity, and it was shut down at the end of September, 1944, when "production of high-grade nodules was approaching 50 per cent rated capacity."

Difficulties responsible for slow progress and low capacity were summarized by Vedensky as follows:

1. From sheer necessity, the jump had to be made from a pilot plant treating 3 tons daily to a plant of 1,000 tons daily capacity.

2. Despite efforts to obtain standard equipment, it was not always available, and even some of the best manufacturers had to supply inferior products.

3. There existed a lack of competent plant designers, which frequently resulted in unworkable designs.

4. Because of labor shortages, operation of the plant often had to be entrusted to inexperienced men.

5. Difficulties in obtaining parts and supplies frequently delayed necessary plant alterations and repairs.

In addition, it may be stated that major troubles were encountered from the ore itself, which contained considerable amounts of calcium, magnesium, sodium, and potassium, causing many difficulties in most sections of the plant.

While allowance can be made for war-emergency conditions, it would

[1] D. N. Vedensky, How the SO_2 Process Worked on Three Kids Manganese Ore, *Engineering and Mining Journal*, p. 58, July, 1946.

seem that some of the difficulties summarized by Vedensky need not have occurred and others would certainly not be present in normal times. It is also possible that a more amenable ore, *e.g.*, that of the Cuyuna range, might have given more favorable results. Analyses of ores treated by the plant are shown in Table 83.

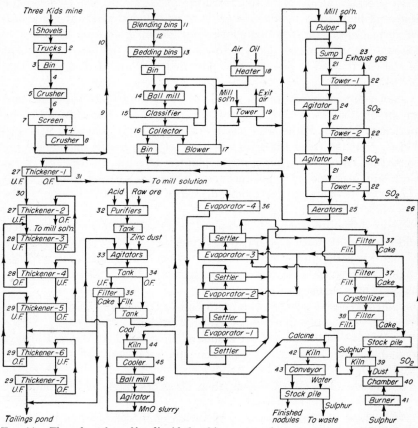

FIG. 44.   Flow sheet for sulfur dioxide leaching process for manganese ore, Manganese Ore Co., Henderson, Nev.

Ore from the bedding bins was dry-ground, then pulped with mill solution and leached in packed towers, against incoming sulfur dioxide gas, thus converting manganese dioxide into soluble manganese sulfate and some thionates. Leached pulp was washed in a thickener circuit by countercurrent decantation.

Pregnant solution from the primary thickener was purified by adding sulfuric acid and raw ore, then neutralized by manganous oxide prepared

in a small reducing kiln. Following filtration of iron and aluminum
hydroxides, the neutral solution was evaporated to yield crystals containing manganese sulfate, manganese dithionate, and alkali dithionates,
which were filtered off, then sent to a roasting kiln.

TABLE 83.   TYPICAL ANALYSES OF THREE KIDS ORE TREATED BY MANGANESE ORE
Co.

Constituent	Stockpile 1, composite %	Stockpile 2, composite %	Stockpile 3, composite %
Mn...................	29.5	24.1	18.2
Na....................	1.34	1.01	1.45
K.....................	1.96	1.77	1.84
Ca....................	1.00	1.42	2.14
Mg....................	0.92	0.86	1.70
S.....................	0.81	0.65	0.60
SiO_2.................	25.15	32.25	42.25
Al_2O_3................	5.65	7.00	8.50
Fe....................	1.35	2.02	2.07
CO_2..................	0.64	1.23	1.07
Ignition loss...........	12.65	12.23	9.51

TABLE 84.   TYPICAL ANALYSES OF UNWASHED NODULES, MANGANESE ORE CO.

	Mn	Ca	Mg	Fe	S	Na	K
Oct., 1943.......	68.1	0.20	0.10	0.56	tr.	0.75	
Dec., 1943......	63.6	0.40	0.32	0.15	0.49	0.13	
Early 1944.....	58.8	0.89	0.95	0.68	2.18	2.04	1.43
Late 1944.......	61.1	0.54	0.74	0.56	1.6	1.96	1.1

TABLE 85.   TYPICAL ANALYSIS OF WASHED NODULES, MANGANESE ORE CO.

Mn.............	64.78
S...............	0.25
Fe..............	0.56
P..............	0.010
SiO_2............	2.82

In the kiln, manganese oxide (Mn_3O_4) and SO_2 were produced, the SO_2
going back to the leaching plant, together with make-up SO_2, and the
calcine going to a nodulizing kiln. Because the nodules still carried
excessive sulfur as undecomposed Na_2SO_4, they were heap-leached with
water as a final step in the process.

   Leaching Plant. It is stated that packed towers were chosen in
preference to agitators because of "apparent simplicity," although
Three Kids was the only ore responsive to tower leaching and it also gave

better results in agitation. The towers gave much trouble due to plugging with $CaSO_4$, excessive losses of SO_2 occurred, manganese extraction had to be sacrificed, the towers redesigned, and finally two 50-ft. stacks were built to keep the exhaust gases out of the plant.

The following reactions are stated to occur in the towers:

1. Formation of sulfate:

$$MnO_2 + H_2SO_3 = MnSO_4 + H_2O$$

2. Formation of thionates:

$$MnO_2 + 2H_2SO_3 = Mn_2S_2O_6 + 2H_2O$$

3. Formation of thiosulfate:

$$S^{++} + H_2SO_3 = S_2O_3 + 2H^+$$

4. Formation of sulfite:

$$Mn^{++} + H_2SO_3 = MnSO_3 + 2H^+$$

In the plant, inhibition of the above side reactions was stated to be dependent on a low pH in the towers and this in turn on the formation of sulfuric acid in the process:

$$H_2SO_3 + \tfrac{1}{2}O_2 = H_2SO_4$$

The Pan-American aerators shown in the flow sheet were intended to form sulfuric acid by oxidizing residual sulfur dioxide.

For comparison, it may be stated that early work at Douglas, Ariz., for the Phelps Dodge Corp., demonstrated that the effects of side reactions producing dithionates and other substances could be minimized by bringing the solutions after leaching into contact with excess manganese dioxide ore. It was also demonstrated that by bringing sulfur dioxide into contact with pulp countercurrently, practically complete SO_2 absorption and good extractions were obtained. This was done in a revolving cylinder leaching device which worked well on a test-plant scale and on a large scale would have eliminated the tower troubles described by the author.

Trouble at the Three Kids plant was experienced by calcium sulfate plugging the leaching towers. The stainless steel blades of the fan-controlling draft through the towers and elsewhere failed after about two weeks of operation.

The thickener washing efficiency in 1944 was 97.4 per cent with six thickeners and 98.6 per cent with seven.

Purification.   Solution purification before evaporation was carried out by adding sulfuric acid to convert bisulfite ions to free sulfur dioxide, oxidizing the latter by adding raw ore, and subsequently neutralizing the sulfuric acid by adding manganous oxide, MnO, slurry to raise the pH to about 5.5, iron and aluminum hydroxides coming down at this point. Copper was brought down from 100 to less than 10 mg per l by adding zinc dust in about twice the theoretical amount.   The manganous oxide was prepared in a small rotary kiln.

Evaporation.   On the basis of pilot-plant work, the evaporator was designed to make two products, $MnSO_4 \cdot H_2O$ crystals to go to the roasting kiln, and alkali thionate crystals to be stockpiled for eventual recovery of sulfur.   For various reasons, this scheme did not work out and sulfates and dithionates were sent together to the roasting kiln, where the alkali salts caused much trouble by fusion and ring formation.

Further difficulty was caused at first by high concentration of sulfite in the leach solutions which yielded sulfur dioxide on heating.   Until this was changed by adding sulfuric acid and manganese dioxide, as stated previously, corrosion in the evaporators caused sufficient damage to require retubing.   Calcium carbonate and sulfate scale also formed in the evaporator tubes to an extent that required periodic acid boil-outs.

In passing it may be noted that for an ore of this character, with high soluble-alkali and alkaline-earth impurities, much of this nightmare of alkali thionates, evaporation, purification, and roasting troubles could have been avoided by a simple preliminary leach of the raw ore with quite dilute sulfuric acid and washing.   This would probably mean no greater cost than the operation as described, in which sulfuric acid was used, and by removal of the trouble-forming constituents most of the difficulties due to their presence would have disappeared.

Roasting.   Pilot-plant work indicated that manganese sulfate could be roasted in a rotary kiln with very high recovery of sulfur for reuse in leaching.   The roasting temperature is such that little if any sulfur trioxide forms.

More lost-time difficulties were said to have been caused by operation of the roasting kiln than in any other plant section.   Most of this trouble was caused by large amounts of alkali salts in the roaster feed.

In June 1944, the ring problem was solved with a power-operated boring bar, equipped with a chisel bit and water jets.   When rings formed, the heat was turned off, the bar driven in, the bit dug into the base of the rings, and steam from the water jets exploded rings and wall cake. During the last month of operation before shutdown, the hope of attaining 50 per cent of the rated capacity was blasted by an explosion in the kiln.

It is stated that pilot-plant test work showed the process to be applicable to a considerable variety of manganese ores, including those of the Cuyuna Range. Despite the difficulties met by the Manganese Ore Co., the process is basically simple. With a less refractory ore, competent plant design, and reasonably capable operation, not under wartime conditions, it seems probable that quite different results would be obtained.

TIN

Leaching methods for tin are metallurgically feasible and a considerable number have been proposed (see page 9). For example, it should be possible to give a cassiterite concentrate a reducing roast that would render the tin soluble in an acid or basic solution. The tin could be precipitated as pure SnO_2, or it could be recovered electrolytically if desired. Such processes have been under test but details are not currently available.

The only leaching of tin ore now done on a commercial scale is the leaching of impurities out of tin concentrates prior to smelting. The general method has been known and practiced for many years. It consists of a reducing roast that renders the impurities soluble in a hydrochloric acid solution. These impurities include iron, arsenic, antimony, copper, lead, and others. The residue can be smelted in the regular two-stage process used for tin. The practice at the Longhorn tin smelter at Texas City, Tex., is typical.[1]

The Longhorn tin smelter was finished in April, 1942. It was designed and is operated by engineers of Mining Equipment Corp., a subsidiary of the Billiton Co., the Dutch tin-mining and smelting firm. The plant is owned by the Reconstruction Finance Corp.

Three classes of ores or concentrates are recognized at the Longhorn smelter. Class A consists of 50 to 60 per cent tin ore, with only minor amounts of impurities. High-grade alluvial concentrates make up most of this category. They are smelted directly without prior roasting and leaching.

Class B material, largely Bolivian concentrates, carries 40 to 50 per cent tin and significant quantities of iron, silica, antimony, arsenic, and other impurities. These concentrates are roasted and leached before smelting.

Class C material, the poorer grade of Bolivian concentrates, contains 18 to 35 per cent tin and is very high in silica, iron, lead, copper, antimony, etc. This material has to be roasted, leached, dried, and perhaps roasted again before it can be smelted. Contrary to 1943 practice, there is no

---

[1] R. H. Ramsey, Longhorn Tin—A Wartime Problem Solved, *Engineering and Mining Journal*, June, 1943.

longer any attempt made in the plant at gravity concentration of class C ores.

Roasting.   All plant feed is crushed to minus $\frac{1}{4}$ in.   There are seven F. L. Smidth Unax rotary kilns available for roasting.   They are 4 ft in diameter and 46 ft long.   Roasting is at 600 to 700°C under a natural gas flame.   Calcine is cooled in this reducing atmosphere to 100°C before leaving the kilns and their accompanying enclosed coolers.

The kiln charge is made up of ore, petroleum coke, and salt, the proportions depending on the composition of the ore being treated.   High-iron ores need more coke; high-lead ores need more salt.   The objective is, of course, to render all the impurities soluble in hydrochloric acid. Iron, for example, must be removed as completely as possible in the leach because there is no other easy way to get it out of the plant.   Therefore, the roast has to produce as much ferrous oxide in the calcine as feasible.

Large amounts of dust are produced in the kilns.   The coarse fraction of the dust is recovered in Buell cyclones.   The fines are picked up in a 20,000-cfm Cottrell plant.   The cyclone dust goes back to the kilns; the Cottrell dust goes on to a completely separate treatment.   Because this finer dust is so high in arsenic and antimony, it cannot be smelted with the main body of the calcine.   It is treated in a separate furnace and produces "common" tin.

Leaching.   Class B ores are leached in ball digesters, which are spheres 10 ft in diameter, swung on hollow trunnions, and lined with rubber and two layers of acidproof brick.   Each charge carries about 10 tons of calcine and 18°Bé hydrochloric acid.   The sphere revolves during the 6 to 8 hr of digestion at 1 rpm, driven by a $7\frac{1}{2}$-hp gear motor. Steam at 28 lb pressure is injected during digestion, which sends the temperature of the pulp up to about 110°C.   Consumption of acid formerly came to about 100 tons daily, but an acid-recovery plant has recently been installed that materially lowers this figure.   Following this leaching, the class B material is dried and is then ready for the reverberatory furnaces.

Class C material is leached separately in the same type of digester and under similar conditions.   The residue is dried and reroasted, however, before it is smelted.

Both B and C material are discharged from the digesters in the same way.   The sphere is tipped with one port opened so that the liquor can drain out through a screen filter in the opening.   When the solution so draining has been removed and the residue washed by decantation, the sphere is completely opened and the residue is discharged.

The slimes and waste liquor that drain away from the residue are thickened and filtered. The filtrate goes to a new acid-recovery plant, where both hydrochloric acid and several miscellaneous metals are recovered. The precipitate is pulped with lime to neutralize it, then filtered once more, and put back through the roasters.

Smelting. Briefly, the residues from leaching are smelted in two stages in 30-ton batches in reverberatory furnaces. In the first, only enough reducing agent is added to bring down most of the tin, leaving a good part of it to form a slag with the remaining iron. In the second stage, this slag is resmelted with more reducing agent to bring down a tin-iron alloy called "hardhead." The slag from this second stage is low enough in tin to be discarded.

The hardhead goes back to the first stage and is smelted with new leach residue, where the iron in the hardhead (about 20 per cent) helps reduce some of the tin in the new feed. Primary furnaces are fired at about 2300°F, secondary furnaces at 2800°F. Dust and fume are passed through a Cottrell plant.

Final purification of tin takes place in drossing kettles. Steam is bubbled up through the molten tin to pick up the last of any remaining iron, and aluminum is stirred through the bath to catch any antimony or arsenic. Dross used to be skimmed off with paddles but an ingenious system has since been devised whereby the molten tin is pumped through a steel cylinder containing a metal filter element that effectively removes the dross. Tin metal goes on to an automatic casting device, and the dross is resmelted separately.

URANIUM AND RADIUM

The following is a description of the process used at Port Hope, Ont., for treating pitchblende ore from Great Bear Lake.[1]

PITCHBLENDE ORE

Ore as received from the mine contains over 50 per cent uranium oxide and considerable amounts of silver. It is first roasted at 1100°C to decompose sulfide and carbonate minerals and to volatilize some of the arsenic and antimony. The roasted ore is then mixed with 5 to 10 per cent of salt and roasted to convert the uranium and silver to chlorides. After cooling, the calcine is ground and then leached for 6 hr with 50 per cent sulfuric acid. Barium chloride is next added to collect the radium, hydrochloric acid to complete the precipitation of the silver, and a few per cent of sodium nitrate to oxidize the uranium.

[1] S. L. Johnstone, *Industrial Chemist*, January, 1949.

Uranium. The solution is next filtered, the insoluble being reserved for the extraction of silver and radium. To the acid solution is added an excess of sodium carbonate to precipitate compounds of iron, manganese, and most of the copper, leaving the uranium in solution as sodium uranyl carbonate. After filtration, the solution is heated with excess of sulfuric acid and the uranium is precipitated, as sodium uranate, by adding caustic soda.

Radium, Silver, and Lead. The insoluble matter from the original sulfuric acid leach, which contains radium, silver, lead, and some impurities, is agitated with a solution containing a calculated amount of sodium thiosulfate. This dissolves the silver chloride, which is recovered from the solution by precipitation with sodium sulfide.

The silver sulfide is sent to refiners for treatment. About 95 per cent of the silver present in the ore is recovered. The residue from the thiosulfate leach contains from 12 to 18 per cent of lead sulfate which is removed by boiling with caustic soda solution.

The insoluble portion is next heated for 6 hr in an autoclave with a solution of sodium carbonate, whereby the radium and barium sulfates are converted to carbonates. These are filtered off and dissolved in strong hydrochloric acid.

Sulfuric acid is added to the solution and the impure barium and radium sulfates allowed to settle. The crude sulfates are again converted into carbonates, which after washing are dissolved in hydrobromic acid. The resultant solution is treated with barium hydroxide and sulfide to precipitate the last traces of metallic impurities. The radium in the solution, about one part to 400,000 parts by barium, is recovered by a complicated series of fractional crystallizations. About 90 per cent of the radium present in the ore is recovered.

CARNOTITE ORE

Three general processes have been evolved for the treatment of carnotite ores: (1) acid leach, (2) alkaline leach followed by acid treatment, (3) fusion with acid sodium sulfate.

Operations (1) and (2) have been referred to briefly in Chap. 1, page 27. The alkaline-leach method has come to be preferred for Colorado Plateau carnotite ores, and recent practice in this method will be described in the following pages.

Sodium carbonate leaching of Colorado Plateau carnotite ores was done for the first time on a continuous, rather than a batch, basis in the new Atomic Energy Commission mill at Monticello, Utah, operated by the

Galigher Co., of Salt Lake City.   The following description is abstracted from an article on the plant.[1]

Carnotite, which is a mixture of oxides of uranium, vanadium, and potassium, is treated in the Monticello mill by a process closely resembling countercurrent cyanidation.   These are the steps in the process:

1. Crushing ore to minus 10 mesh.
2. Roasting ore with salt.
3. Quenching calcine in hot sodium carbonate solution.
4. Grinding to 65 mesh.
5. Agitation leaching in 3 to 9 per cent sodium carbonate solution.
6. Countercurrent washing and filtration.
7. Precipitation of uranium and vanadium with sulfuric acid.
8. Purification of uranium and vanadium oxides by fusion and leaching.

Crushing.   The plant treats about 100 tons of ore daily.   The ore is brought to the Monticello mill by a number of operators, most of them small-scale miners.   These small lots are sampled and graded, then stockpiled for treatment according to type of ore.   The following types are recognized at present:

1. High vanadium, low lime.
2. High vanadium, high lime.
3. Low vanadium, low lime.
4. Low vanadium, high lime.
5. Asphaltic.

These ores formerly had to be treated separately but present practice makes it possible to treat the first two and the last three types simultaneously.

The chief aim in the crushing section of the mill is to reduce the particle size to minus 10 mesh with minimum creation of dust or fines.   The reason is that the carnotite mineral occurs as a coating, or cementing, layer around sand grains.   When the rock is crushed, the carnotite tends to concentrate in the finer sizes and the loss of uranium in dust can easily become excessive.

A 2- by 20-in. Cedarapids hammer-mill type of crusher is used to keep formation of fines to a minimum.   A vibrating screen is run in closed circuit with the crusher.

The dust collection system consists of a 9- by 4-ft precleaner dust chamber where coarse dust is dropped out and returned to the fine-ore

[1] John A. Butler, Utah's New Uranium Mill, *Engineering and Mining Journal*, p. 56, March, 1951.

belt, a No. 16 type N Rotoclone, and a 6-ft Callow cone treating the overflow of the Rotoclone.

Water circulates through the Rotoclone at all times to guard against break-through and loss of dust.   There is so much fine dust in the carnotite ores that this circulating water was found to carry significant quantities of uranium; hence, the Callow cone to pick up this very fine dust. The underflow goes back to the crusher along with the Rotoclone sludge.

The crushing plant runs one shift a day, six days a week.

Roasting and Leaching.   Roasting and leaching circuits at Monticello are designed to treat two classes of ores.   The first, or type 1 ores, includes the high-vanadium ores.   The second, or type 2, includes the low-vanadium and asphaltic ores.   The differences in treatment are in the temperature of the roast, the quantity of salt added, and the strength of the sodium carbonate leach solution.   Both ores are roasted in an 8-hearth, 18-ft-diameter Skinner roaster.

The type 1, high-vanadium ores have a lime content less than 2.0 per cent.   They are treated by mixing with 6 to 9 per cent of salt, roasting at 850°C, and quenching in hot 3 per cent sodium carbonate.   After quenching, the calcine is ground to natural-grain size, about 65 mesh, in a 5- by 6-ft ball mill in closed circuit with a 48-in. screw classifier.   The charge of $1\frac{1}{2}$-in. balls is held on the light side because grinding need only separate the sand grains.   Dust collection from the roaster is by balloon chamber and Rotoclone.

It has been found most important to quench the calcine immediately on discharge from the roaster in order to get high recovery of the uranium and vanadium.   If the calcine takes a minute or more to cool from 850 to 750°C, the recovery of uranium is cut 10 to 15 per cent.   Vanadium extraction is also lowered.   Therefore the calcine is discharged from the roaster by a short shaking feeder directly into high-pressure solution jets that shoot the calcine into pipes leading to the ball-mill-classifier circuit.

Galigher 10- by 10-ft agitators are used.   The pulp is kept at about 94°C by steam coils.   Oversize propellors are provided because the ore settles so rapidly that it is hard to keep it in suspension.   Quenching and leaching are carried out at a pulp density of around 45 per cent solids because this practice has been found helpful in holding down accumulation of impurities.   A more dilute mixture would allow a build-up of soluble impurities, but the thick pulp means that a larger proportion of the solution, and hence a larger proportion of the impurities, is drawn off each day to the precipitation section.

Enough solution is taken to the precipitation units each day to hold the pregnant liquor just below 2.00 gpl of uranium oxide.   A higher concentration causes reprecipitation of uranium in the leaching and washing circuits.

The pulp is leached in three agitators in series and thickened in four 30-ft thickeners.   Driessen-type cones, made from 6-in. pipe, are used to deslime the underflow from the third thickener when type 2 ores are treated.   Wilfley sand pumps are used for thickener underflows because of the sandy nature of the pulp.

Type 1 ores are filtered on Oliver horizontal filters and four washes are possible because the ore filters so fast.   An extraction of 93 per cent of the uranium and 85 per cent of the vanadium is obtained on type 1 ores.

Type 2 ores, including the asphaltic or Temple Mountain and the low-vanadium ores, are more difficult to treat because only about 40 per cent of the vanadium is recoverable by any normal leaching procedure.   The methods worked out at Monticello have been successful in raising uranium recovery, at least to about 85 per cent.

In treating these ores, salt is omitted from the roast and the roasting temperature is held at 550°C.   The leach solutions run about 7 to 9 per cent sodium carbonate.   More than ordinary difficulty was encountered with type 2 ores by reason of fouling of the leach solutions with impurities.   This was remedied by the shift from 25 to 45 per cent solids in the leach pulp.   Because the type 2 ores carry a great deal more primary slime than the type 1 ores, it is necessary to deslime the former and filter sands and slimes separately.   The Driessen-type cones that deslime the underflow from the third thickener help this separation by producing a slime-free sand fraction.

Uranium Precipitation.   Uranium is precipitated as a "yellow cake" (sodium uranyl vanadate) from the pregnant liquor by addition of sulfuric acid.   Liquor is pumped from storage tanks to two 12- by 12-ft rubber-lined agitators.   Concentrated sulfuric acid is added to the sodium carbonate liquor to a pH of 6 and the solution is heated by live-steam injection until all carbon dioxide has been expelled.   The pH is further adjusted by additions of acid; heating and agitation are continued until the filtrate shows 10 ppm or less of uranium oxide.   The precipitation operator checks the filtrate for completeness of precipitation by means of a bead test which takes about 10 min.

The yellow precipitate is filtered by pumping the solution through 36- by 36-in. Sperry presses.   Filtrate goes to vanadium precipitation. Yellow cake cleaned from the presses, which contains up to 70 per cent moisture and assays 45 per cent uranium oxide and 17 per cent vanadium oxide (dry basis), is dried to about 10 per cent moisture by spreading on cast-iron plates which cover the top of the flue from the fusion furnace.

It is then mixed with fluxes which consist of soda ash, salt, and sawdust, and fused in a tilting-hearth reverberatory-type oil-fired furnace.

This furnace, which is the first of its type in use for fusing uranium yellow cake, was designed and built by the Monticello staff. It is patterned after cupelling furnaces as used in the refining of gold bullion. The tilting hearth has as advantage that no tapping is necessary. When a charge is fused and is quiescent, the hearth is tilted forward by means of a hydraulic cylinder. Another advantage of this type of furnace is that the hearth can be lowered and moved out from under the arch on a truck when repairs have to be made.

The arch is built of fire-clay brick, while the hearth has a rammed magnesite lining. No water-jacketing or cooling is necessary.

The melt from the reducing fusion is poured into curved-bottom pans, $4\frac{1}{2}$ ft long by 4 ft wide and, when cool, is broken with a hammer into pieces 4 in. or smaller in size. These are charged onto a $\frac{1}{8}$-in. screen set 2 ft below the top of a 6- by 6-ft agitator. The agitator is filled to 6 in. above the screen with warm water.

Vanadium in this fused material is readily soluble in water; the uranium is in the form of insoluble oxides. The chunks of fused material dissolve rapidly and become sufficiently fine to pass through the screen. The pulp is pumped to 10- by 10-ft Galigher agitators which overflow back to the 6- by 6-ft agitator. This leaching dissolves the vanadium while the uranium becomes a very fine black powder.

When titrations show that the liquor contains approximately 25 gpl vanadium oxide, pumping from the smaller agitator is stopped. Agitation in the larger agitator is also stopped and the uranium oxide allowed to settle. The vanadium liquor is siphoned off and is pumped through a 36- by 36-in. iron-frame-and-plate Sperry press.

Thickened uranium oxide pulp in the 10- by 10-ft agitator is given two warm-water decantation washes; these washes are used for subsequent leaching of fused yellow cake. After decantation of the second wash, the thickened black uranium oxide pulp is pumped to the Sperry press.

Black cake in the press is blown first with steam, then with air, before cleaning the press. Black cake from the press is placed in pans and dried to 0.10 to 0.20 per cent moisture in a steam-heated drying oven. It is then packaged in drums for shipment to the AEC. The finished product contains a high per cent of uranium oxide and a fractional percentage of vanadium oxide.

Vanadium Precipitation. The filtrates from uranium precipitation and those from uranium refining have to be treated somewhat differently.

These filtrates are precipitated in 8- by 8-ft rubber-lined agitators (similar to those used for uranium precipitation) by pH control. Vanadium in the filtrate from the uranium precipitation is already oxidized and requires only the addition of sulfuric acid until a pH of 2.5 is reached, together with heating to approximately 80°C, to obtain a readily filterable vanadium oxide red cake.

Vanadium in the filtrate from the uranium refining section is highly reduced and the solution is high in caustic soda. Acid is added until a pH of 2 to 3 is obtained; then enough sodium chlorate is added to oxidize the vanadium completely. The liquor is heated to approximately 80°C and the final pH is adjusted by addition of either acid or soda ash to obtain a red cake of desirable physical properties.

This red cake is of lower grade and does not filter as readily as that obtained from filtrate from uranium precipitation. These solutions, which contain 20 to 25 gpl vanadium oxide, are precipitated to 0.25 gpl or less. Red cake (vanadium oxide) is filtered from the solution in rectangular, rubber-lined, filter-bottom tanks. After washing with hot ammonium sulfate solution and hot water, the red cake is shoveled into a wooden bin, which has sufficient capacity to store red cake for 15 days, if necessary.

The wet red cake, which contains 60 to 70 per cent moisture, is slushed to the back end of a reverberatory-type furnace, 8 ft wide by 11 ft long (outside dimensions). The bottom of this furnace consists of a water-jacketed, sloping, steel hearth, and the sides and arch are made of fire-clay brick. There is no back in the furnace, this being formed by the wet red cake being piled up at that end. An Airoil burner plays directly on the pile of wet red cake in the furnace and as this dries and fuses it flows continuously onto a straight-line caster. From the caster the flake vanadium oxide is dropped directly into drums ready for shipment.

METALLIC URANIUM

Before 1941 the demand for metallic uranium was very small and the product offered for sale was usually rather impure. It has been authoritatively stated that in 1941, when a demand arose in the United States for the metal for fission purposes, the only material available consisted of a few grams of fairly pure metal and a few pounds of a very impure pyropheric powder. However, a good supply of black uranium oxide from Canadian sources, containing about 2 per cent of impurities, was available.

Later it became possible to obtain relatively large amounts of the black oxide, with total impurities under 1 per cent and including only a few parts per million of boron. This material was not pure enough for the production of metallic uranium for fission purposes and a process was developed for the large-scale removal of all impurities by a single ether-extraction of uranyl nitrate, and the conversion of this salt to the brown oxide, UO_2. This forms the starting point for the reduction to metal.

The process first employed in the United States was the electrolysis of potassium uranyl fluoride, KUF_5, and later uranium tetrafluoride. The cost at the start was about \$1,000 per lb but improvements in the process and plant expansion enabled refined metal to be produced at \$22 per lb by 1943. In the process used later, a mixture of potassium uranous fluoride and equal parts of calcium and sodium chlorides was electrolyzed at a fairly low temperature to produce metallic uranium as a loosely adherent deposit on the cathode. In 1945, the cost of production of refined uranium was estimated to be about \$10 per lb and that of plutonium \$20 per g.

CADMIUM

The following describes an interesting example of cadmium recovery methods at Risdon, Tasmania,[1] in the electrolytic zinc plant there.

Cadmium-copper precipitate, a by-product of the purification stage in the zinc plant, is composed mainly of zinc, cadmium, and copper in amounts that vary, depending on the efficiency of precipitation and the cadmium and copper content of the impure solution treated.

The composition range is approximately: cadmium 10–12 per cent, copper 6–8 per cent, and zinc 30–35 per cent. As received at the cadmium plant, the precipitate is a dark gray to black press cake produced by filter-pressing the flocculent cadmium-copper precipitate formed when impure zinc solution is agitated with zinc dust.

The treatment, in addition to recovering cadmium as metal, yields a copper product as a residue and recovers in solution for return to the zinc plant the excess of zinc dust used during purification.

The recovery of cadmium metal is approximately 200 tons per year. Both cadmium and copper recovery vary with zinc production tonnage, composition of the original concentrates, degree of roasting, and other operational factors.

The operations involved can be best described by dividing the process into the following stages:

1. Oxidation and grinding of the cadmium-copper precipitate.
2. Leaching and filtering.
3. Precipitation of cadmium.

[1] G. H. Anderson, Recovery of Cadmium, Electrolytic Zinc Co. of Australasia, *Metals Transactions*, p. 205, March, 1949. See also W. C. Snow, Electrolytic Zinc at Risdon, Tasmania, *Trans. AIME*, Vol. 121, p. 501.

4. Oxidation and grinding of the precipitated cadmium.
5. Leaching oxidized cadmium precipitate and purification of leach solution.
6. Electrolysis.
7. Melting, casting, and packing.

A feature of the process is the use of two distinct solution circuits. Spent electrolyte from the zinc plant circuit, containing about 10 per cent sulfuric acid, is used as the primary solvent of the cadmium and zinc present in the oxidized precipitate.   When the cadmium is later separated by precipitation and filtering, the filtrate, originally zinc-plant spent electrolyte and now fortified in zinc, is returned to the zinc plant.

The precipitated cadmium, after oxidation, is redissolved in spent electrolyte from cadmium electrolysis, which solution is in closed circuit within the cadmium plant, except for discards to the zinc-plant circuit. Details of various operations follow.

1. Oxidation and Grinding of the Cadmium-copper Precipitate.   The precipitate, having had a preliminary drying by compressed air in Dehne filter presses in the zinc plant, is trucked to a storage platform.

After 48 hr exposure to atmosphere, oxidation is sufficient to enable all cadmium and zinc, but only a portion of the copper to be dissolved in dilute sulfuric acid.   The oxidized precipitate is shoveled into trucks and, after weighing and sampling, is broken in a shallow, mild, steel trough by rotating right- and left-handed blades.

Return solution (see stage 3) is added to form a pulp which passes to a tube mill 5 ft long and 3 ft in diameter, with cast-steel liners and loaded with flint pebbles.   The use of return solution is restricted to produce a thick pulp which is elevated to a wooden storage tank of 3,200-gal capacity, provided with air agitation.

2. Leaching and Filtering.   Leaching is carried out in a wooden tank of approximately 14,000-gal capacity, having a conical bottom and provided with both mechanical and air agitation.

Discharge is through a plug cock but, in addition, the tank has a side discharge to which is fitted, inside the tank, an armored rubber hose for decanting clear solution after settlement of the solids.

The tank is covered and ventilated to atmosphere.   Approximately 7,000 to 8,000 gal of zinc-plant spent electrolyte containing 90 to 95 gpl sulfuric acid and 45 to 50 gpl zinc is run into the leaching tank.   After agitation is started, the ground cadmium-copper precipitate is charged until the acidity of the solution falls to 5 to 6 gpl sulfuric acid.   Agitation is continued for another 5 to 6 hr, when the acidity is reduced to 1 to 2 gpl sulfuric acid.   Ground limestone is added slowly until a pH of 3 to 4 is reached.

Approximately 30 min later a sample is taken, tested for copper, and the calculated quantity of zinc dust required to remove copper in excess of 0.5 gpl is added.

Control of the copper content of the solution is important and is considered to have three distinct advantages: (1) its subsequent precipitation with the cadmium in section 3 prevents coagulation of the cadmium into metallic balls and facilitates filtering; (2) during the cadmium circuit

TABLE 86. METALLURGICAL AND OPERATING DATA, CADMIUM RECOVERY PLANT, ELECTROLYTIC ZINC CO. OF AUSTRALASIA
(Average figures for year ending June 30, 1948; 6.85 tons treated per day)

Weight, %

Assays, Cd-Cu precipitate:

Cd	10.85
Cu	6.7
Zn	33.6
Pb	0.6
Ag, oz per ton	2.30
Cd extracted by leaching	98.7
Cu solubility	68.5
Zn dust used per ton leached, lb	269
Limestone used per ton leached, lb	25
Cu residue factor	12.8
Cu residue made per filter cake, lb	921
Wash displacement	1.83

Cu residue assays:

Cu	46.5
Cd	1.07
Zn	5.85
Pb	6.0
Ag, oz per ton	18

leach (Sec. 5), arsenic is precipitated or otherwise eliminated; (3) its presence ensures a minimum of zinc and cadmium in the copper residue.

If no copper is in the leach solution, sufficient sulfated copper residue is added to give the desired content. Sulfated copper residue is made by mixing copper residue and sulfuric acid and storing in heaps for 1 or 2 days.

Approximately 30 min after the addition of the calculated amount of zinc dust, a further test is taken to determine copper in solution. If necessary, further additions of zinc dust are made.

Agitation is continued for another hour, after which solids are allowed to settle for 3 to 4 hr, when clear solution is decanted and pumped to the cadmium precipitating tank.

The remaining pulp is agitated, air-lifted to a wooden storage tank, and filtered in a small Moore filter unit.

The filtrate and washings are pumped by wet vacuum pumps to the cadmium precipitation tank containing the decanted leach solution. The filter cake is discharged to a hopper and fed to an oil-fired rotary dryer 15 ft long and 3 ft 9 in. in diameter, consisting of a mild-steel shell, lined with 10 gauge stainless steel sheet and fitted with suitable angle lifters.

The dried copper residue is bagged for shipment to a copper refinery at Port Kembla in New South Wales.

3. Precipitation of Cadmium. The precipitation tank is identical with the leach tank already described, except that no decantation hose is fitted and air agitation is not used.

To the decanted solution, filtrate, and washings from the 8,000-gal leaching operation described in Sec. 2, about 600 lb of zinc dust is added after agitation has commenced. Filtered samples of the solution are tested with hydrogen sulfide from time to time and further additions of zinc dust are made until only a trace of cadmium remains.

Approximately 45 to 60 min later, if a similar test indicates a satisfactory cadmium content, the pulp is filtered in two 27-in. Dehne filter presses. The filtrate, known as "return solution," after by-passing for a few minutes, goes to a storage tank prior to its return to the zinc-plant circuit.

When the filter presses are full of precipitate, pumping is stopped and a water wash given until a 1.025 sp gr shows that the precipitate is almost free of zinc sulfate.

After drying with compressed air, the washed precipitate is discharged to hoppers over a drying and oxidizing hearth. For the year ending June 30, 1948, zinc-dust efficiency was 58.1 per cent and the quantity of cadmium left in the return solution averaged 1.08 gpl.

4. Oxidation and Grinding of Precipitated Cadmium. The oxidizing hearth is of brick, with a hearth of cast-iron plates approximately 11 by 9 ft, mounted so that gases from an oil burner first pass under the hearth and then over the precipitate which, when dropped from the hoppers above, is raked evenly over the hearth to a depth of 4 to 6 in.

Because the precipitate oxidizes readily, a maximum gas temperature of 300°C is set at the rising flue from under the hearth to above the charge, but rarely is this limit necessary. Hand rabbling proceeds at intervals until the color of the precipitate indicates that oxidation is complete, when the material is discharged by hand to a ventilated hopper. The precipitate is then screw-fed to a mild-steel ball mill 4 ft long and 2 ft 6 in. in diameter, loaded with 1½- and ¾-in. steel balls. Cadmium-cell feed solution is added to produce a reasonably thick mill discharge, which is stored in a wooden tank ready for air-lifting to the leach tank (stage 5) when required.

For ventilation, a fan handling 10,000 to 15,000 cfm is connected to the hood over the oxidized precipitate hopper and to a hood over the mill feed screw discharge point. The dust-laden air is delivered to the base of a water-irrigated wooden scrubbing tower mounted over a concrete sump from which the water is recirculated by means of a pump while the settled pulp is withdrawn at intervals and pumped to the leach tank. Average figures for the year ending June 30, 1948, were: total cadmium in the precipitate, 69.3 per cent; acid solution, cadmium, 68.5 per cent; zinc, 5.5 per cent; oxidation of cadmium, 97.7 per cent.

5. Leaching and Purification. Variations in the sulfuric acid content of the leach solution are made from time to time in order to hold both the cadmium content and the volume of the cell feed circuit reasonably constant.

If both are about normal, leaching is done with normal cadmium-cell-spent electrolyte, but if the cadmium content is low, the cell-spent electrolyte is fortified with 10 to 20 gpl sulfuric acid. If the volume needs increasing, approximately 600 gal of spent electrolyte is supplemented with 800 gal of water and the whole acidified to 150 gpl sulfuric acid. In all cases the volume is 1,400 to 1,500 gal and the subsequent leaching operation is the same.

Leaching of the ground cadmium precipitate pulp is carried out in a mechanically agitated lead-lined tank, having a working capacity of 2,400 gal, and ventilated by the suction fan mentioned in stage 4.

The desired volume of leaching solution having been run to the leach tank, pulp from the storage tank is charged until the acidity of the solution is approximately, but not less than, 10 gpl sulfuric acid.

A sample of the pulp is filtered and tested for copper by the sodium sulfide method and if an excessive amount of copper is present, it is reduced by the addition of unoxidized cadmium precipitate.

Leaching is continued until the acidity is reduced to 1 to 2 gpl sulfuric acid, when tests are made for copper and arsenic (Gutzeit's test) and, if present, more unoxidized precipitate is added. Agitation is continued for 1 hr after copper and arsenic have been reduced to 0.5 and 0.1 mg per l, respectively. If, after neutralizing with hydrated lime, a further test for arsenic is found satisfactory, the pulp is pumped to a Kroog filter press.

The filtrate is by-passed to the leach tank until free from solid particles, as indicated by filtering 500 cc through filter paper, and when clarity is satisfactory the filtrate is diverted to one of two lead-lined wooden storage tanks, each of 3,200-gal capacity, where, if necessary, water is added to reduce cadmium to the desired content of gpl.

By discarding spent electrolyte to the original cadmium–copper precipitate leach and rebuilding the circuit with fortified spent electrolyte and water leaches, the impurities are controlled to 30 to 40 g zinc, 0.7 to 0.8 g iron, and 30 to 35 mg chlorine, per liter.

The residue collected in the Kroog press during filtering of the cadmium leach pulp is returned to the cadmium–copper precipitate mixer (stage 1).

TABLE 87. LEACHING DATA, CADMIUM PLANT, ELECTROLYTIC ZINC CO. OF AUSTRALASIA

(Average figures for the year ending June 30, 1948)

Cd extraction from acid-soluble Cd in precipitate by leaching, %	92.5
Cd extraction from total Cd in precipitate by leaching, %	89.2
Cd leach residue factor, %	25.8
Cd leach residue:	
Assay, Cd, %	28.7
Cu, %	31.9
H_2SO_4 used per ton Cd dissolved, tons	0.287
Zn dust used per ton Cd dissolved, lb	2470
Hydrated lime used per ton Cd dissolved, lb	56.3
Feed solution assay:	
Cd, gpl	150.7
Zn, gpl	37.55
Fe, gpl	0.79
Mn, gpl	2.35
Cl, mg per l	30
Cu, mg per l	0.82
As, mg per l	0.1

6. Electrolysis. The cell room contains 20 cells arranged in five rows of four cells, each of which is of 3-in. timber, lined first with 8-lb lead, and then with 2 in. of a 40 per cent sulfur–60 per cent sand mixture, which has given good service. Only two linings have failed in 25 years. Internal dimensions of the cells, which have a volume of 208 gal, are 5 ft square and 2 ft 6 in. deep, while the cross section is semioctagonal.

The lead in the 10 half-round, 23-in. radius anodes contains 0.01 per cent silver, which gives added rigidity and extends the 4-year life to 5 years.

Mounted on a 3-in.-diameter mild-steel shaft and separated at $5\frac{1}{2}$-in. spacing by rubber-covered aluminum sleeves are nine aluminum cathodes, 4 ft in diameter and $\frac{1}{4}$ in. thick, each of which has a submerged surface area of 8 sq ft and lasts 7 to 8 years. To enable the stripped cadmium sheet to be readily broken into four conveniently sized quadrants, each side of the cathode is radially grooved at 90 deg spacing to a depth of $\frac{1}{32}$ in. Before assembly, each cathode is given a matte surface by scrubbing with a steel wire brush and sandstone. Once each year the cathode assembly is dismantled, inspected, cleaned and, if necessary, faulty parts replaced.

Cathodes are rotated at 10 rpm by suitably driven link chains through gearing from which the cathode assembly may be disengaged without stopping the driving mechanism. Electrically the cells are arranged in series. Current is supplied by two motor-driven parallel-connected generators, rotating at 960 rpm, and each capable of supplying 650 amp over a range of 25 to 70 volts.

Anode bus bars of $1\frac{1}{4}$-in.-square copper are arranged to give the anode head bars an edge contact. Between adjacent cells is a hinged section for short-circuiting a cell when cathode assemblies are removed for stripping.

The series circuit is made complete by means of a 9-in.-diameter brass collector keyed to the cathode shaft and contacting brushes connected by copper cable to the following anode bus bar. Cell voltage is approximately 3.5 volts per cell.

Feed solution containing 150 gpl cadmium gravitates from the feed storage tanks through iron pipes of uniform length, flanged together for ease of cleaning.

Each cell has a separate feed pipe through which the rate of feed is controlled to hold the acidity of the cell solution at 85 to 90 gpl sulfuric acid. Titrations with caustic soda using Congo Red indicator are made every 4 hr.

Spent electrolyte overflows from each cell to a launder common to each row and gravitates to a storage tank.

Glue solution containing 0.14 lb glue per gal is added every 4 hr at a rate equivalent to $2\frac{1}{2}$ to 3 lb glue per ton cadmium deposited. During deposition, the cadmium surface tends to form "trees." These are wiped off at intervals with a slotted wooden tool to which rubber strips are attached to make contact with each face of the cathode simultaneously. Trees are cleaned from the cells monthly and are returned to the tube mill grinding the original cadmium-copper precipitate.

Stripping periods are either 48 or 96 hr, depending on the current density demanded by production. When the current density on the immersed cathode surface is between 10 and 12 amp per sq ft, quite a reasonable current efficiency is obtained and the deposit adheres to the cathode. When the current density is higher, the stripping period is reduced to 48 hr because beyond this time the current efficiency is found to decrease and the deposited cadmium sheets tend to become detached.

The production of cadmium is not regular, owing to variation in the amount of incoming cadmium; consequently both the number of cells used and the current density are varied. While it is aimed to operate at

10 to 12 amp per sq ft, at times a higher density is necessary. When the deposit is about to be stripped, the cell concerned is short-circuited by means of the hinged section of the anode bus bar, hooks suspended from a bridle of convenient length are attached to fittings on the cathode shaft, and the whole cathode assembly is lifted by means of a traveling chain block and lowered to trestles at the end of the cell row.

The deposit is removed by means of stripping knives, broken into quadrants, stacked almost vertically in portable racks, weighed, and transferred to the melting section.

Before returning the assembly to the cell, each aluminum cathode is hosed, scrubbed with a stiff bristle brush and, if necessary, given a light rubbing with sandstone.

TABLE 88. ELECTROLYSIS DATA, CADMIUM PLANT, ELECTROLYTIC ZINC CO. OF AUSTRALASIA

(Average figures for year ending June 30, 1948)

Average current, amp	800
Current efficiency, %	88.7
Current density, amp per sq ft	11.0
Cd "trees" produced, % of Cd deposited	6.11
Number of cells in use	17.6
Discard solution assays:	
Cd, gpl	68.2
Zn, gpl	37.2
H_2SO_4, gpl	84.5

Melting, Casting, and Packing. The cadmium sheets are melted, under a cover of molten rosin, in an oil-fired cast-iron pot having a capacity of approximately 2,500 lb cadmium. The molten cadmium is handled from the pot to the molds in a mild-steel ladle, the pouring spout of which is in the form of a pipe reaching almost to the bottom to prevent dross or flux entering the mold.

Molds are either lubricated with stearin or No. 3 Shell grease or sprayed with a fine mist of dilute sulfuric acid in order to give a clean bright surface to the castings. After inspection, the castings are packed in Tasmanian oak cases in which are inserted sheets of waxed paper and cardboard to keep the castings from contact with the wood.

Periodically dross is ladled from the surface of the molten cadmium in the melting pot into mild-steel trays and after cooling and weighing is ground in a Berdan grinding pan from which a stream of water carries off the slime to a settling pond, the overflow from which passes into the cadmium-copper precipitate pulp circuit.

The dross slime, collected in a settler, is fed to one of the zinc-plant roasting furnaces and eventually returns, via the zinc circuit, to the cadmium plant. Clean cadmium prills are removed from the pan, dried, weighed, and remelted.

It is planned to replace the rosin flux with one of three parts ammonium chloride and eight parts zinc oxide which, in addition to enabling all cell trees to be remelted direct, will dispense with grinding and the return of the dross slime through the zinc circuit and, as a result, cadmium losses will be reduced.

The melting furnace is enclosed in a mild-steel hood from which rosin vapor is exhausted but, before being discharged to atmosphere, passes in series through three vertical wire-packed mild-steel cylinders in which approximately 60 to 70 per cent of the rosin is condensed for further use.

TABLE 89. MELTING AND REFINING DATA, CADMIUM PLANT, ELECTROLYTIC ZINC CO.
OF AUSTRALASIA
(Average figures for year ending June 30, 1948)

	Per Cent
Melting efficiency (including returned prills)............	95.91
Cd prill recovered from dross.........................	7.56
Cd in dross slime to roasting plant....................	1.35
Unaccounted melting loss.............................	2.74
Rosin used (% cathodes melted)......................	3.02
Rosin distillate recovered (% total rosin used)..........	68.3
Cd assays:	
Cd...	99.9590
Cu...	0.0009
Zn...	0.0263
Pb...	0.0136
Fe...	0.0002
Metal distribution:	
Cd as metal..	79.68
Cd in return solution...............................	11.13
Cd in copper residue...............................	1.27
Unaccounted loss...................................	7.92
	100.00

VANADIUM

An interesting example of vanadium leaching, other than carnotite treatment, is furnished by the plant of Rhodesia-Broken Hill Development Co. in Africa. The principal vanadium mineral is descloizite, a lead-zinc vanadate, which is considered quite difficult to treat for its vanadium content.

The material leached in the vanadium plant at Rhodesia-Broken Hill includes various vanadium ores, lead and zinc oxides and zinc silicates, and vanadium gravity-concentration middlings. These are blended to give a product carrying about 4 per cent vanadium oxide and not over 18 per cent zinc. This ratio is important because too high a zinc content in

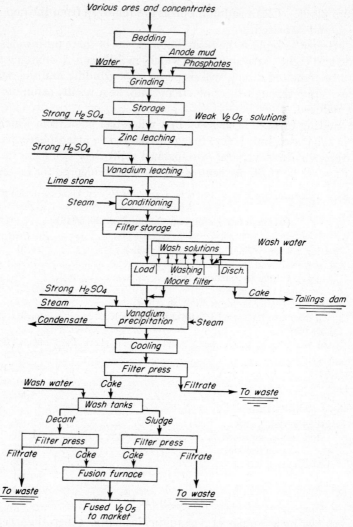

Fig. 45.   Flow sheet for vanadium-leaching process, Rhodesia-Broken Hill Development Co., Ltd.

the leach solutions tends to throw vanadium out of solution prematurely. It has been found preferable to keep the zinc content of the solutions to not more than 100 to 125 gpl.

The flow sheet of the plant is shown in Fig. 45.   For a discussion of treatment of zinc concentrates, see Chap. 7.   Vanadium plant feed is made up of the following elements in the ratios given: 90,000 lb of the blended ore mentioned in the foregoing paragraph; 11,000 gal of water;

2,000 to 3,000 lb of anode mud (60 to 65 per cent manganese dioxide); 600 lb of superphosphate. The purpose of the manganese dioxide is to provide an oxidizing environment to put the vanadium into solution as V_2O_5 rather than V_2O_4. Purpose of the superphosphate is to increase the stability of the V_2O_5. This pulp is ground in a ball mill and pumped to storage tanks.

Leaching. Leaching is done by batch agitation and is essentially a two-stage process, although it is conducted in one tank. The agitators are 17- by 17- ft redwood tanks, unlined. They are provided with two mechanical agitation propellors in each tank, with Pachuca-type air-lift columns and with steam coils.

In the first stage of leaching, weak vanadium oxide solution from the filter wash is added to the pulp just described, until the total volume is about 15,000 gal. This takes about 1,000 to 2,000 gal. Agitation is started and about 3,000 gal of strong sulfuric acid (70%) is run in slowly. The aim is to keep the temperature from rising above 45°C and to hold the free acid below 2.0 gpl. The reason for this precaution is that the zinc will dissolve in this weak acid but the vanadium is not affected. Furthermore, the silica does not readily gel in this weak acid.

For the second stage, strong acid is added quickly because there is no longer any danger of a rapid rise in temperature. The acid and the vanadium oxide concentrations are checked repeatedly and the leach is finished when the acid concentration increases markedly with no corresponding increase in vanadium content. The solution at this point usually carries about 20 to 25 gpl of acid and the same concentration of vanadium oxide. The pulp then goes to the conditioning tanks.

Conditioning for Silica. The object of the conditioning period is the same as that described in Chap. 7 for zinc leaching at Broken Hill, *i.e.*, the prevention of silica gel. Conditioning takes place in 17- by 17-ft redwood tanks, lead-lined and mechanically agitated. The pulp is agitated and ground lime added until it is neutral. This takes about 500 lb calcium carbonate. The pulp is heated by live steam during this period to about 55°C. The filtration rate is checked by filtering small samples of the pulp and agitation continues until a satisfactory filtering rate is achieved. This is possible only when the silica is thrown down in granular form instead of a gel.

Filtration. Moore filters are used and the cake is washed countercurrently. The vanadium pulp is filtered on one unit of forty 6- by 10-ft leaves for a total area of 4,000 sq ft. The leaves are made of wood and the vats underneath lead-lined, of concrete. There are five stages of countercurrent washing. Washed cake goes to the tailing dam. Tailing contains 0.6 per cent vanadium oxide, of which 0.1 per cent is water-soluble.   The filtrate from the cake and the first wash go to solution storage.   This solution carries 15 gpl vanadium oxide.

Precipitation.   Vanadium is precipitated by batch agitation in tanks similar to the conditioning tanks.   About 6,000 gal of solution is drawn from storage, agitated, and heated.   Strong sulfuric acid is then run in to give a concentration of about 5 gpl of acid.   The temperature is brought to 90°C and agitation continued for 12 hr.   The vanadium precipitates during this period as vanadic hydrate.   Precipitation is complete with 0.5 gpl V_2O_5 in solution, which is the saturation point for the oxide in acid solution.   The pulp then goes to the filter presses.

The vanadic hydrate is filtered off in 40-frame, 42- by 42-in. Dehne filter presses, built of wood.   The filtrate, carrying 0.5 gpl V_2O_5 and 4.5 gpl sulfuric acid, is sent to wash.   The precipitate is repulped with water and sent to wash tanks.

Washing is by decantation in redwood, lead-lined tanks of 20,000 gal capacity, provided with agitating propellors.   The cake is agitated for 1 hr with slightly acidulated water, then allowed to settle.   Clear water is decanted and the process repeated.   The decanted solutions are filtered to catch any flocs of vanadic hydrate that may be carried over. The sludge is filtered in a Dehne press, the filtrate going to wash and the cake going to the fusion furnace.

The vanadium cake is fused in a small reverberatory-type furnace, fired with producer gas.   Typical assay of the fused cake is: V_2O_5, 90 to 92 per cent; copper, 0.035 per cent; phosphate, 0.007 to 0.015 per cent; sulfur, 0.015 to 0.020 per cent.   Recovery calculated from V_2O_5 in leach feed and the fused oxide is 75 per cent.   Production in 1948 was running about 30 long tons per month.

COBALT

The extraction of cobalt and nickel by the ammonia process of Caron, and methods for their separation, have been described in Chap. 1.   However, there are ores and minerals carrying cobalt, especially sulfides, for which ammonia leaching is not suitable.[1]   A notable example is the ore of the Rhokana Corp., N'kana, Northern Rhodesia.   Pilot-plant treatment for cobalt production from flotation concentrate from these ores has been described by Talbot and Hepker.[2]   As a result of this work, a cobalt-

[1] This statement must be regarded in the light of the new leaching process developed by the Chemical Construction Corp. See H. L. Waldron, Is the Chemico Metals Technique Tomorrow's Metallurgy? *Engineering and Mining Journal*, p. 80, June, 1952.

[2] H. L. Talbot and H. N. Hepker, Production of Electrolytic Cobalt from a Copper-Cobalt Flotation Concentrate, *Bulletin Institution of Mining and Metallurgy*, No. 514, 1949.

leaching and electrolytic plant was constructed by the Rhokana Corp. in Northern Rhodesia.

Permission for abstracting Talbot and Hepker's paper has been given by W. J. Felton, secretary of the Institution of Mining and Metallurgy in London. Data on the final plant have been furnished by Talbot, through A. D. Marriott, representative of the Dorr Co. in Africa.

Cobalt Pilot-plant Operation. The principal copper minerals in the Rhokana ore are bornite and chalcopyrite. Cobalt occurs as the sulfide, carrollite, and as an oxide mineral, asbolite, which is not recoverable by flotation. Typical concentrator assays are the following:

	% Copper	% Cobalt
Mill feed....................	3.22	0.104
Copper concentrate..........	47.60	0.56
Cobalt concentrate..........	31.22	2.75
Mill tailing.................	0.38	0.04

The cobalt concentrate formerly was smelted separately in a reverberatory furnace, cobalt entering the matte along with copper. During converting, cobalt slags off with the iron and the converter slag is granulated, mixed with coke, and smelted in an electric-arc furnace. Cobalt is thereby recovered as an alloy of about 37 per cent cobalt, 12 per cent copper, and 50 per cent iron, and this alloy shipped overseas for refining. The over-all cobalt recovery from ore to alloy was about 14 per cent. Changes in the ratio of iron to cobalt meant decreased recovery and difficulty in producing an alloy acceptable to the refiners.

Pyrite and the cobalt mineral, carrollite, have quite similar flotation characteristics and no satisfactory separation method was found. Investigations were accordingly started for developing a leaching procedure.

Arsenic, antimony, molybdenum, and tungsten were present only in trace quantities. The concentrate from current production used for these tests analyzed:

	Per Cent
Copper...........	32.49
Cobalt............	3.21
Iron..............	12.71
Sulfur............	22.75
Silica............	15.92
Alumina..........	4.00
CaO.............	1.15
MgO.............	1.62

Two methods were investigated, designated as the "matte-leach" and "roast-leach" processes. A brief summary of the first is as follows:

The Matte Leach.   The cobalt concentrate, mixed with limestone, coal, and converter slag, was smelted in a reverberatory furnace to produce a matte to be leached.   The matte, ground dry to 65 mesh, was leached with hot sulfuric acid solution in batches.

Cobalt and iron were dissolved, the copper remaining in the residue, which was returned to the smelter for copper recovery.   Cobalt was separated from iron in the leach solution by adding a soluble sulfide at a controlled pH, the cobalt being precipitated as sulfide and recovered by filtration.   The filter cake was given a sulfating roast and leached with hot water.   Final traces of iron were precipitated from the resulting solution by oxidation with air and addition of limestone.

The purified solution, containing from 20 to 25 gpl cobalt, was then electrolyzed and the stripped metal melted and granulated for shipment.

Under proper conditions, as described, a leach extraction of over 95 per cent of the cobalt was obtained.   Furnace recoveries in four runs averaged 98.1 and 95.6 per cent of copper and cobalt, respectively.   Selective precipitation of the cobalt gave 96 per cent recovery of the cobalt in the form of a precipitate with 9 per cent cobalt and 9 per cent iron.   Hot-water leach of this material after sulfating gave a recovery of 90 per cent of the cobalt.   Over-all extraction of cobalt from concentrate to leach solution was accordingly $96.5 \times 96 \times 90 =$ about 83 per cent.

The Roast Leach.   The cobalt concentrate was given a sulfating roast under closely controlled conditions, converting the cobalt to water-soluble sulfate and rendering the iron and copper relatively insoluble.   The calcine was then leached with hot water, the pulp filtered and then purified to remove the small amount of iron and copper present.

The cobalt was precipitated from the purified solution as hydroxide by the addition of milk of lime.   After filtering, the cobalt hydroxide cake was redissolved in spent solution from electrolysis.   By this means, acid build-up and cobalt concentration in the circulating electrolyte were controlled, magnesium build-up was prevented, and solution balance assisted. The solution was electrolyzed and the cathode metal melted and granulated for market.

From 70 to 75 per cent of the cobalt in the concentrate was rendered water-soluble by the sulfating roast.   It was believed that the extraction would be over 85 per cent with a properly designated multiple-hearth roaster.

Test-plant electrolytic details were as follows: the cell was lead-lined, 20 in. long, 12. in. wide, and 14 in. deep.   It contained four anodes and three cathodes.   Spacing was $4\frac{1}{2}$ in. and clearances between the electrodes and the cell lining were 3 in. at the sides, $4\frac{1}{2}$ in. from the bottom, and $3\frac{1}{4}$ in. at the ends. The cathodes were mild-steel plates 6 in. wide, $\frac{3}{16}$ in. thick, with 9-in. submergence. The anodes were of grid construction to maintain the anode current density at about 20 amp per sq ft in order to prevent deposition of cobalt oxides at the anode. Cell operating data were

Duration of run, hr	72
Ampere hours used	2342.5
Average amperes through cell	32.6
Cathode current density (amp per sq ft)	14.5
Average temperature, cell discharge	58.4
Circulation rate, g per lb Co deposited	100
Average pH, cell feed	5.95
Average pH, cell discharge	1.77
Cobalt metal deposited, lb	4.65
Cathode current efficiency, %	81.8
Total kwhr consumed	7.00
Kwhr per lb Co deposited	1.51
Cell voltage, calculated from above	2.97

Increased circulation raised the pH of the cell discharge to 2.7 and the current efficiency to 87 per cent. Light machine grooving of the cathode plates resulted in a firm, adherent deposit, which could be built up to $\frac{1}{4}$ in. thickness and readily stripped. At 15 amp per sq ft, 12-day cathodes could be built up and readily stripped. The cathode metal had the following average analysis:

	Per Cent
Cobalt	99.89
Copper	0.041
Iron	0.032
Sulphur	0.019
Calcium	0.006
Nickel	Not found
Zinc	Not found
Manganese	Not found
Magnesium	Not found
Silicon	Not found

Because the ore carries about 0.1 per cent cobalt and the tonnage treated is 3,000,000 to 3,500,000 per year, the cobalt content of the ore treated is from 3,000 to 3,500 tons per year.

The flow sheet of the operating-scale cobalt plant, built by Rhokana, is shown in Fig. 46.

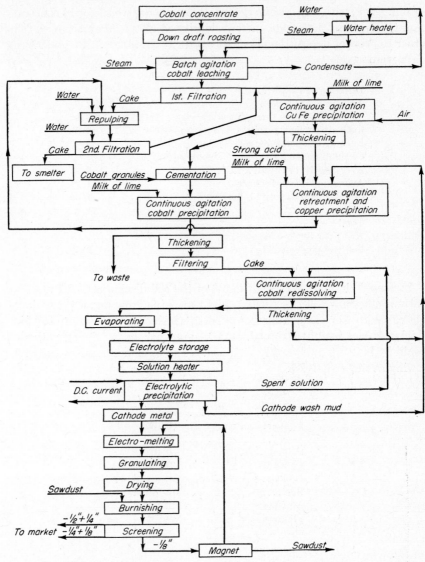

Fig. 46. Flow sheet of cobalt-recovery plant, Rhokana Corporation, N'kana, Northern Rhodesia, Africa.

The following is an equipment list:

TABLE 90.   MAJOR EQUIPMENT, RHOKANA CORPORATION, COBALT PLANT

Six Herreshoff (1 spare) 8-hearth roasters
One Cottrell dust collecting system
Three calcine leaching agitators 11 by 12 ft, with steam coils
One hot-water tank, 10 by 12 ft
Four (1 spare) copper-iron purification tanks, 11 by 16 ft (Wallace type)
Two cobalt precipitation agitators
Three filter-feed storage agitators, 10 by 12 ft
Four (1 spare) cobalt hydroxide dissolution agitators, 13 by 14 ft
Five (1 spare) re-treatment agitators, 5 by 5 ft
One copper–iron purification thickener, 40 ft diam
One cobalt precipitation thickener, 40 ft diam
One cobalt hydroxide dissolution thickener, 50 ft diam
Five drum filters (2 spare) 11½ by 12 ft long

All equipment in contact with solution or pulp to be acidproof construction.

Plans for Final Plant.   The ore averages about 3 per cent copper and 0.1 per cent cobalt, the latter occurring mainly as carrollite ($CuCo_2S_4$). The copper minerals are principally chalcopyrite and bornite. Using minimum amounts of reagents, the easily floatable copper minerals are floated first, producing a smelting-grade concentration of 40 to 45 per cent copper, after which a cobalt concentrate is made, averaging 3 per cent cobalt, 25 to 30 per cent copper, and 15 to 20 per cent iron. Before flotation, 1.5 lb per ton of lime is ground in with the ore in order to keep the cobalt out of the first concentrate.

Roasting Cobalt Concentrate.   Roasting is done in five 8-hearth Herreshoff roasters, the daily capacity being 150 tons of concentrate. The roasting is by downward draft, in three successive stages:

1. The first stage is an oxide roast carried out at not over 600°C in order to avoid the formation of cobalt ferrites.

2. The second stage is a sulfating roast at 580 to 620°C, during which the CoO and CuO are largely converted to the sulfates, the reaction with SO_2 being catalyzed by Fe_2O_3.

3. The third stage at 680 to 710°C is a further sulfating by SO_2, and decomposition and interchange of $CuSO_4$ in the bed according to the reaction: $CuSO_4 + CoO = CoSO_4 + CuO$.

The cobalt and iron water-solubility is expected to be 80 to 85 per cent and 1 to 2 per cent, respectively.

The calcine is cooled and conveyed to a hopper in a water-jacketed screw conveyor serving all roasters. There is an automatic hopper weigher mounted on a Telpher crawl to serve the leach agitators. The cooled calcine is moved by pneumatic conveyor to the calcine-storage bin.

Lime slaking is in a ball mill in a closed circuit with a classifier.   Milk of lime is stored in two 16- by 18-ft mechanical agitators.   Cobalt concentrate weighs 130 lb per cu ft, calcine 90 lb per cu ft.

Leaching of Calcine.   Leaching of calcine is by batch agitation in mechanical agitators.   The calcine feed, as weighted, is charged into water heated to 70°C.   The heat of reaction raises the temperature to 80 to 90°C and this temperature is maintained by steam coils.   Agitation is continued for 1 hr in a pulp dilution of 1:1.   The cobalt dissolves in about 10 min but continued agitation precipitates copper because the pulp becomes more basic, owing to the magnesium and calcium present. The agitation is stopped when the pH reaches 3.5.   This is very important because a higher pH precipitates cobalt and any such precipitate here would be lost.

Leached calcine is continuously filtered in two stages.   The first stage dewaters only.   The filter effluent contains 25 gpl cobalt and 7 to 8 gpl copper.   The cake is repulped with water and pumped to the second filtration, where it is washed by means of a water spray on the cake.   The second filter effluent carries 7.0 to 5.0 gpl cobalt.   The cake is shipped to copper smelting.   The combined effluents from both filters, containing about 15.0 gpl cobalt, 5.0 gpl copper, and 0.3 gpl iron, are pumped to the copper-iron purification.

The solution is purified by continuous agitation in mechanical air agitators, in which the air helps oxidation of the iron.   The agitation time is about 6 hr.   The agitator feed solution is at about 3.5 pH.   Milk of lime is added to bring the pH up to 5.5, about one-half of the lime being added to the first agitator and one-quarter to each of the second and third agitators.

Most of the copper and all of the iron is precipitated.   A small amount of the cobalt (3 to 5 per cent) may precipitate with the copper.   The agitator discharge solution, containing 15.0 gpl cobalt, 0.2 gpl copper, and no iron, flows to the thickener.   The thickener overflow moves by gravity to the cementation step and the copper-iron sludge is pumped to re-treatment.

Precipitation of Copper and Cobalt.   The copper-cementation boxes are similar to those used for copper precipitation by scrap iron.   The cobalt granules are about $\frac{1}{4}$ in. in size and have to be annealed at 900°C for 1 hr.   They are inactive unless annealed.   The reason for this is unknown but is probably due to a film coating of some kind.   Passage of the solution around the granules is by upward percolation.   The granules are cleaned periodically by removing them from the boxes and freeing them from the copper powder.   The effluent from the cementation, containing 15 gpl cobalt, less than 0.001 gpl copper, and no iron, is pumped to cobalt precipitation.

Cobalt is precipitated by continuous agitation in mechanical agitators, the agitation time being about $2\frac{1}{2}$ hr. The agitator feed solution is at pH 5.5 and milk of lime is added in sufficient amount to raise the pH to 8.2, at which point the cobalt precipitates as the hydroxide, $Co(OH)_2$. The agitator discharge is by gravity to thickener. The thickener underflow (cobalt sludge) is pumped to continuous filtration. The thickener overflow and the filter effluent are pumped to waste. The filter cake (cobalt hydroxide) at 45 to 50 per cent solids is repulped with spent solution and pumped to the cobalt-redissolving stage.

Cobalt is redissolved by continuous agitation in mechanical agitators for about 1 hr. Spent solution at pH 1.8 is added to the first agitator and strong acid (98 per cent sulfuric acid) is added to the second agitator in an amount sufficient to bring the pH to between 4.7 and 5. The agitator discharges to a thickener, the underflow from which is pumped to re-treatment to recover any cobalt hydroxide that may not have been dissolved. The thickener overflow is pumped to the pure solution storage, and on the way passes through an evaporator for evaporation of about 5.0 gpm, which is required in order to balance the plant solutions. The total electrolyte to storage is 565 gpm containing 2.5 gpl cobalt.

Electrolysis. The purified electrolyte is heated to 70°C. There are 64 cells, 5 ft long, 4 ft deep, and 3 ft wide. The high flow rate is to prevent build-up of acidity in electrolyte beyond pH 1.8. The anodes are of grid construction, of antimonial lead, and carry 20 amp per sq ft, in order to prevent deposition of cobalt oxide on the anode. If cobalt oxide production is desired, the anode current density is reduced to 10 amp per sq ft. The cathodes are mild steel plates carrying a current density of 15 amp per sq ft. Cell voltage is 3.2 volts, and current efficiency 80 to 85 per cent.

A re-treatment section handles sludge from the copper-iron purification, sludge from cobalt redissolution, and cathode washing sludge. Treatment includes four agitators, the first two for cobalt dissolution and the second two for copper precipitation. Strong acid (98 per cent sulfuric) is added to the first agitator to bring the pH to 3.6. Milk of lime is then added to the third and fourth agitators to bring the pH to 5.5, at which point copper precipitates. The agitator discharge is pumped to the second calcine filter to recover cobalt in solution.

The cobalt cathodes are melted in an electric furnace and the molten metal granulated, the granule sizes ranging from $\frac{1}{2}$ in. down. The granules are then dried, burnished with sawdust, and screened on a double-deck vibrating screen, the upper and lower decks with $\frac{1}{4}$ in. and $\frac{1}{8}$ in. respectively. The two coarse sizes are packed and shipped to market. The minus-$\frac{1}{8}$-in. screen undersize is separated from sawdust by magnetic separation and returned to the melt. Some of the medium-size granules are used for copper cementation after annealing.

IRON

A considerable amount of work has been done on leaching and electrolytic processes for the extraction and production of iron from ores. The following is abstracted from an article by R. D. Pike.[1]

In 1846, Bottger described the use of a bath containing ferrous sulfate and ammonium chloride for the electrodeposition of iron. Other early workers were Kramer, Bietz, Klein, Jacobi, and Lerez. Siemens (U.S. Patent 415,576) described leaching a sulfide mineral with ferric chloride or sulfate and depositing iron in a diaphragm cell. This patent disclosed the general basic principles followed by later workers, including Pike.

The Burgess process, operated for some years by the Western Electric Co., used soluble iron anodes. By this method cathodes undesirably high in carbon, sulfur, or both were often produced.

The so-called Grenoble process, operated commercially at Grenoble, France, employed a hot neutral solution of ferrous chloride to which iron oxide was added for control of ferric iron, with cast-iron anodes and rapidly rotating mandrels for cathodes. A plant using this procedure was installed by Perin at Niagara Falls.

Eustis, about 1920, began pilot-plant testing of the Siemens principles employing pyrrhotite ores from Canada.[2] His work was followed by that of Traill and McCleland,[3] which was on a laboratory scale, and met difficulties in producing a thick iron deposit. An interesting extension of the general idea was the treatment of ilmenite for making electrolytic iron and titanium oxide. In this process, the iron oxide of the ilmenite was reduced to sponge iron before leaching.

Pike and his associates used chloride solutions. Their procedure was to leach unroasted copper concentrate with hot ferric chloride solutions in autoclaves, separating the dissolved copper by cementation with iron, and electrolyzing the resulting iron solution to produce metallic iron. A diaphragm cell was used with graphite anodes and rotating cathodes.

[1] R. D. Pike *et al.*, Electrolytic Iron from Sulphide Ores, *Trans. AIME, Iron & Steel Division*, 1930.

[2] D. Belcher, *Transactions American Electrochemical Society*, 1924.

[3] R. J. Traill and W. R. McCleland, Investigations in Ore Dressing and Metallurgy, *Bulletin* 72, Department of Mines, Mines Branch, Canada.

The iron produced averaged about 0.005 per cent carbon, 0.007 per cent sulfur, and 0.006 per cent copper. There was no phosphorus, silicon, manganese, nickel, cobalt, cadmium, arsenic, zinc, tin, or lead. The iron could be plated to a thickness of about 0.2 in. and was apparently of exceptional physical quality. For the complete details of operation, the original article should be consulted.

CHAPTER 9

THE HISTORY OF HYDROMETALLURGY

Neither reagents suitable for leaching ores, nor the chemical knowledge to use them, nor the economic conditions for successful production of metal by wet processes came into existence until comparatively recent times. That is why hydrometallurgical processes as a source of metals date back only a few centuries. Pyrometallurgical processes, of course, have a history hundreds of years longer.

Men first produced and used the metals they could find free in nature, like gold, native copper, and meteoric iron. In the late Stone Age, such metals were known but had no use beyond ornamentation. Discovery of smelting ushered in the Bronze and Iron Ages, when metals first served as utensils and weapons. Pyrometallurgical methods were used exclusively.

Copper was undoubtedly the first metal to be produced by wet methods. The first, and for many years the only, technique was by cementation on iron from mine waters or similar solutions carrying copper. Although this reaction was one of the first known chemical facts, its usefulness was overlooked and its nature misinterpreted. From a practical point of view, no one thought the reaction useful because it was difficult and expensive to get metallic iron, itself. Why use it up in obtaining copper?

The alchemists clung to the reaction as a strong argument for transmutation of metals. Anyone could easily see it happen by poking an iron rod into the alchemist's solution. Paracelsus and Basil Valentine mentioned the reaction more soberly as early as 1500 A.D. Not until about 1750 did iron become commonplace enough to be used as a copper precipitant. Its first such use was probably at Rio Tinto in Spain. Up to that time, at Rio Tinto and in the ancient (3000 B.C.) copper mines of Cyprus, the copper-bearing mine waters had been regarded as a nuisance because they corroded the miners' tools.

EARLY METHODS (1550 A.D.)

Hydrometallurgical methods seem to have begun with a technique for recovering vitriol ($FeSO_4$) from mine waters, or from leach solutions, that was in use around the middle of the sixteenth century. It was described in *Pirotecnica of Vannoccio Biringuccio*, Chap. 5.

The method is interesting in that it is quite similar to the large-scale weathering technique practiced later at Rio Tinto. Another interesting feature was the addition of metallic iron to the liquor to reduce ferric iron to ferrous, although the report fails to mention any resulting precipitation of copper.

Biringuccio suggested leaving the ore to be leached in a heap out in the open for 5 or 6 months, exposed to the action of the weather. The heap must be turned over several times and any lumps broken up. Then it must be left under cover for another 6 or 8 months.

The ore may then be put into a leaching tank and stirred up with water until, in the judgment of the operator, all the vitriol is leached out and solution is sufficiently high in dissolved iron. The slurry should then be allowed to settle and the clear liquor drained off into another tank.

In the separate tank, the liquor should be boiled down to a concentrated solution, at which point some iron should be thrown in and the boiling continued to bring down the crystals of vitriol. Biringuccio also described the processes of recrystallization and return of mother liquor.

Biringuccio wrote, "Vitriol is also found reduced to its ultimate purity by nature itself, without art. This is thrown forward by the heat, like a skin on the mixed ore when it is weathered." This obviously refers to an important factor in modern heap leaching, which is the salt that is brought out to the surfaces of mineral particles by capillary action.

In describing production of alum, Biringuccio mentioned the presence of "marcasites," which was his name for any sulfide. Such ores were roasted in heaps. It seems to be an early example of a sulfatizing roast.

The tanks Biringuccio described were about 43 ft long, 21 ft wide, and 8 ft deep. If they were half-filled with water, it would mean about 3,600 cu ft, corresponding to about 13,626 gal or 100,000 l.

A rough idea of the capacity of the method can be gained by assuming that Biringuccio's vitriol solution, after stirring in the first tank, might carry 1 per cent iron, corresponding to about 50 gpl $FeSO_4 \cdot 7H_2O$. For his 100,000 l, he would then have about 11,000 lb, or 5½ tons, of dissolved vitriol. If his raw material contained about 20 per cent water-soluble vitriol, this would mean a charge in his leaching tank of about 27 tons of ore.

Charging, leaching, and settling would probably take about 4 days. The slurry might settle so that 80 per cent of the solution could be drawn off. This would amount to about 11,000 gal, or a maximum of 2,750 gal per day to his evaporating section. Ten boilers for evaporating would mean 275 gal or about 40 cu ft each. Assuming 1 day for evaporation, the plant must have had a capacity of about ½ to 1 ton of vitriol per day.

Extension of this method to recovery of metal had to wait for availability of cheap iron to precipitate the copper. Heap leaching for copper probably began at Rio Tinto about 1752. The method was like the one Biringuccio outlined, a leaching by weathering piles of ore in the open air, followed by iron cementation of the liquor that drained off the heaps.

The method is essentially the same as is now in use at several large copper mines in the Southwestern United States. Ore that is too low-grade to treat in the mill, but is too high-grade to be discarded completely, is leached by simply spraying water over the piles of broken ore.

Heap-leaching can be speeded up considerably if the ore is first roasted and the copper converted to a readily soluble form. Heap- or stall-roasting works well but spreads a pall of sulfur dioxide over all the countryside. Heap roasting went on at Rio Tinto until 1888, when it was forbidden by law.

As chemical knowledge accumulated, and more experience with leaching was built up, a host of methods for copper leaching were gradually tried out. Only a few of these can be mentioned, owing to space limitations, but because of their historical interest they will be described briefly.

RECENT METHODS—COPPER LEACHING

The various processes for copper leaching that have been tested or tried out in recent years may be divided into two classes: (1) sulfate and sulfite methods, (2) chloride methods.

Sulfate and Sulfite Methods

Heap leaching and iron precipitation are too well known for any further comment here. A modern development of heap leaching in the Southwestern United States is described in Chap. 4.

Heap roasting, followed by leaching to extract copper, was used at Rio Tinto for years. It was banned in 1888 after the practice had devastated the countryside for miles around. Stall roasting, practiced in several localities, met the same objection. In fact, any roasting operation in which sulfur dioxide is discharged into the atmosphere may become troublesome. Near many of the larger copper smelters in the United States, "smoke farming"—i.e., collection of damages from the smelting company—was at one time more profitable than dirt farming.

Sulfating roasting, with or without addition of reagents, such as sodium sulfate or pyrite, was tested by several English and German inventors early in the nineteenth century. It was tried out for extraction of copper from pyrite cinders, but the Longmaid-Henderson chloridizing roast gave better extraction and also recovered metals other than copper. Development of improved techniques has given the sulfating roast new importance. With the Dorr FluoSolids roaster, it is possible to get practically

100 per cent production of sulfate, against earlier conversions of not more than 78 per cent. In the light of this fact, further consideration may be given to roasting-leaching techniques for many sulfide copper concentrates or other products.

Sulfur dioxide leaching (Neill process) involved a reaction between CuO and SO_2 to form $CuSO_3$, which is insoluble in water. In the presence of excess cupric oxide, CuO, a cupro-cupric sulfite was formed that was soluble in solutions containing an excess of sulfur dioxide. The copper sulfite was precipitated by boiling off the SO_2. A pilot-plant test at Coconino, Ariz., brought out several difficulties, among them the impossibility of getting a strong SO_2 solution from a weak SO_2 gas, premature precipitation of the sulfite before solution separation, and weakness of copper solution formed. Some difficulties were overcome but the work was never carried to completion.

Sulfur dioxide precipitation (Van Arsdale method) was developed in an attempt to produce acid cheaply for leaching. The proposal was to oxidize sulfur dioxide with air in solutions of iron and copper sulfates. The method is similar to the oxidation obtained in one of the Hunt and Douglas methods described in the following pages. When these solutions, carrying sulfur dioxide under pressure, were heated, metallic copper precipitated quite unexpectedly. The method is described elsewhere in this volume (page 140) and it has possibilities for modern use.

Ferrous sulfate leaching (Elliott process) was a proposal (U.S. Patent 814,836) to leach copper ore with a hot neutral solution of ferrous sulfate. Air had to be introduced to oxidize the ferrous to ferric sulfate, which actually did the leaching. When the copper was precipitated on iron, the ferrous sulfate was regenerated. Theoretically the reactions are

$$12FeSO_4 + 3O_2 = 4Fe_2(SO_4)_3 + 2Fe_2O_3 \qquad (1)$$
$$3CuO + Fe_2(SO_4)_3 = 3CuSO_4 + Fe_2O_3 \qquad (2)$$
$$CuSO_4 + Fe = Cu + FeSO_4 \qquad (3)$$

In these equations, iron and copper are in balance, but in practice much iron is lost through precipitation of basic iron salts when the neutral solution of ferric sulfate is heated. These salts carry down a lot of copper and for this and other reasons the proposal is regarded as having no commercial importance.

Greene-Cananea, in Mexico, once tried to leach mill tailings and flue dust by a similar method. Copper content varied from 0.54 to 0.89 per cent, and from 0.27 to 0.66 per cent of readily soluble zinc was present. The air oxidation proved to be quite inefficient. Iron precipitation was troublesome unless acid was added but in that event the process became a simple leach with sulfuric acid. The tests showed that ferric sulfate was a satisfactory solvent for various forms of copper but the regeneration of this reagent by oxidizing the ferrous sulfate was not successful. It should be kept in mind, however, that ferric sulfate is a valuable copper solvent and that it can be regenerated easily by electrolysis, as was shown years later at Inspiration.

Sulfating roast and lime precipitation (Bradley process)[1] was tried in a pilot plant at Anaconda. It comprised a sulfatizing roast, leaching, treatment of liquor with calcium chloride, filtration of calcium sulfate, precipitation of $Fe(OH)_3$ and aluminum hydroxide by cupric oxide and calcium hydroxide, filtration of oxide precipitates, and precipitation of cupric oxide by calcium carbonate.

It was found that in a chloride solution of iron, aluminum, and copper, the calcium carbonate first brought down $Fe(OH)_3$ and then $CuCl_2 \cdot 3Cu(OH)_2$ with some aluminum hydroxide. The method proved unsuccessful.

The Laist process was tried out at Anaconda in a plant built to treat accumulated mill tailings totaling about 20,000,000 tons. These contained about 0.64 per cent copper and 0.48 oz silver per ton. About one-fourth of this copper content was oxidized; the rest was sulfide copper. The process involved oxidizing roasting, leaching with sulfuric acid, ferric sulfate, and salt, washing, precipitation on iron, briquetting and smelting the precipitate.

This was probably the first large-scale copper-leaching plant in the country. It was successful metallurgically and economically, and was described in detail by F. C. Laist and H. W. Aldrich.[2]

Electrolytic processes for copper, in the early stages of development, usually featured anodic depolarization and production of ferric iron, in addition to acid, as a solvent for copper. Diaphragm cells were usually used.

Although diaphragm cells are not seriously considered for modern copper electrolytic plants, they are used successfully for other electrolytic processes. There seems no reason why diaphragm cells could not be adapted to copper electrolysis, if it seemed desirable. Production and use of ferric iron as a solvent has been worked out at Inspiration.

Anode composition was at one time a serious problem. Greenawalt stated, in 1912, "For sulfate solutions, no really satisfactory anode has yet been discovered, although most conceivable substances have been

[1] H. O. Hofman and C. R. Hayward, *Metallurgy of Copper*, 2d ed., p. 317, McGraw-Hill Book Company, Inc., New York, 1924.

[2] F. C. Laist and H. W. Aldrich, The 2,000-ton Leaching Plant at Anaconda, *Trans. AIME*, Vol. 60, p. 866.

tried.   Lead, on the whole, has given the best results for sulfate solutions. The purity of the lead is an important factor."

This statement sounds strange today, in view of the almost universal use of lead anodes in both copper and zinc sulfate electrolysis.   Pure lead is used in only one zinc plant and in that one for special local reasons. Union Miniere, for example, started with pure lead anodes but found them unusable.   They were replaced by the customary antimony-lead alloy.   Antimony does not go into solution, as Greenawalt feared, nor are carbon or graphite anodes "absolutely worthless" for sulfate solutions, as he stated.   They have advantages for certain conditions and are quite durable for copper electrolysis, provided they are properly depolarized.[1]

Keith process was one of the earliest copper-leaching-electrolysis methods tried out in the United States.   The plant was set up at Arlington, N.J., and treated ore from the mine located there, which was the first copper ore body worked in the United States.   The steps were roasting, leaching with spent electrolyte, electrolysis with lead anodes and copper starting sheets plated on lead cathodes.

The cells were arranged in series.   Current density was decreased in succeeding cells by increasing their size and the number of electrodes in them.   The purpose of this reduction in current density was to maintain a reguline deposit as the solution became weaker in copper content down through the cells.

Actually this procedure was unnecessary because the spent electrolyte had to be recirculated anyway, and there could be nothing gained by stripping the solution of copper below the point at which reguline deposition became difficult.   The effect of ferric iron was not considered.   If it were present in increasing amounts as deposition proceeded, the described current-density reduction would have resulted in a corresponding reduction in ampere efficiency.

Siemens-Halske process included a special roast, a leach with spent electrolyte containing ferric sulfate and free sulfuric acid, and electrolysis in a special diaphragm cell in which electrodes and diaphragm were horizontal.   The cathode compartment was uppermost and contained a copper cathode.   In use, the solution deposited copper and then flowed slowly through the asbestos diaphragm into the lower anode compartment, where ferrous iron was oxidized to ferric.   This horizontal diaphragm cell was impracticable in commercial use, although the theoretical voltage was low.

Laszczynski process (U.S. Patent 757,817, April, 1904) was based on a cell in which solutions carrying considerable iron could be electrolyzed

---

[1] For a discussion of these points, see *Trans. AIME*, Vol. 60.

without oxidation of ferrous to ferric iron.   This was brought about by wrapping a cover, or envelope, of porous fabric around the insoluble lead anode.   The result was that only sulfuric acid was produced at the anode and there was no anodic depolarization effect.   This is the precise opposite of the Siemens-Halske and similar processes in which the solution flow is from the cathode to the anode compartment.   Ampere efficiency was stated as nearly 100 per cent, which is understandable since ferric iron was not in contact with the cathode.   Power consumed was about 1.3 kwhr per lb of copper deposited.   There was no apparent advantage in this procedure over modern methods of electrolysis.   In the complete absence of anodic depolarization, the lead anodes probably suffered considerably from peroxidation.

Carmichael and Tossizza processes were somewhat similar.   The Carmichael process[1] consisted of roasting, leaching with a hot 5 per cent sulfuric acid solution, followed by electrolysis.   The solution from the ore was saturated with sulfur dioxide gas which was also blown into the electrolyte in the cells.   Sulfuric acid was generated from the gaseous sulfur dioxide, which also acted as a depolarizer.   Current density was 6 amp per sq ft at a voltage of 1.5, and an ampere efficiency of about 90 per cent. Tossizza (U.S. Patent 710,346, Sept. 30, 1902) claimed a considerably smaller voltage by a similar use of sulfur dioxide.

As a depolarizing agent sulfur dioxide is less practicable and efficient than ferrous sulfate.   The atmosphere in any tank house is usually not too agreeable.   Blowing sulfur dioxide through the electrolyte during electrolysis would make it unbreathable.

Ramen process (U.S. Patent 913,430, Feb. 23, 1909) put half of the lixiviant into the cathode compartment of a diaphragm cell, while the remainder was precipitated by iron, and the resultant liquor sent to the anode compartment.   No details are available on any practical application of this proposal.

Marchese and Gunther processes, which were tried on a commercial scale at Stolberg and Mansfeld, Germany, used soluble anodes of copper matte and white metal, respectively.   They were never successful, and with modern smelting and refining methods the incentive for direct electrolysis of matte or white metal no longer exists.

CHLORIDE PROCESSES

Doetsch and Froelich processes were operated for a time in Spain. The Doetsch method involved leaching cupric sulfide by ferric chloride, precipitation of copper by iron, and regeneration of the solvent chloride.

[1] *Electrochemical Industry,* April, 1903.

The Froelich process was quite similar, the reduced ferric chloride being regenerated by air.

Hunt and Douglas processes included two methods, known as the No. 1 and the No. 2 Hunt and Douglas processes. They were developed by the late James Douglas, pioneer American copper hydrometallurgist. He was responsible not only for much leaching progress but also for the first United States electrolytic copper refining. In Arizona he introduced the water-jacketed copper blast furnace and the copper converter, which he adopted after a visit to Italy where such a converter was first used. Both of his leaching processes at one time were of considerable practical importance.

Process No. 1 was a neutral leaching method making use of the solvent action of hot ferrous chloride brine on oxidized or roasted copper ore. The reactions are somewhat complicated but may possibly be simplified as follows:

$$CuO + FeCl_2 + H_2O = CuCl_2 + Fe(OH)_2$$

The ferrous hydroxide, $Fe(OH)_2$, in the presence of air then readily oxidizes to $Fe(OH)_3$. Cuprous chloride may also be formed, probably in greater amount than the cupric chloride:

$$3CuO + 2FeCl_2 + 3H_2O = 2CuCl + CuCl_2 + 2Fe(OH)_3$$

In this case, the cuprous chloride was held in solution by excess of either ferrous chloride or sodium chloride brine. In the process, leaching was followed by filtration and precipitation on iron, thereby regenerating the solvent, ferrous chloride. During agitation, it is probable that a certain amount of ferric chloride was formed, since the ferrous compound in neutral solution is readily oxidizable.

If the process is carried out according to the foregoing, and the solutions used cyclically, iron is built up. Accordingly the oxidation of ferrous to ferric chloride and its precipitation as basic salt on heating would furnish a means of controlling excess ferric iron. Such precipitated iron products, however, also carry down appreciable amounts of copper, thereby reducing extraction. Disadvantages of the procedure were mainly filtration or settling troubles, and the fact that ferrous chloride is only an indifferent solvent for copper.

In process No. 2, these difficulties were recognized and more or less obviated by an acid regenerative system, of which there were several variations. The main steps were

1. Solution of oxide copper by acid:

$$CuO + H_2SO_4 = CuSO_4 + H_2O$$

2. Addition of a chloride, which could be either ferrous, calcium, or sodium chloride, resulting in conversion of a part of the copper in solution to chloride:

$$2CuSO_4 + FeCl_2 = CuSO_4 + CuCl_2 + FeSO_4$$
$$2CuSO_4 + CaCl_2 = CuSO_4 + CuCl_2 + CaSO_4$$

3. Precipitation of the copper as cuprous chloride by passing sulfur dioxide into the solution:

$$CuSO_4 + CuCl_2 + SO_2 + 2H_2O = 2CuCl + 2H_2SO_4$$

4. Several methods of treating the precipitated cuprous chloride have been proposed. Iron would release copper and form ferrous chloride. Treatment of the cuprous chloride with lime was theoretically possible, yielding cuprous hydroxide and calcium chloride, but use of lime also gave copper oxychloride. Iron precipitation was also not entirely satisfactory. A later proposed modification was electrolysis of the wet, solid cuprous chloride with a copper cathode, in contact with the precipitate, and an insoluble anode, according to:

$$2CuCl + H_2O + E.E. = 2Cu + 2HCl + O$$

Oxygen and hydrochloric acid were evolved at the anode, the acid being absorbed in a tower filled with oxide ore.

The method used much later at Chuquicamata and Andes for dechloridizing copper liquors may be considered a modification of this process.

It is rather curious that Hunt and Douglas missed the simple and efficient dissolution of cuprous chloride in brine, and the precipitation of copper by iron, thereby regenerating the brine. It was used at Chuquicamata, but not for treating the Hunt and Douglas cuprous chloride.

Hoepfner process of electrolysis took place in a diaphragm cell, in which the solvent was cupric chloride. This was intended to act on either cupric oxide or sulfide, thereby being reduced to cuprous chloride. Brine was of course used to hold the cuprous chloride in solution.

The steps of the method were (1) leaching with cupric chloride, (2) dividing the solution, part going to a cathode compartment and the remainder to the anode compartment of an electrolytic cell, (3) electrolysis, during which copper was deposited on sheet copper cathodes and chlorine set free at the anode, converting cuprous to cupric chloride, (4) combining the cathode and anode compartment exit liquors and using these as a solvent in step (1).

To a certain extent, this method has attractive theoretical advantages. The copper is deposited from cuprous solution, thereby giving a high yield per unit of power. In addition the cuprous chloride at the anode theoretically acts as a depolarizing agent, absorbing free chlorine and resulting in a low voltage. Voltage was stated to be about 0.8. Later work reduced this voltage still further to less than 0.5, as stated.[1]

The proposal was tested on a pilot-plant scale under the direction of the late D. H. Browne, and a humorous account of his many troubles with the method was published in an early volume of the American Electrochemical Society. The main difficulties involved materials of construction for the corrosive solutions, imperfect solution of cupric sulfide and consequent low extractions, and short life of the diaphragms and carbon anodes. A modern diaphragm design and a better utilization of anodic depolarization might have obviated the two last-named difficulties.

ZINC PROCESSES

As with copper, zinc pyrometallurgy long preceded zinc leaching. Both came much later than copper metallurgy. Zinc metal was mentioned by Agricola but the first commercial production of zinc was in China. The date of its first production there is not known. The first commercial production in Europe of zinc by distillation was in England, around 1740.

Due to the high voltage required for zinc electrolysis as compared with copper, power is a very considerable item in production costs. Early attempts at anodic depolarization were made involving sulfur dioxide, the anodic oxidation of chromates, etc., but without practical results. It may be noted that the presence of even small amounts of sulfur dioxide in a zinc electrolyte leads to immediate production of hydrogen sulfide by cathodic reactions. The result is the precipitation of zinc sulfide.

Due mainly to the necessity for extreme purity of solutions, any possibility of anodic depolarization for zinc electrolysis is probably hopeless, with the possible exception of electrical depolarization, no account of which has been published. Electrical depolarization is mentioned elsewhere in this volume. Laboratory-scale tests (data unpublished) have shown the possibility of plating out good reguline zinc at lower than usual plant voltages by the use of electrical depolarization.

The Gordon process, operated by the Metals Extraction Corp. at Salida, Col., was an ammonia process similar to that for copper and nickel, except that reduction to metal, as is done for ammonia leaching of copper and nickel, was not possible.

The method was applied to a zinc–lead sulfide ore. This was roasted and leached with "gas-house liquor." The solution reaction is stated to be:

$$ZnO + 2NH_4OH + 2CO_2 = ZnCO_3(NH_4)_2CO_3 \cdot H_2O$$

[1] Cohen and Lanz, *Z. Electrochemie*, Vol. 2, p. 25, 1895.

Copper and cadmium were precipitated from the solution by passing it over metallic zinc. The ammonia and carbon dioxide were then driven off in stills and condensed for reuse, the zinc being precipitated as $ZnO \cdot ZnCO_3$ or possibly as $Zn(OH)_2CO_3$. The precipitate was then calcined to zinc oxide. The washed residue containing lead, iron, gold, and silver was shipped to a smelter. Modern selective flotation removed the incentive for this process.

Waring process started with a smelting step on a complex ore, in which volatile metals were vaporized and a matte and slag were formed. The matte supposedly carried only the copper, gold, and unvaporized silver. The fume contained zinc, lead, a little silver, and various impurities, and was treated by an ammonium carbonate solution which separated zinc from the other metals. The purified liquors were distilled, yielding zinc carbonate for calcination, as with the Gordon process. Zinc "fume" is now treated by standard leaching and electrolytic methods.

Campbell process was a laboratory-tested proposal for electrolysis of zinc ammonium carbonate solutions, obtained as in the Gordon process. It proved unworkable.

Coolbaugh process was a method for producing a marketable zinc sulfate from ordinary ores. It consisted of a sulfatizing roast, followed by leaching and air agitation for precipitating the iron group. The residue, carrying lead, silver, gold, and copper, was sent to a smelter. The solution was further purified by adding zinc dust. Purified liquor was evaporated by spray-drying to zinc sulfate crystals, which were shipped.

Sulfatization in the roasting step was probably far from complete and development of modern sulfatizing equipment may result in new opportunities for this method of producing zinc sulfate for making lithopone.

Bisulfite process and associated methods are quite similar to the Neill process for leaching copper. Zinc sulfite, $ZnSO_3$, is insoluble in water, but it can be made soluble by an excess of sulfur dioxide, probably forming $ZnH_2(SO_3)_2$. It was proposed to precipitate the insoluble zinc sulfite once more by driving off the excess sulfur dioxide. The zinc sulfite was to be calcined to zinc oxide. A small plant was built in England around 1912 to test the method but results there were not satisfactory.

ZINC ELECTROLYSIS

The first proposal for zinc leaching and electrolysis, which was quite similar to modern methods, was made by L. Letrange of Paris, around 1880. Modern zinc leaching and electrolysis was begun by the Anaconda Co. and the Consolidated Mining & Smelting Co. of Canada, around 1915.

Commercially, the incentive for this development was the availability of large tonnages of mixed copper-lead-zinc ores, carrying precious-metal values, that were not suitable for the conventional zinc retort process.

Ashcroft processes were two in number. The first included roasting zinc sulfide to oxide, leaching with a solution of ferric chloride, and electrolysis in two stages. In the first stage, iron anodes were used, thereby adding to the solution iron which had supposedly been depleted during leaching. In the second stage, the cells had insoluble anodes. Zinc was supposed to be deposited and the ferrous iron added in the first stage oxidized to ferric chloride by chlorine produced at the anode. Voltages were probably low, due to soluble anodes in the first electrolytic step and to the anodic depolarization in the second step. Because these chloride solutions carried large amounts of iron, which is fatal in sulfate zinc electrolysis, it is probable that no zinc could be plated satisfactorily from them.

The second Ashcroft process was radically different. It consisted of the following steps: suspension of finely ground zinc sulfide ore in molten zinc chloride through which chlorine was blown, leaching of the resulting chloride mass with water, removal of metals other than zinc from solution, evaporation of the resulting zinc chloride solution, and fusion of the solid zinc chloride. Part of the fused chloride was returned to the first step and the remainder was electrolyzed in the molten state.

Malm process included treating zinc sulfide ore in a rotating kiln with dilute chlorine gas, leaching with water, purifying the solution, evaporation of the solution to solid zinc chloride, and fusion and electrolysis of the molten zinc chloride. Tests of the method were made in three localities on a pilot-plant scale between 1907 and 1917, but were unsuccessful.

Hoepfner process for zinc must be distinguished from the Hoepfner process for copper, described previously. The zinc process was started in Germany to recover the metal from leach liquor from the chloridizing roasting of pyrites cinders. The solutions were freed from iron and heavy metals other than zinc, and electrolyzed in a special diaphragm cell, using carbon anodes. The diaphragm was required in order to keep chlorine away from the cathodes, where it would cause serious re-solution if accompanied by small amounts of iron. Hoepfner used rotating cathodes and retort carbon anodes. Chlorine was evolved at the anode and absorbed in lime to make bleaching powder. A Hoepfner plant was in operation for a number of years at the works of the Brunner, Mond Co. in England. Hoepfner's processes and equipment were described by Günther.[1]

---

[1] W. Günther, *Darstellung des Zinks auf Electrolytischem Wege*, W. Knapp, Halle, 1904.

LEAD PROCESSES

A great deal of experimental work has been done on methods for lead leaching and several processes have been commercially applied, although due to various causes none is operating at present.

The principal raw materials for these processes were:

Electrolytic zinc plant tailing, which contains zinc as ferrite and sulfide, lead mostly as sulfate, and some silver and copper. Brine leaching of this material extracts most of the lead and a large part of the silver and copper. However, the zinc is not affected and present practice is to smelt these residues for lead. This also recovers the silver, and the lead slags can be treated by "fuming" to recover the zinc.

Lead sulfate flue dust from lead and zinc smelters can be treated only in limited quantities by a lead smelter.

Lead sulfate sludges from sulfuric acid chambers are produced at a rate of about 3 lb lead as sulfate per ton of sulfuric acid made. This material, similarly to the flue dust, is not wanted by lead smelters.

Oxidized ores of lead (carbonate or sulfate) can be treated by lead leaching with brines if lime is absent. Mixed ores, not carrying lime but with lead sulfide in addition to oxidized compounds, can be treated if iron is used in the solutions. The lead is precipitated by electrolysis, regenerating ferric iron. Oxidized lead ores carrying silver were given a chloridizing roast at two plants in Utah, and lead and silver were recovered by brine-leaching.

Mill tailing (carrying lead sulfide and silver) and *complex zinc–lead–iron sulfide ores.* Selective flotation has been so improved that at present there are apparently no pressing problems in this field. It is possible, however, to recover lead from zinc concentrates carrying small amounts of lead by direct ferric iron leaching (without roasting) and electrolysis. There should be a small field at present for this method.

Table 91 from Ralston[1] gives data as to methods of converting lead to soluble forms.

Chloridizing roasting was carried out by the Tintic Standard Mining Co. on low-grade oxidized lead ore of the following average analysis:

$$
\begin{array}{ll}
\text{Au, oz per ton} \dots\dots\dots & 0.025 \\
\text{Ag, oz per ton} \dots\dots\dots & 17.0 \\
\text{Cu, \%} \dots\dots\dots\dots & 0.35 \\
\text{Pb, \%} \dots\dots\dots\dots & 4.00 \\
\text{SiO}_2, \% \dots\dots\dots & 56.0 \\
\text{Fe}_2\text{O}_3, \text{Al}_2\text{O}_3, \% \dots\dots & 16.3 \\
\text{CaO, \%} \dots\dots\dots & 0.33 \\
\text{Zn, \%} \dots\dots\dots\dots & 0.12 \\
\text{S, \%} \dots\dots\dots\dots & 2.5 \\
\end{array}
$$

[1] O. C. Ralston, Hydrometallurgy of Lead, *Trans. AIME*, Vol. 70, p. 447.

TABLE 91. METHODS OF CONVERTING LEAD TO SOLUBLE FORMS

Name	Method	Reference
Larson	Chloridizing roasting	Min. & Sci. Pr. (1917) 115, 275
Ganelin Amalgamated Zinc Co. of Australia H. Hey	Use of $ZnCl_2$ instead of NaCl in roasting	U.S. Pat. 1,396,740 U.S. Pat. 1,402,733 U.S. Pat. 1,452,857-8
Amalgamated Zinc Co. of Australia H. Hey	Heating ore in an atmosphere of HCl	Brit. Pat. 159,135, 1921 U.S. Pat. 1,384,465, 1921
Middleton	Heating $FeCl_3$ or $CuCl_2$ to 150°–250°	U.S. Pat. 1,403,516, 1922
F. E. Elmore	Chloridizing roasting with $CaCl_2$ or $MgCl_2$ at 400°–500°C	Brit. Pat. 162,026, 1919
H. J. E. Hamilton	Selective chloridizing roasting	Brit. Pat. 152,289, 1920
Elmore	Action of 95% H_2SO_4	U.S. Pat. 1,441,072, 1923
Christensen	Action of various H_2SO_4 strengths	U.S. Pats. 1,415,796, 1,434,084, 1,434,086, 1,434,088, 1,435,891
Elmore	Slightly acid NaCl brine	Brit. Pats. 127,641, 181,-239, 184,628
Hanney	$FeCl_3$ in strong brine	U.S. Pat. 1,456,798
Collins	$FeCl_3$ in strong brine	Brit. Pat. 166,929, 1920
Christensen	$FeCl_3$ in strong brine	Various U.S. Pats., 1914, 1922, 1923
Leaching Solutions		
Nathansohn	Chloride solution plus excess Cl	Brit. Pat. 187,195, 1921
Gainton	Chloride brine and low percentage of excess Cl	
De Luce	FeCl (12%) and $FeCl_3$ (15%)	U.S. Pat. 1,251,485
Precipitation of Lead		
U.S. Bureau of Mines	Electrolysis, Fe anodes	
Flynn and Van Arsdale	Electrolysis, Fe anodes Depolarization, insoluble anodes	U.S. Pat. 1,448,547, 1918
Christensen and Snyder	Zinc hydroxide electrolysis, $FeCl_2$, insoluble anodes	
Sulman and Picard	Na_2CO_3, Na_2S, and CaO	U.S. Pat. 1,268,547, 1918
Tintic Standard Co	Scrap iron	
Tintic Milling Co	Sponge iron	

The ore was pulverized, mixed with coal dust and salt, and blast-roasted in a furnace of the Holt-Dern type. The chloridized ore was then treated in wooden leaching vats with strong brine. A barren solution and a water wash followed the leach solution. The pregnant solution was pumped to towers, where it passed the roaster gases and absorbed sulfuric, sulfurous, and hydrochloric acids. It was then passed to the silver precipitators where copper replaced the silver. The solution was then run over scrap iron in launders to recover the copper, was heated by live steam to about 75°C, and passed to launders containing baled tin-plate scrap. One pound of iron precipitated 2.6 lb of lead. The lead precipitate analyzed:

Ag, oz per ton	2–5
Cu, %	3–5
Pb, %	78–83
Fe, %	3
Insoluble, %	3
As, %	0.7
Zn, %	0.7

The plant cost was small and operating costs low, so that the operation was commercially profitable. A similar operation at Tintic Milling Co. at Park City, Utah, used sponge iron for precipitating the lead. Precipitation was from cold solution. The sponge iron was made locally from a low-grade iron ore.

Electrolytic precipitation in a modification of Tainton's process was tested by the Bunker Hill & Sullivan Co. The steps were roasting at about 500°C; a water wash to remove soluble sulfates; a brine leach, carrying chlorine, applied in agitators, thickeners, and a wood-lined Burt filter; introduction of calcium chloride to precipitate sulfate as calcium sulfate; precipitation of lead and silver in an electrolytic cell with rotating sheet-iron cathodes and graphite anodes.

Similar work at Trail, British Columbia, showed that the process would be more economical than smelting only when the zinc-plant residues carried less than 18 to 20 per cent lead.

Leaching of zinc-plant residue for lead was tested by the Anaconda Co. late in 1919, using the soluble anode process developed by the Bureau of Mines. Anodes and cathodes were ½-in. iron plates. The electrolyte flow was about 2 gpm for each 1000 amp, and 14.74 lb lead was precipitated per kwhr from a solution carrying about 10 gpl of lead. Lead content was reduced to about 2 gpl. Difficulties were encountered in melting the product, which yielded only 59 per cent of its lead content as metal; also from dilution of the brine from the 40 per cent water content of the residues. Work was abandoned when favorable smelting rates were obtained on the material.

Flynn and Van Arsdale[1] did test-plant work on leaching a partly oxidized lead ore carrying silver, using acidified brine carrying ferrous iron, and electrolysis with graphite anodes. The ferrous iron was sufficient to inhibit chlorine evolution at the anode. Lead and silver extractions were satisfactory but gold extraction was nil. The anodes were durable.

Many other processes have been tried with varying success. It is significant that, although a number of large companies have investigated lead leaching thoroughly, in every case the work was abandoned and the plants dismantled. While it is possible that the many troubles met in lead leaching might be solved by proper process selection and plant design, the combination of these troubles and economic considerations make any extended application of lead leaching very improbable.

[1] F. N. Flynn, and G. D. Van Arsdale, *Engineering and Mining Journal*, Vol. 109, p. 487, 1920; also U.S. Patent, 1, 448, 923.

CHAPTER 10

THE FUTURE OF HYDROMETALLURGY

A discussion of the outlook for hydrometallurgy is written with full knowledge of the thinness of the ice upon which all forecasters skate. To say positively that this or that event will, or will not, happen is only to lessen the odds on an eventual ducking. Here, for example, is an opinion of the future of hydrometallurgy given by a man who had every reason to believe that the ice ahead, so to speak, was as solid as it looked.

"I desire, however, to point out," he said, "that a class of processes (hydrometallurgical) which has been given up in almost every case in which it has been tried in the United States, is not one in which to seek the means of starting a new mining and metallurgical enterprise."

The book on copper smelting in the introduction to which this statement can be found was published in 1907. It was no doubt still on the shelves of certain engineers when, a few years later, they designed and built the history-making leaching plants at Ohio Copper, Chuquicamata, and Ajo.

This chapter will not, therefore, contain any sweeping generalizations about the future of hydrometallurgy for base metals. The material in this book and the day-to-day experience of the industry are evidence enough of the secure place won by leaching in the production of metals. It seems fairly certain, too, that interest in hydrometallurgical methods will increase, rather than lessen, in the future, simply because wet methods offer a good chance of solving the problems posed by the complex, low-grade, and impure ores on which our industrial future depends.

As an example of the place of hydrometallurgy in mineral dressing progress, the Pine Creek plant of U.S. Vanadium Co. near Bishop, Calif., is excellent because it compresses so much experience in so short a time. The ore treated at Pine Creek contains tungsten (as scheelite), copper, and molybdenum. Originally, gravity concentration methods were used and a fair recovery of the tungsten was made. But times changed, and that recovery was no longer good enough. A flotation technique was then worked out that for some years produced a satisfactory scheelite concentrate with a good recovery.

But times changed again, and still more was demanded of the Pine

Creek metallurgists. They were asked to get the last bit of molybdenum out of the scheelite concentrate and they found they could do it only by leaching.

Today, the flow sheet includes separation of a copper and a molybdenum product by flotation, plus flotation of a scheelite concentrate carrying some molybdenum. In the leaching plant, both molybdenum and scheelite are dissolved by alkali digestion. The molybdenum is then precipitated as the sulfide, which is filtered off and roasted to the trioxide. The tungsten is then precipitated as calcium tungstate, filtered off, and nodulized for shipment.

This experience might well serve as a demonstration piece of the course of the industry. Over the years, the standards of purity set by consumers of metals steadily increase; grade and purity of available ores of most metals steadily decrease. If this trend continues, greater and greater reliance must be placed on those processes that turn out products of greatest purity. Hydrometallurgical processes are preëminent in this respect.

However, in considering where leaching processes fit into the technology of the future, one must answer two questions: (1) What do hydrometallurgical processes cost? (2) What new ideas are available to make hydrometallurgical processes cheaper, more efficient, and wider in scope? The remainder of this chapter will consider those two questions.

WHAT DOES LEACHING COST?

In attempting to answer this question on the cost of building and operating a modern leaching plant, one immediately runs into the hard fact that hardly anyone will publish accurate and detailed cost figures these days.

Costs have soared so wildly in recent years that most plant managements almost refuse to believe the evidence of their own private calculations on cost. Time and again the comment is heard, "Oh, our cost data are meaningless. They don't represent normal conditions." Unfortunately, it is increasingly apparent that abnormality is becoming normal. It is becoming painfully clear that there are almost no more "low-cost" metal producers left in the world.

One can only make a rough check of costs by simple, although admittedly inexact, calculations based on annual reports. For example, take Inspiration Consolidated Copper Co., in Arizona, one of the best-known and best-operated copper leaching plants in the world. The following calculation is based on Inspiration's report for 1950.

COPPER PRODUCTION, 1950

	Pounds Fine Copper
From ores:	
Electrolytic copper...	58,892,007
Blister copper...	13,811,484
Total (equivalent of 17.75 lb per ton of ore treated)..............	72,703,491
From leaching in place......................................	4,178,194
Grand total...	76,881,686

COPPER DELIVERIES, 1950

Value of deliveries...	$17,567,960.78
Cost of deliveries (last in–first out basis, including all charges except Federal income tax and depreciation).........................	$11,609,028.47

SALES FROM STOCKS, 1950 (CALCULATED FROM DATA GIVEN)

	Pounds (Calc.)
Finished copper on hand, Dec. 31, 1949........................	9,642,500
Finished copper on hand, Dec. 31, 1950........................	3,917,200
Copper sold from stocks......................................	5,725,300
New copper sold, 1950..	76,881,685
Sold from stocks, 1950.......................................	5,725,300
Total copper deliveries......................................	82,606,985
Cost of copper deliveries.....................................	$11,609,028.47
Calculated cost of copper.....................................	14.1 cents per lb

The price of copper as the year began was 18½ cents; as the year ended, it was 24½ cents. The average price reported by *Engineering and Mining Journal* for 1950 was 21.2 cents per lb.

The foregoing figure for the cost of Inspirations's copper is only a very rough guidepost, inasmuch as it is based on incomplete data and also represents the combination of underground mining, open-pit mining, leaching in heaps, leaching in vats, and production of blister and electrolytic copper.

By comparison, a calculation was made, based on the 1950 annual report of Miami Copper Co., neighbor of Inspiration, which obtains all its ore from underground mining, and whose copper is recovered by flotation and smelting. Miami mines what is probably the lowest-grade underground orebody in production in the world (0.667 per cent copper). Its operations are models of efficiency.

METALS PRODUCED, 1950

Copper, Miami....................	46,553,778 lb
Copper, Castle Dome..............	44,795,706 lb
Molybdenum.....................	627,288 lb
Cost of metal production..........	$15,824,141*
Calculated cost of copper..........	16.6 cents per lb

* Includes all charges except rent, depletion, depreciation, exploration, and Federal taxes.

WHAT DO LEACHING PLANTS COST?

As is the case with operating costs, it is next to impossible to secure for publication detailed cost data on building leaching plants. All one can do is attempt to obtain accurate data on a confidential basis, or to extend data published years ago, making some allowance for the intervening inflation.

For example, in Liddell's *Handbook of Nonferrous Metallurgy*, Laist, Caples, and Wever state that "first cost of an electrolytic zinc plant, including all auxiliary departments, water systems, tramming systems, bins, etc., will vary from $30,000 to $40,000 per ton of daily zinc capacity," depending on size, location, type of construction, and availability of supplies and labor.

This, of course, was true in 1926, but a quarter of a century later the costs would run to probably three times these figures. In fact, the cost of a new electrolytic zinc plant has about doubled in the 10 years following Pearl Harbor. A plant that was designed to produce around 85 tons per day of electrolytic zinc cost about $8,000,000 in 1941. This figure included large power and acid plants. If the plant had been built in 1951, a good estimate would have put the cost at about $15,000,000.

With this general relationship in mind, it is obvious that considerable caution must be used in drawing conclusions from any cost data that are as old as those presented on the following pages. However, these data are the only measure one can get of the first cost of a leaching plant and they are certainly interesting as a starting point for estimating costs of the future. Two sets of data will be presented; one shows detailed costs of the leaching plant at Inspiration and the other gives the costs of the Nicaro Nickel plant in Cuba.

INSPIRATION—CONSTRUCTION COSTS

Installation costs of the main percolation leaching plant of Inspiration have been described by Booth.[1]

The estimated plant cost was $6,000,000, the actual installed cost being $5,840,650, a remarkably close agreement with the original estimate. Later, it was found necessary to separate slimes and to build a slimes and leaching plant, which cost about $724,338. This made the total plant cost $6,564,988.

The design was for a capacity of 9,000 tons ore per day, to recover about 20 lb of copper per ton, the equivalent of a daily maximum cathode production of 100 tons. On this basis, the total plant cost was about $729 per ton of ore per day, and about $65,649 per ton of copper produced

[1] George H. Booth, Detailed Costs, Inspiration Copper Leaching Plant, *Engineering and Mining Journal*, Vol. 124, No. 3, July 16, 1927.

TABLE 92. COST OF COMPLETED STRUCTURES AT THE INSPIRATION PLANT

	Total costs	Per ton Cu per day (100 tons)	Per ton ore per day (9,000 tons)
Roll plant............................	$ 404,750	$ 4,047	$ 44.97
Screening plant........................	103.050	1,030	11.45
Conveyor system......................	263,850	2,638	29.31
Sampling mill.........................	20,200	202	2.24
Leaching tanks (13)...................	1,394,150	13,941	154.80
Solution tanks (11)....................	368,900	3,689	40.98
Electrolytic tank house................	939,200	9,392	104.35
Motor generator house................	303,700	3,037	33.74
Transmission lines and transformers......	118,300	1,183	13.14
Anode casting machine at smelter........	19,000	190	2.11
Tailing railroad.......................	283,250	2,832	31.47
Solution heating......................	103,550	1,035	11.50
Copper-precipitating launders...........	112,600	1,126	12.51
Acid storage..........................	27,950	279	3.10
Oil house............................	4,800	48	0.53
Lead shop............................	18,800	188	2.08
Water supply.........................	57,950	579	6.43
Telephone and signal systems..........	5,200	52	0.57
Office and laboratory..................	25,250	252	2.80
Total...............................	$4,574,450	$45,745	$508.27

TABLE 93. COST OF WORK OTHER THAN STRUCTURES

Clearing site and moving buildings...............	$ 89,000
Grading..	401,500
Changes in railroad tracks.......................	23,250
Alterations to existing structures.................	16,550
Construction office and warehouse................	9,200
Concrete mixing plant...........................	28,450
Lead work, not chargeable to structures...........	48,400
Construction shops.............................	12,600
Construction equipment and tools................	36,950
Temporary power lines and power.................	22,550
Temporary water lines and water.................	10,250
Temporary telephones...........................	400
Handling supplies...............................	34,250
Crawler crane operation.........................	8,300
Stable expense.................................	13,400
Compressed air.................................	2,600
Miscellaneous..................................	18,300
Total...	$775,950

Total per ton ore, $86.20

Total per ton Cu per day, $7,759

per day.[1] The capacity of the slime-treatment plant was about 500 tons per day, which gives an installation cost of about $1,450 per ton per day.

In the Inspiration plant, the largest single expense was for leaching vats and solution- and wash-storage tanks, which cost $1,763,050 or about 27 per cent of the total, including the fines plant. The next largest

TABLE 94. OVERHEAD COSTS OF LEACHING PLANT

Engineering design and field	$257,600
Supervision and inspectors	89,800
Timekeeping and clerical work	16,500
Testing materials	3,950
Miscellaneous labor, including watchmen	28,150
Fire protection	2,300
Toilets and lavatories	1,550
Insurance and compensation	18,800
Transporation of employees	6,500
Overhead from existing shops	2,850
Proportion of expense for purchasing and supply departments	62,250
Total	$490,250

Total per ton ore per day, $54.47
Total per ton Cu per day, $4,902

TABLE 95. MISCELLANEOUS INSPIRATION PLANT DATA

Grading for plant and tailing railroad, 369,000 cu yd
Tailing railroad and yard tracks, new work, 2¾ mi
Tailing hauling equipment:
   Twenty 45-cu yd Magor side-dump cars
   Switching-type Porter locomotive, 113 tons
Structural steel for building and gantry cranes, 2,650 tons
Lumber used in completed structure, 4,000,000 bd ft
Lead for vat linings, 3,400 tons
Copper for electrical and other equipment, 550 tons
Belt conveyors, total installed length, over 3,900 ft
Pumps for acid solutions:
   Byron-Jackson lead, horizontal, 26 installed
   Byron-Jackson lead, vertical, 13 installed
Cast-lead valves, total 264, of 4, 8, 10, 12 and 14 in., Resisto, United Lead, and Autisell types

single item was $939,000 for the electrolytic tank house, equal to about 14 per cent of the total. The tank house, plus motor-generator house, transmission lines, and transformers, amounted to $1,361,200, equal to about 20 per cent of the total.

The figure of $65,649, total installed cost per ton of copper produced, is very much higher than the cost given in 1926 by Laist for an electrolytic

[1] Booth's original data gave a daily output of 90 tons of cathode copper. Actual production was 100 tons; therefore Booth's figures have been altered accordingly.

zinc plant.   His estimate was from $30,000 to $40,000 per ton of zinc metal produced per day.   The costs, however, are not comparable.   It must be remembered that the quoted Inspiration costs include crushing, screening, and conveying systems which are not needed for a zinc plant treating concentrate.

TABLE 96.   INSPIRATION FINES LEACHING PLANT

Capacity, normal, 500 tons per 24 hr
Capacity, maximum, 700 tons per 24 hr
Installation costs:

Steel and erection......................................	$ 95,353	
Excavation and concrete work...........................	167,620	
Concrete materials.....................................	38,421	
Concrete mixing plant and operation....................	13,683	
		$315,077

Excavation per cu yd, $1
Concrete per cu yd, $30

Dorr equipment..	$196,867	
Other equipment.......................................	121,448	
Miscellaneous equipment (lead piping, railway spur and railway alterations, launders, and engineering fee)............	90,946	
		$409,261
Total, ready for operation...		$724,338

Cost per ton fines per day, normal capacity, $1,448
Cost per ton fines per day, maximum capacity, $1,035
Cost of erecting all equipment, $40,000

TABLE 97.   SUMMARY OF INSPIRATION PLANT COSTS

	Total costs	Per ton ore per day	Per ton Cu per day
Cost of completed structures (Table 92)..	$4,574,450	$508.27	$45,745
Work not part of structures (Table 93)...	775,950	86.20	7,759
Overhead costs (Table 94)..............	490,250	54.47	4,902
Slimes plant (Table 96)................	724,338	80.48	7,243
Total.................................	$6,564,988	$729.42	$65,649

Other important factors are that leaching-plant costs for either copper or zinc vary considerably with the grade of material treated and with the resulting strength and volume of solutions.   The Inspiration plant treats ore carrying about 20 lb of copper per ton, but the raw material to a zinc-leaching plant is concentrate varying from 35 to 55 per cent zinc as sulfide, recoveries from which may be from 80 to 95 per cent by leaching. Also tank-house installation costs are roughly inversely proportional to the current density used. Current density at present used in copper plants varies from 10 to 15 amp per sq ft of cathode surface. Zinc plants use about 30 amp per sq ft for the low-density system and 60 to 100 amp for higher-density plants.

Therefore, if roasting, leaching, and electrolysis are considered for treatment of copper concentrate, not ore, it seems probable that plant

TABLE 98. COST OF A ROASTING PLANT
Three Wedge-type roasters at Beattie Gold

Insulating brick, insulation, etc...................	$ 75,000
Silocel brick.................................	4,244
Structural steel...............................	136,923
Roasters......................................	64,000
Service, engineering, and erection..............	1,731
Cottrell plant.................................	105,000
Waste heat boiler.............................	16,650
Coal pulverizer...............................	15,704
Stack...	28,463
Conveyor......................................	2,907
Pyrometer, recording..........................	12,801
Weightometer.................................	2,030
Acidproof cement and sodium silicate.............	1,074
Conveyor belts................................	6,000
Castings and manhole assembling................	5,075
Excavation....................................	10,600
Foundations...................................	15,000
Floors..	3,000
Multiclones, 3................................	21,000
Draft fans, 3, hot gas.........................	3,664
Draft fan, 1,125,000 cfm......................	3,870
Total...	$599,860
Total cost to 3/30/38.........................	$843,664

installation costs would be considerably below the Inspiration figure of $65,649 per ton of copper per day, reduced to 1926 price levels. They might be of the same order of magnitude as for a zinc plant, per ton of metal produced. It must be remembered, as already pointed out, that plant costs have risen about three times since these data were published.

Table 98 gives the cost of installing a roasting plant at a Canadian mine in 1937–1938. Three roasters were installed, making a total installed cost per roaster of $281,000 each. The gross hearth area was 6,400 sq ft per roaster, giving a cost of $44 per sq ft or $21,700 per hearth (25 ft in diameter).

The unit area was 64 sq ft per ton at maximum daily tonnage of 300 tons. Rated capacity was accordingly 100 tons per day per furnace, and installed cost $2,810 per ton ore per day.

Cost of a Nickel-leaching Plant

The Caron process for leaching nickel ores (see page 270) was used during the Second World War by the Nicaro Nickel Co. in Cuba. The plant was financed by the Defense Plant Corp. and was operated by Freeport Sulphur Co. Owing to a growing shortage of nickel, the plant was reactivated in 1951 for the government by Mining Equipment Co., a

TABLE 99.   INSTALLATION COSTS, NICARO NICKEL CO., ORIENTE, CUBA, PLANCOR 690

1. Land and land improvements:		
Land	$	93,621.48
Land improvements		418,288.55
Total item 1	$	511,910.03
2. Buildings, building installation, etc.:		
Buildings	$	9,130,528.43
Building installations		712,715.68
Leasehold improvements		652,709.34
Off-leasehold improvements		605,456.22
Total item 3		$11,101,409.67
3. Machinery and equipment:		
Process machinery		$14,008,920.82
Auxiliary equipment		3,669,549.37
Electric power and telephone distribution		549,480.38
Laboratory and testing equipment		46,336.36
Furniture and fixtures		273,663.25
Shop equipment		222,674.94
Auxiliary tanks and pipe lines		1,096,994.55
Total item 3		$19,867,619.67
4. Portable tools and automotive equipment:		
Portable tools	$	205,454.48
Automotive equipment		318,494.14
Total item 4	$	523,948.62
5. Materials and supplies (for contingencies)		($237,335.91)
Total all items		$31,767,552.08

subsidiary of N. V. Billiton, the Dutch tin mining company, which also operates the Texas tin smelter. National Lead Co. later took over Billiton's interest.

The installation and operating costs of the Nicaro plant are of interest because the process used is similar in many ways to the ammonia-leaching process for native copper. Also, ammonia leaching seems to have some promise for treating sulfide copper ores and cobalt ores. There are reasons for caution in using these data, however.

For one thing, the Nicaro plant was built under war conditions when cost was no object in comparison with the military urgency of getting the plant into production. Unquestionably, this fact was reflected in costs

TABLE 100. TOTAL OPERATING COSTS, NICARO NICKEL CO.
(Before amortization, interest, and depletion)

	Dec., 1946	Entire year, 1946	Total to Dec. 31, 1946
Production costs:			
Ore production..............	$ 39,557.85	$ 580,299.94	$ 1,784,500.79
Metallurgical plant...........	330,665.21	3,898,911.17	10,581,191.01
General production...........	47,380.75	668,691.74	2,563,266.92
Administrative..............	63,084.28	405,494.60	1,336,929.81
Townsite operation...........	13,635.32	182,767.64	633,362.78
Railroad and commissary.....	668.42	(12,321.21)	(30,369.18)
Total......................	$494,991.83	$5,723,843.88	$16,868,882.13
Other costs:			
Pilot-plant operation.........	....	....	$ 211,337.06
New York and Miami offices..	$ 19,555.18	$ 198,516.78	643,222.65
Freight and handling.........	17,248.00	212,466.00	820,820.00
Management fee.............	17,140.00	197,023.00	469,031.00
Storage and outloading.......	2,157.73	36,063.55	66,554.72
Selling expense..............	7,439.00	84,082.00	224,532.00
Total......................	$ 63,539.91	$ 728,151.33	$ 2,435,497.43
Grand total, all costs..........	$558,531.74	$6,451,995.21	$19,304,379.56

TABLE 101. OPERATING COSTS PER POUND OF METAL, NICARO NICKEL CO.*
(Operating cost per lb Ni + Co)

	Dec., 1946	Entire year, 1946	Total to Dec. 31, 1946
Production cost.........................	$0.230	$0.231	$0.285
Pilot-plant operation....................	......	......	0.004
New York and Miami offices............	0.009	0.008	0.011
Freight and handling...................	0.008	0.009	0.014
Management fee.......................	0.008	0.008	0.008
Storage and outloading.................	0.001	0.001	0.001
Selling expense........................	0.004	0.003	0.004
Total.................................	$0.260	$0.260	$0.327

* For the purpose of computing Nicaro's management fee (3 per cent of market value of product), the "market value" of nickel oxide was established in the contract between Nicaro and Metals Reserve Co. as $26\frac{1}{2}$ cents per lb. Actual market value of nickel oxide in December, 1946, was $27\frac{1}{2}$ cents per lb, rising to $29\frac{1}{2}$ cents in January, 1947.

that were far higher than they would normally have been.   Expert opinion has it that the plant might have been built for one-third of its final cost if normal procedures could have been followed.

For another, the Caron process differs from ammonia leaching of native copper in that the nickel mineral has to be given a reducing roast

TABLE 102.   PRODUCTION COST SUMMARY, NICARO NICKEL CO., 1943–1946

	Cost per ton ore handled	% of total Cuban cost	Cost per lb Ni	% of all costs
Cuban plant:				
Ore production.................	$0.545	10.5	$0.0284	8.74
Metallurgical plant..............	3.406	63.0	0.1780	54.82
General production expense.......	0.809	15.0	0.0423	13.02
Administration expense..........	0.452	8.0	0.0236	7.27
Townsite operations.............	0.202	3.7	0.0106	3.26
Commissary operations...........	......	(0.2)		
Total Cuban operating costs......	$5.414	100.00	$0.2829	87.11
Shutdown expense.................	......	......	0.0009	0.28
Freight and handling in Cuba.......	......	......	0.0032	0.99
Freight and handling in United States	......	......	0.0144	4.43
Wilmington plant.................	......	......	0.0082	2.52
New York office:				
Administration..................	......	......	0.0099	3.05
Selling.........................	......	......	0.0028	0.86
Pilot-plant expense................	......	......	0.0033	1.02

Total cost per pound of nickel plus cobalt based on all operating costs, except interest and depreciation, was $0.3256.   This is based on the recovery of 63,571,414 lb of Ni + Co from 3,323,075 tons dry ore, a recovery of 19.13 lb per ton.   On the above installation costs, interest and depreciation at 15 per cent would amount to $0.157 per lb Ni + Co, on an output of 32,000,000 lb per year, giving a total production cost of $0.4826.

to make it soluble in ammonia.   A further difference is that nickel is precipitated from the leach liquor as a carbonate, which must be calcined before shipment.   Both these steps add to plant and operating costs. The data given herewith are abstracted from an official government publication.[1]

[1] H. A. Tobelmann and H. J. Morgan, "Review of the Nicaro Nickel Project, Plancor 690," Office of the Publication Board, U.S. Department of Commerce, Washington, D.C.

TABLE 103. OPERATING COSTS, BEST YEAR (1945), NICARO NICKEL CO.

	Labor*		Materials†		Other cost‡	Total	
	Cost	%	Cost	%	Cost	Cost	%
Ore production	$ 240,111.10	9.4	$ 81,038.94	2.4	$220,382.89	$ 541,532.93	9.2
Metallurgical plant	912,734.51	35.5	2,284,605.79	67.4	618,317.67	3,814,657.97	65.0
General production expenses	655,051.15	25.5	909,917.95	26.9	756,518.87§	808,450.23	13.8
Railroad operation	175,811.29	6.8	54,563.03	1.6	230,374.32§		
Administrative expenses	342,898.56	13.4	32,164.38	0.9	115,085.95	490,148.89	8.4
Townsite	203,336.31	7.9	31,683.72	0.8	26,224.35§	208,795.68	3.6
Commissary	38,430.61	1.5	4,841.36	.....	50,300.08§	7,028.11§	
Total	$2,568,373.53	100.0	$3,398,815.17	100.0	$109,631.11§	$5,857,557.59	100.0

Total Ni + Co produced in 1945, lb............ 24,031,800

	Labor cost	Materials cost	Other cost	Total cost
Cost per lb of Ni produced	$0.107	$0.141	$0.005	$0.243
Cost per ton of ore treated	$2.12	$2.80	......	$4.83

* *Labor* covers all payrolls, taxes, workmen's compensation, public liability insurance, etc.
† *Materials* covers all supplies, plus freight and handling.
‡ *Other* covers telephone, telegraph, legal fees, interior fees, rentals of boats, cars, etc. Income in this account is rental from houses, profit on commissary, distributed railroad cost, and power distribution.
§ Indicates a credit.

It was originally proposed that the plant treat 2,000 tons of high-grade ore (serpentine) per day and produce 20,000,000 lb of nickel per year, the original cost estimate being close to $9,500,000. It was then decided to treat both limonite and serpentine in the existing ratio, increasing the capacity to 2,400 tons ore per day. Due to increasing costs the estimate for this capacity was nearer to $15,000,000.

TABLE 104. METALLURGICAL RESULTS, NICARO NICKEL CO., 1943–1946

	Dec., 1946	Entire year, 1946	Total to Dec. 31, 1946
Ore fed to dryers, dry tons........	110,709	1,255,083	3,160,878
Estimated stack losses............	3,224	37,554	105,412
Ore ground and delivered to silos..	107,485	1,217,529	3,055,466
Ore fed to process, dry tons.......	105,985	1,218,079	3,047,391
Grade of ore fed, % Ni...........	1.40	1.44	1.40
Ni in ore fed, lb.................	2,967,580	35,159,634	85,354,341
In process change................	18,532	29,346	291,998
Ni to account for, lb.............	2,986,112	35,188,980	85,062,343
Ni oxide recovery, lb.............	2,788,398	32,080,259	76,963,650
Ni + Co recovery, lb.............	2,156,000	24,782,800	59,131,314
Ni + Co recovery, %............	72.20	70.43	69.52

Production of nickel oxide	Lb Ni oxide	Lb Ni + Co contained	% Ni + Co contained
1943............................	3,431	2,415	70.24
1944............................	13,811,866	10,314,299	74.68
1945............................	31,068,094	24,031,800	77.35
1946............................	32,080,259	24,782,800	77.25
Total to Dec. 31, 1946...........	76,963,650	59,131,314	76.83

Estimated reserves as of Dec. 31, 1946.......... 25,001,673 tons
Estimated grade of reserves, % Ni...............1.45

From military necessity and other reasons the capacity was again raised to 3,600 tons of ore per day and a new estimate of $19,300,000 was authorized in May, 1942. In November, 1942, it was found that an additional $10,000,000 was required to complete the project and further increases later brought the total amount available for construction, approved December, 1944, to about $33,500,000. The designed capacity was approximately 32,000,000 lb of nickel per year.

The actual installation cost was about $9,300 per ton of ore daily capacity. At a daily capacity of 45 tons per day of nickel as oxide, the installation cost per ton of metal per day was about $744,444. Installation and operating cost data are given in the preceding tables.

It is interesting to note that in a little over a year from the time the first estimate of costs on Nicaro was submitted, the following were major increases in costs, described in a letter to the Secretary of Commerce from the War Production Board, dated Nov. 21, 1942:

1. Cost of common labor had risen 80 per cent because of Cuban government decrees and increased demand for labor for airport projects.
2. Rising costs of materials pushed building costs up 30 per cent.
3. Tremendous increases in ocean freight rates pushed freight costs up $2,000,000.
4. Construction equipment, normally furnished by contractors, had to be bought for them by Nicaro.

All in all, the project furnishes an interesting, and rare, detailed cost study of a leaching process. Anyone who uses these figures must, of course, make due allowance for the extraordinary conditions under which the plant was built and run. It is also true that costs, in general, were even further inflated by 1952 than they had been in 1946.

DEVELOPING A PROCESS

In development of a leaching process, whether one is working out a new method or applying an old technique to new material, there are certain definite steps that must be gone through. Failure to work through any one of these steps carefully and completely will inevitably endanger the success of the operation. These steps are

1. Determination of the size, analysis, and probable variation in character of the orebody to be handled.
2. Taking of accurate, representative samples for testing.
3. Examination of physical character of ore.
4. Laboratory investigation.
5. Test-plant work.
6. Pilot-plant operation.

Much of what will be said in this section is, or should be, self-evident. Yet there are numerous examples that one might cite, from both recent and more remote experience, that indicate how neglect of the obvious can add to metallurgical problems and multiply costs. Unless blessed with good fortune, one simply cannot afford to base plant construction on unsystematic or incomplete procedures at any point in the foregoing outline of process testing and development.   The following paragraphs discuss these points.

1. Size of the ore body is frequently determined by drilling, a procedure over which the metallurgist usually has no control.   Ordinarily it is a simple process, yet before the metallurgist assumes responsibility for the reliability of the process he develops, he should satisfy himself that the drilling campaign has given him an accurate picture of the ore his process will one day treat.   For example, although one large copper ore body was thoroughly drilled some years ago, and its grade accurately determined, large-scale production disclosed presence of primary slimes that interfered seriously with metal recovery in the percolation leaching system that had been designed for the plant.

It is, of course, hardly up to the metallurgist to direct the drilling program.   Yet he can and should insist that exploration be extended in any direction in which he is in doubt as to the kind of ore he will have to handle.   He should be on the lookout for anything in his test work that may indicate a possible occurrence of refractory ore that can be checked by exploration.

2. It is almost impossible to provide one sample, or a hundred samples, that will be "truly representative" of an orebody that may contain millions of tons of ore.   Few orebodies are so happily uniform.

However, it is possible, *and it is essential*, that sampling should indicate the approximate average grade and character of the orebody, and should also indicate the extremes of variation in grade and character that are likely to be encountered as mining progresses.   To know the extremes of all factors is fully as important as to know the average.

For preliminary laboratory-scale work, cores or cuttings from the drilling campaign are usually used.   The size of sample needed varies, of course, but should run from 100 to 500 lb, depending on the size and complexity of the orebody.

For test-plant work, one needs a supply of ore running not less than 500 to 2,000 lb per day of operation.   By "test plant" is meant the small-scale sort of plant that can be set up in a laboratory and run continuously.   Over a period of two or three months of investigation, a carload or two of ore might be required.

For pilot-plant work, when a large or complex plant is being developed, the scale of work should be increased to permit handling 10 to 25 tons of ore daily.   This simply means duplicating the final process, but in smaller sizes of equipment.

3. Determination of physical character of ore should include study of grindability, screen analyses for different degrees of crushing and grind-

ing, moisture content, microscopic examination, nature of soluble constituents—any factor, in short, that may affect the behavior of the ore in
handling, crushing, grinding, leaching, and dewatering. There have been
embarrassing instances where neglect of one such factor has, for example,
produced a plant design where the first ore into the new plant got no
farther than the chute under the primary crusher. The slope of the chute
was too flat to carry the ore, which had turned out to be unexpectedly
sticky.

4. The laboratory work has the objective of determining the main steps
in the process to be developed. Equipment and methods of testing
should simulate actual practice as closely as possible, but there is still a
large factor of experience that must be applied in extending laboratory
tests to plant practice. And even with long experience to back one up,
it is still unsafe to base estimates of extraction, acid consumption, etc., on
so-called "tests" involving a few grams of material stirred up in a beaker
of acid on a hot plate. Laboratory work should be directed by a man
with experience in correlating laboratory and field work, with imagination
enough to foresee the problems he will meet in the field, and with judgment enough to make sure he is properly preparing his technique to meet
them.

5. Test-plant work is called upon to try out the flow sheet that has been
indicated by the laboratory investigation. The scale of work is small
enough so that there is no great loss if major changes in flow sheet have to
be made. When the test-plant work is completed, the metallurgist should
be sure of the units of equipment he wants for the final plant and of how
they are to be strung together.

6. The pilot plant is a further check on the flow sheet and equipment
and should be run with units of commercial size. The chief aim of the
pilot plant is, however, to furnish accurate data on the sizes and specifications of equipment in the final plant and to furnish accurate estimates of
installation and operating costs. There is no value in skimping on pilot-
plant work, unless some overriding emergency requires it.

Pilot-plant work should be continued until all possible factors have been
considered and provided for. For example, a short pilot-plant run may
hide a ruinous build-up of impurities that a longer campaign would have
disclosed. A long program also gives ample opportunity to detect the
oversights that creep into every testing job. An extremely expensive
revision in a new plant once had to be made because a simple diversion of
material from one launder to another had gone unnoticed in the brief
pilot-plant run on the process.

For detailed discussions of pilot-plant operations that led to full-scale leaching plants, note the descriptions of development of the Inspiration plant, the Katanga plant, and the Nicaro Nickel plant.[1]

Although it is impossible to list all the data that should be obtained from a test program on an ore to be leached, owing to the wide variation in individual problems, it is possible to suggest the more obvious questions to which an adequate research campaign should provide answers:

1. Where is the orebody located?
2. What is the proven tonnage?
3. What is complete ore analysis, including trace elements?
4. Do the samples submitted indicate both average grade and character and the extremes of these factors in the orebody?
5. What are local unit costs of labor, power, fuel, reagents, and other supplies?   How readily will supplies be available in this location?
6. What treatment method and flow sheet will be used?
7. What is the proposed final scale of operations?
8. Are samples submitted adequate in quantity for preliminary, test-plant, and pilot-plant work?
9. What does microscopic examination of ore show?
10. What is complete list of minerals present?   What are their physical and chemical characteristics?
11. What is grindability of ore, screen analyses, etc.?
12. Is percolation or agitation to be used?
13. If percolation, furnish these data: mesh to which crushed, screen analyses of fractions, depth of bed, percolation rate, time of contact, strength of solvent, composition of solvent and leach effluent, accumulation of impurities, solvent consumption and regeneration, makeup solvent required, number and quantity of washes, moisture in final residue, analysis of residue, extraction.
14. If agitation, furnish these data: degree of grinding, settling rate in various solution strengths, underflow pulp dilution, number of CCD thickeners, analysis of final residue, plus other applicable data from "percolation."
15. Will solution discard be required; if so, how much, and how dispose of it?
16. Must solution be purified?   How?   What are allowable limits of impurities?

[1] G. D. Van Arsdale, Leaching with Ferric Sulphate at Inspiration, *Trans. AIME*, February, 1926.

A. E. Wheeler and H. Y. Eagle, Leaching Operations at the Union Miniere du Haut Katanga, *Trans. AIME*, Vol. 106, p. 609.

M. F. Dufour and R. C. Hills, Nickel from Cuba, *Chemical Industries*, p. 62, October, 1945.

NEW IDEAS FOR HYDROMETALLURGY

Along with the more or less routine development of leaching flow sheets, as outlined in the foregoing pages, hydrometallurgists must be constantly on the lookout for new ideas and new methods that will broaden the range and the usefulness of leaching techniques. As already indicated, the future will very likely see even greater dependence on leaching techniques than at present, and the metallurgist's job is to be ready with effective and efficient processes when those demands are made. In the following pages are presented some ideas that may perhaps be useful in developing such new processes.

Crushing and Grinding. The hydrometallurgist can expect, and must keep alive to, a steady advance in the quality and efficiency of the mechanisms available to him for crushing and grinding. These will be equally useful to all varieties of mineral beneficiation, however, and few of them will be so directly applicable to hydrometallurgy as to aid in developing new leaching techniques.

One method that does hold such promise is the technique of grinding materials extremely fine in turbulent-air chambers. The Fluid Energy mill of C. H. Wheeler Co., Philadelphia, is an example. In this mill the material to be ground is whirled about through a roughly circular path in an enclosed tube under the impulse of a strong air current. Material ground below the limiting size is withdrawn through a kind of air classifier. Grinding, of course, is done dry.

Because the grinding medium in this and similar methods is the material itself, there is little energy wasted in grinding steel or lifting heavy masses of such medium. It is possible economically to carry grinding much finer by this method than by normal grinding procedures.

Work done with this method has already shown that certain chemical and physical properties of materials are quite different when they are ground extremely fine than those they exhibit in the coarse state. It would make an interesting study to determine the feasibility of a leaching process in which fine grinding was necessary in any case in order to liberate the desired mineral, and in which extremely fine grinding was tried.

Material ground in the Fluid Energy mill, for example, could be collected in a cyclone and then pulped at the bottom of it with a strong leaching solution. The technique is used in several plants simply to collect dust under water. Although no data are available, there is a strong possibility that grinding to micron size might radically speed up certain leaching reactions that are so slow as to be useless on ore ground to a size measured in meshes.

The reactions of normal leaching processes may be speeded up so markedly that the leaching tanks of the future might well be reduced to the simple pump and pipe line connecting the cyclone-repulping unit with a series of thickeners. Of course, material ground so fine might not thicken readily and the effect of gravity might need amplifying, as in a centrifuge or a cyclone of the DorrClone type.

Roasting. As pointed out in the chapter on roasting, the FluoSolids process is the latest step in the long progression of roasting techniques from the days of simple heap roasting. The aim through the years has been to attain maximum contact between material and gas by stirring or rabbling; to provide healthier working conditions around the roaster; to achieve a precise control of temperature, calcine composition, and all other roasting factors.

Considerable detail has already been given (page 58) on the FluoSolids process and it is mentioned here only to emphasize that its potentialities are as yet almost untapped. Already in use for calcining lime and for roasting arsenical gold ores, the method also has a great potential in the nonferrous field. These are some of the possibilities:

1. Return to chlorine as a solvent for gold by means of a chloridizing roast in the FluoSolids reactor.
2. Roasting pyrite economically to produce a high-strength exit gas (14 to 15 per cent sulfur dioxide) for making sulfuric acid.
3. Minimizing formation of ferrites in zinc roasting and control of zinc sulfate formation, through temperature control in the FluoSolids reactor. Calcine would be removed from exit gases at high temperatures to prevent sulfate formation by cooling down in a sulfur dioxide atmosphere.
4. Production of copper sulfate in roasting sulfide concentrates. Nearly all copper can be made water-soluble by proper control of the reactor. Such a sulfating roast, followed by electrolysis, offers economic advantages over conventional milling and smelting methods.

Leaching. All one can be sure of in discussing the future of leaching is that new techniques are going to be worked out over the next few years that would have been dismissed as fantastic by the metallurgists of yesterday. Here are some examples of present trends:

It seems likely that sulfide copper ores can be leached with ammonia, as native copper ores are now. H. A. Tobelmann, consulting metallurgist, has done considerable work on this problem and feels that it may be solved one day. Prof. F. A. Forward of the University of British Columbia has worked out a process for dissolution of chalcocite with ammonia-leach solutions, and attempts are being made to apply the process commercially. It has been found possible to leach cobalt ores with ammonia and at the time this was being written, a full-scale project using this process was under development. There are problems, such as the requirement that the pulp be digested in an autoclave at high pressure and temperature, but the prospect of finding a solution using this technique is an inviting one.

There are laboratories where work is under way to apply leaching to low-grade iron ores. At present, there seems little likelihood that leaching of iron ores could compete economically with magnetic separation or flotation. Yet, for handling some of the more difficult iron ores on which this country may some day have to depend, leaching may be the ideal method.

Leaching would be the right way to handle impure and low-grade tin ores, like the poorer grade of Bolivian ores, if one could easily reduce the cassiterite to make it soluble in alkali-leach solutions. To this end, work should be done and some already has been done (see page 9) to find out how best to give cassiterite a reducing roast. What actually is most effective in reduction? Is it carbon in the coal or coke with which the charge might be mixed? Is it carbon monoxide or dioxide in the furnace atmosphere? Or is it a combination of hydrocarbons, produced from the coal or coke in the charge, that actually does the trick? There seem to be no published data available to give an adequate answer to these questions.

Jet Leaching for Manganese. In the event that this country should one day be thrown back on its own resources of manganese, leaching of domestic manganese ores will become a tremendously important industry. In that event, the technique of leaching such ores will have to be made much more efficient than it is now.

Partly to have it on the record for possible future use, and partly because it is an excellent example of ingenious reasoning in research and development, the following description is presented of what came to be called "jet leaching." The technique showed good promise of commercial feasibility, but for lack of time to test it thoroughly, it never got beyond the laboratory. It was developed, by the way, before jet planes came into general use and the name is in no way an attempt to tie up supersonic speed with leaching.

Jet leaching was conceived by Wayne C. Hazen during the course of some pilot-plant work on the sulfur dioxide leaching of the Three Kids manganese ore. The metallurgical work was directed by D. N. Vedensky of Pan-American Engineering Co. for the Manganese Ore Co. during the Second World War. The technique, as tested in the Pan-American laboratory, has not been mentioned in print hitherto and, as far as the writer knows, no further work has been done on it.

The problem in leaching the Three Kids ore was to dissolve the manganese dioxide in the ore with a solution of sulfur dioxide in water. Percolation was tried first but was given up when precipitation of calcium and other sulfates repeatedly cemented up the beds of ore and burst the tubes used for leaching tests. Leaching in conventional agitators was tried next, using ore dry-ground to 48 mesh and running both ore and sulfur dioxide into the agitator tanks. Leaching went extremely slowly, largely because it took so long to get the required volume of SO_2 into the solution.

An obvious solution was to pulp the raw ore in a flotation cell and add the SO_2 through the air inlet. A flotation machine is, after all, nothing but a means of keeping a pulp in suspension while a gas (air) is rapidly and thoroughly disseminated through it. This method speeded up the leaching process greatly, and for a time it was thought that the answer had been found.

However, largely for mechanical reasons, it was found more practicable to do the leaching in packed towers, using the flotation cells as a means of driving the last of the SO_2 out of the leached pulp and of generating in it a small amount of sulfuric acid.

While the pilot plant work was going ahead with the tower-leaching method, Hazen cast about for another means of getting a rapid and intimate mixing of relatively large amounts of gas with small amounts of pulp. It was apparent that in the agitators and the flotation machines the approach had been to disperse the large quantity of gas into the small quantity of pulp. The tower-leaching technique, with pulp trickling down against an upward flow of gas, was an admittedly inefficient method of approaching the problem from the other direction, i.e., to disperse the small amount of pulp into the large amount of gas.

On the face of it, the latter approach would seem to lead to a readier solution than the former. Investigation of the literature showed that several methods have been tried for dispersing pulp rapidly in a large volume of gas.

For example, a technique apparently developed in Germany makes use of a long shallow trough set on the floor of a chamber through which the gas in question is flowing. The pulp to be dispersed flows into the trough. So arranged that its surface just touches the surface of the pulp in the trough is a cylinder that can be rotated at high speed. The spinning cylinder whips the pulp up into a fan-shaped cloud, completely filling the chamber with a fog of the pulp. Some elementary tests indicated that this method could, indeed, be applied to leaching Three Kids ore with sulfur dioxide.

More extensive tests were run, however, on leaching by means of the jet-pump idea, which makes use of the simple laboratory-aspirator principle. The pulp is pumped at fairly high velocity through a nozzle into a throat. Gas is admitted at this point and the kinetic energy of the pulp is such that it forces the gas ahead of it into the throat, creating a vacuum behind it and drawing in more gas.

A series of tests was run to determine what arrangement of jet and throat gave maximum intake of air. The following conclusions were reached, as outlined in Hazen's report:

1. Contrary to the original assumption, a venturi type of throat seems to hinder, rather than help, induction of large quantities of air into the pulp. It aids in producing a high vacuum in the throat but this is not the best condition for the leaching process.

2. The jet nozzle should be designed to produce a spray of fine droplets that completely fill the throat below it.

3. There should be approximately 6 sq in. of throat area for each gpm issuing from the jet. This is an extremely rough approximation and the point needs much more thorough investigation.

4. Lengthening the throat beyond the minimum is not helpful from the point of view of gas induction.

5. The amount of gas induced varies with the pressure on the jet but too high a jet pressure introduces mechanical difficulties.

Jet-leaching Tests. Tests were then run to find out whether or not the ore could be leached by this method. Three Kids ore, as then being treated in the pilot plant, was ground to minus 65 mesh and pulped with low-strength manganese liquor from pilot plant. This was pumped through the various nozzles used for testing by means of a small acidproof pump. The leaching units were arranged as shown in the accompanying sketch (Fig. 47).

In the first series of tests, the pulp, after passing through the jet and the leaching tube, fell into a small box, where the gas was separated for reuse. Gas was recirculated because of the fear that excess oxygen in the feed might generate sulfuric acid and because it was undesirable to vent the gas, which might carry large quantities of sulfur dioxide, inside the pilot plant. The pulp was also recycled because there was no other way of handling it.

Sulfur dioxide was admitted at 50 lb per hr until the pulp began to lighten in color, indicating dissolution of manganese dioxide. Thereafter it was admitted at 30 lb per hr until leaching was judged complete. The results shown in Table 105 are qualitative only, in that much pulp was lost in these first tests.

This test indicated that it was possible to get a 95 per cent extraction of the manganese in a rather short time, considering that it took only a second or so for the pulp to drop the length of the leaching tube. Assuming that the pulp was recycled about six times, the indicated reaction time was quite short.

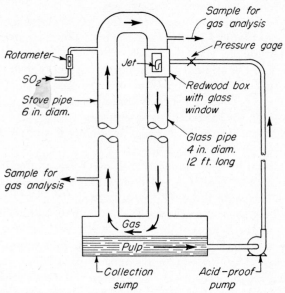

FIG. 47. Arrangement of units for testing jet leaching of manganese ore with sulfur dioxide.

The second test was run to find out what strength of sulfur dioxide could be completely absorbed in one pass. In this test a smaller jet was used, one that would give a bushy spray. The flow of pulp was cut down to 7.9 gpm, and the bushiness of the spray, together with the reduced pulp volume, cut down the flow of gas. It was found possible to absorb all the sulfur dioxide from 50 cfm of gas carrying 2.9 per cent of SO_2. In this test, the length of throat was extended to 28 ft. Pulp was recycled but gas was allowed to escape. Analyses were made of exit as well as entering gases.

Following these tests, another leaching run was made. The results, recorded in Table 106, show that about 46 per cent of the sulfur dioxide going to the leaching system was being absorbed at the rate of flow used. Assuming 1.4 lb SO_2 for each lb of manganese dissolved, this absorption corresponds to a rate of 17.52 lb of manganese dissolved per hr. The low

TABLE 105. JET-LEACHING TESTS, FIRST SERIES

Flow of pulp through jet	15.8 gpm
Gage pressure at jet	35.0 psi
Calculated gas volume	101.0 cfm
Length of discharge tube	12.0 ft

Cumulative time, min	SO_2 in gas, %	SO_2 added, lb per hour	Mn in discharge solids, %	Temperature of pulp, °F
0	7.0	50.0	31.3	
23	7.4	50.0	27.8	
24	12.0	75.0		
46	12.3	75.0	24.1	
47	7.3	50.0	25.9	86
60	7.3	50.0	20.7	90
90	7.2	50.0	13.7	93
120	7.8	50.0	9.9	100
130	8.8	50.0	2.7	103
140	5.7	30.0		
150	5.6	30.0	1.0	105

TABLE 106. JET-LEACHING TESTS, THIRD SERIES

Flow of pulp through jet	7.9 gpm
Gage pressure at jet	36.0 psi
Calculated gas volume	55.0 cfm
Length of discharge tube	28.0 ft

Cumulative time, min	Intake gas, % SO_2	Exit gas, % SO_2	SO_2, added, lb per hour	Exit solution, pH	Mn in discharge solids, %
0	9.1	4.9	52.5	3.7	29.4
6	...	...	52.5	3.5	19.1
30	...	6.1	52.5	1.8	1.9
45	7.6	4.1	30.0		
48	...	...	30.0	1.6	
50	4.4	2.4	15.0	1.6	0.34

tailing assay obtained showed that leaching was as thorough as for any other method tried in the plant.

Several other tests that were run indicated the following conclusions:

1. Power requirement for this type of leaching was calculated at about 0.7 hp per long ton of ore per day. Large-scale work should use power at an even lower rate.

2. A smooth, narrow stream of pulp from the jet drew in the greatest

flow of gas (150 cfm for only 4.4 gpm of pulp), but absorption of SO_2 was low.

3. A bushy jet of pulp absorbed most SO_2 and seemed to give the best leaching conditions, but the nature of the jet was seen to vary with the pressure on the pulp and with other factors. Therefore, adjustment of jet to pressure and to kind and dilution of pulp was adjudged a research problem in itself.

4. The technique seemed to present these advantages: only one moving part (the pump); simplified design that should be easy to expand to large units; no fan needed to circulate gas; fast leaching, thus cutting down retention time and size of units needed.

Significance of the Tests. This obviously incomplete investigation of a new method of leaching is presented in some detail, not alone for the sake of its possible usefulness to future research on manganese ores, or to leaching tests in general, but for its interest as an example of willingness to try new ideas. This investigator was thinking as he worked, he was constantly dissatisfied with what he was doing, and was open to ideas that might give him a better way.

Note the reasoning that led to a trial of jet leaching. It went below the surface of the problem to an analysis, simple though it was, of the more fundamental nature of it. And from there it tried to follow a path to the best solution of that problem. That is why this example is recommended as an object lesson in research technique. First the dissatisfaction with the existing process; then the analysis of the basic problem; then the careful development of the idea.

It is necessary, of course, to curb the restlessness of this ideal researcher with strong and wise direction that will, at some point, call a halt to further changes and fix upon an optimum technique. Lacking this, it will never be possible to reach a workable plant process. The proper combination of these two ingredients will alone make for the greatest progress possible. And that is the kind of progress that the future will demand of the base-metal hydrometallurgist.

INDEX

Skinner furnace installations, 56, 212, 219, 223–224, 231, 256–257
Smidth, F. L., kiln at Nicaro Nickel Co., 273
Snow, W. C., cadmium from electrolytic zinc, 299
  electrolytic zinc at Risdon, 254
Solution analyses, electrolytic zinc plants, 125
Sperry filter-press installations, 219, 223–224
Sulfates, anhydrous, dissociation of, 6
  hydrated, decomposition of, 7
Sulfides, effect of roasting temperatures on solubility, 65
  roasting of, 2
Sullivan, J. D., chemistry of copper leaching, 13
Sullivan Mining Co., Kellogg, Idaho, agitation equipment, 83
  antimony leaching, 29
  solution analyses, 125
  solution leaching and washing equipment, 100–102
  Tainton process, for lead, 20
    for zinc, 124
  tank-room data, 127–129, 131
  zinc-electrolysis current density, 17
  zinc hydrometallurgy, 207, 209, 212–217, 240–246
Sunshine Mining Co., 29

T

Taggart, A. F., *Handbook of Mineral Dressing*, 34
Tainton, U. C., lead alloy anodes for zinc, 127
Tainton process, for lead, 20
  at Sullivan plant, 67, 124
  for zinc, 124–126
Talbot, H. L., electrolytic cobalt, 310
Tennessee Copper Co. grinding plant, 31–32
Thickeners, Dorr (*see* Dorr thickeners)
Three Kids Mine, 22, 48
Tin-ore treatment at Longhorn Smelter, leaching, 290–292
  roasting, 9
  smelting, 292
Tobelman, H. A., review of Nicaro nickel project, 346
Trail, British Columbia (*see* Consolidated Mining & Smelting Co.)
Traill, R. J., electrolytic iron, 318
Trumbull, R. C., Pyrites Co. treatment of pyrites cinder, 197
Turbo-mixer Corp. mixers at Nicaro Nickel Co., 273

U

Uranium, from carnotite, 293–299
  from pitchblende, 292–293

Uranium crushing, 294
Uranium leaching, 28–29, 295
Uranium precipitation, 296
Uranium production, 292–299
Uranium roasting and leaching, 295

V

Vanadinite, 27
Vanadium leaching, 26–28
  with acid, 27
Vanadium minerals, 27
  at Rhodesia-Broken Hill Development Co., leaching, from carnotite, 297–298
    from desclosite, 307–310
    flow sheets, 308–309
Vanadium precipitation, 310
Vanadium production, 307–310
Van Arsdale, G. D., and Maier, C. G., electrolytic manganese, 274
  hydrometallurgy of lead, 335
  leaching with ferric sulfate at Inspiration Copper Co., 352
  leaching mixed copper ores, 176
Vedensky, D. N. manganese oxide, SO2 process, 285
Vielle Montagne, zinc hydrometallurgy, 207, 210

W

Wad, manganese ore, 21
Waldron, H. L., cobalt-leaching process, 310
Wash water, Chuquicamata data, 91
  precipitation of copper at Andes, 108
Washing, after agitation, 90
  at A. S. & R. Co., 101–102
  ammonia leach plants, 97–98
  CCD, 92–96
  at Consolidated Mining & Smelting Co., 98–99
  at Electrolytic Zinc Co., 99, 101
  equipment at zinc-leaching plants, 100
  at Nicaro Nickel Co., 98
  at Sullivan Mining Co., 100, 102
Wedge, Utley, sulfating roasting of copper ores, 5
Wedge roasting furnace, at A. S. & R. Co., 65–67
  at Anaconda Copper Mining Co., 69
  installations, 54–55, 194, 206, 212
  at Norske Zinkompani, 251
  at Sullivan Mining Co., 241
Wheeler, A. E., copper leaching at Haut Katanga, 16, 146, 352
Wilfley pump, at Andes Copper Co., 104, 106
  at Inspiration, 38
Woodman, F. W., electrolytic manganese, 275
Woolf, W. G., electrolytic zinc at Sullivan Mining Co., 240, 243
Wyman, W. J., leaching manganese ores, 21